TWO STRIKES
AND
YOU'RE OUT!

BY

TERRY SMITH

Literary genre: crime fiction

TWO STRIKES AND YOU'RE OUT!

ISBN: 1 903607 64 7

Published by Able Publishing 2005

Typesetting and production by:

Able Publishing
13 Station Road
Knebworth
Hertfordshire SG3 6AP

Tel: (01438) 813416 / 812320
Fax: (01438) 815232
Email: books@ablepublishing.co.uk
www.ablepublishing.co.uk

In memory of a remarkable and dear friend,

Peter Frederick Welch,

*a free spirit, entrepreneur and adventurer
who passed away in February 2004.*

"The profit of life consists not in the space but rather in the use. Make use of life while you have it. Whether you have lived enough depends upon yourself, not on the number of your years."

French Philosopher
Michel Eyquem de Montaigne.
(1533-92)

Other books by the same author:

The Art of Armed Robbery

AUTHOR'S NOTE

There are times in our lives when we are encouraged to say, "If only I could turn the clock back?" or "If only I had acted on my intuition at the time things would have been different?" We all know that it is impossible to turn back the clock and that is what makes these seminal moments in our lives even more painful because we should have known better. Boy should we have known better!

For those that have read my first book, *The Art of Armed Robbery,* you will be aware that this is the long awaited and called for sequel. I wanted to keep the same autobiographical format as the first book, but for libel reasons, I have had to present this book as fiction based upon true fact. How much of the book is true and how much of the book is fact is up to the reader. What I will say, however, the fictional format has provided me with the freedom and space that I needed to excavate and expose the level of betrayal and deceit that exists in the modern criminal fraternity. Gone are the days when loyalty and devotion comes naturally. Nowadays family, friends and associates only exhibit loyalty because they love and like you. There are some former villains, however, like a few others and myself, that will never ever let their morals and principles subside into betrayal and treachery. We are the chosen few that have risen up the precious pyramid of honour and respect, while lesser mortals tumbled down the slopes into abject infamy and insignificance.

This book covers a story of gargantuan betrayal and treachery. The only sad and painful aspect of the story is it happened to me. I wished this was not my story and I was reading about someone else. Alas, this is not the case and I feel duty bound to narrate this story so that other people may learn from it and not become a sucker like I did to 'the three men of sin'!

For those that have had the benefit or privilege of reading my first book, you will recall that there were a lot of questions and queries that were left open-ended or unanswered. Due to this new approach, I am now able to fill those gaps, so to speak.

Terry Smith
12 November 2003

CONTENTS

ACKNOWLEDGEMENTS

Very special thanks to Patsy Feeley who without his support this book may have never reached the printers. Also to Billy Todd, Chris Pearman, Brian Richardson, Mickey Reilly and Howard Prosser who had to put up with my incessant mantras about the case. Also to Ibrahim Eidarous, Yasser and all the other innocent Muslim victims in the HSU at Belmarsh who prayed to Allah for me to be returned to my beloved family. God bless you all.

Limitless gratitude and appreciation to Jon Patty, Les Bunker, Phil Hunter (solicitors), James Scobie (barrister) and leading counsel David Nathan QC who restored my faith in humanity.

A massive thanks to my dear friends Mark, Annette and Cassius Blake, Wesley, Lorraine, Lois and the ultimate twins Alfie and Archie. Your loveliness just goes on and on.

Endless gratitude also to Cass Pennant, Nick Paul, Ricky Grover, Terry Orwell, Gary and Sharon, Tony and Martin Bowers for sound advice and encouragement on all issues.

Distinct thanks also to Kane and Joanne, Robert and Lisa, Tony Martins and family, Dean, Christine and family, Danny and family, Sandra Welch and family for exhibiting the rare quality of human warmth and friendship.

Ample appreciation to all the cool cats at Windfall Films, including David Dugan, Oliver, David Glover, Ruldoph Herzog, Jamie Lockhead (getaway driver), Leesa Rumley, Yvonne Bainton (The Matrix) and Chris Morphet for introducing me to the wonders of film. Also great working with Joe Pyle, Peter Scott, Matthew Bevan, Mitch and the endearing kraut Arno Funke. We are still three-nil up!

Thanks for the sterling advice and support from those on the other side of the wall, Johnny Massey, Rooky Lee, Tony Argent, Paul Lyons, Danny Clark, Harry Roberts and especially Charlie Bronson whose literary and artistic talents are astounding.

A very special mention to those that watch over us. Although no longer with us, we know that you are there. My grandmother Dolly

Smith, Nanny Ada Harris, Uncle George Nichols, Young Tommy Hole, Old Tommy Hole, Lenny Carter, Peter Welch, Ava Smith and Reggie. We miss you all.

Lastly, exceptional thanks and gratitude to my peerless wife Tracey, Tel Boy and Sam, Bradley and Nikki, Jade and Sonny for making life so wonderful. Also Pat and Iris Etherden, Suzy and Linda, Paul, Eyeball, Alec, Thomas and Olivia. Patsy, Boozy, Jonathan, Jessica and Maisy. Audrey, Ray, Billy and Carly, Johnny, Val and family, Tony and Janice, Danny, Tina and family, The Thompson family, Lenny and Little Lenny, George and Maggie of the Peacock Pub. God bless you all.

CHAPTER 1:

THE BEGINNING

Where did it all begin? I do not really know? All I do know is that I have led a very special existence.

Please let me introduce myself. My name is Terry, Terry Diamond. I am a 44-year-old organized and professional criminal. I have been involved in crime and its by products all my life. A life that has seen and experienced both a richly encrusted happiness and downbeat despondency. As I recount my tale I will take you on a very special journey. A journey that I hope remains with you for a long, long while.

It all began when I was released from prison after serving a very long prison sentence for armed robbery. I am not proud of being a professional manipulator of fear and terror. I know deep down in my water that it is both morally and legally wrong. But sometimes life is shaped and moulded by external forces beyond our control. The argument goes that we all have free will. The ability to choose and shape our own destiny. I beg to differ, however, because I know that there is something out there that could be both good and evil, auspicious and malevolent. Whether it is up to us to choose our path I do not know. All I know is that we are puppets of some powerful entity and I want to cut the strings and be me!

The reason why I entered the world of armed robbery is very complicated and complex. Or could there be a simple explanation for my criminality? Could it be that my fatal flaw is unrepentant selfishness and greed? I doubt it very much because I am addicted to excitement. I love chaos, drama and anarchy. They say at times of crisis comes forth opportunity. When I experience chaos I see beauty in the making. A spontaneous beauty that can only be expressed during wilful mayhem.

During my prison sentence, which stretched into over a decade in the British penal system, I saw it all – despair, hopelessness, blood spurting violence, suicide, death and mind-deep blackness. But I refused to yield to such negativity, because I believe in faith and hope. I believe in the positive side of the human condition. In short, I believe that we are not alone, that out there someone is watching over us. You may call it a divine guardian, an angel, the Christian God or the Muslim Allah. Believe me, whatever it is, we are not alone.

CHAPTER 2:

LEARNING THE TRADE

Until this nightmare incident that I am able to recount, I was still very much an active and prolific armed robber. It had been my chosen profession. I was taught the trade by the Old School. Put bluntly, by well-respected robbers who transformed every robbery into a work of art. They taught me the game, but it is not a game, it's a serious business with serious consequences. If you do not adhere to its guiding principles of trusting no one, always disguising your face and leaving as little evidence behind at the scene of the crime as possible, you will be history. Either banged up in soul sapping prison for life or buried in loamy soil forever. Not a nice prospect!

At the time of this story, I was hitting the cash-in-transit security companies about once every few months. I had been a consistent and ruthless armed robber in the past, but with age comes forth wisdom and experience. I no longer needed to express myself through the barrel of a gun on such a regular basis. I had, to put it bluntly, "slowed down"! Nonetheless I still possessed an overwhelming fascination for the contents of security vans and trucks. I enjoyed the danger of my chosen profession and I wanted the big one! I wanted to prise, relieve and secure the million pound plus heist. And when I put my mind to something, I know as sure as night follows day that I can accomplish it. I am the guv'nor.

One of the arts of being an organized and professional armed robber is that you trust no one and find your own work or targets to attack. I always found my own work and that way it protected me from the omnipresent threat and menace of informants who want to lure, chaperone and steer you into a sometimes fatal police trap. Uncharacteristically, the idea or plan for my next robbery came from a fellow robber.

Although we did not mix on a social level, we had unswerving respect for each other. We both knew what we were capable of and woe betide anyone who stupidly tried to apprehend us during a robbery. If it came down to either them or us it would be them, as we were not going to volunteer for decades of prisondom. Normally, I would get out early in the mornings in my anonymous little car or on my motorbike and scour our corpulent capital of London and surrounding Home Counties for a big fat juicy security van and then set my plan in motion. I would thoroughly organize the escape route, the getaway vehicles, the tools required, masks, gloves, everything, right down to the large holdalls to carry away our prize. Then I would ring my partner in crime from a payphone and arrange a meet to discuss our next project. My partner trusted my judgement implicitly. He would never question my plans, he would put his life in my hands and we would always come away with the prize. We shared a mutual respect for each other and together we would plunder security vans of all colours and creeds. After a successful mission, we would part company and drift back to our simple suburban existence.

My partner, Harry, came to me with a plan about a security van that left a security depot in South East London and delivered its weekend cargo to a clearing bank depot on an industrial estate in the Home Counties. Repeatedly it did this on a regular basis and was ripe for an organized attack. Harry told me that another firm of designer clad robbers in the wilds of Essex had been planning to rob this security truck and had been given the information about the robbery by a security guard in the company.

Apparently, the security guard had told the robbers from Essex that every week this security vehicle left its South East London security depot with the weekend takings. It delivered them to the clearing bank and collected, for the return run back to base, over a million pounds for the ATM machines in London. It made absolute sense, as there was a constant demand for newly pressed bank notes for these cash machines. In effect the security companies could not fill these cash machines up quick enough. That is until I was there to relieve them of their cassettes, cram-packed with new crisp bank notes. As you opened them after a successful robbery, all you could see were bricks of banknotes packed tightly together, like thirty packs of playing cards on top of each other.

In the 1970s, because the security companies were being consistently hit by robbers, who seized their booty as the security guards transferred the money across the pavement, the insurance companies decided to set a limit on the money that could be carried across the pavement from the security vehicle to the bank or factory. The limit was £25,000.

Prior to that, however, one specialized bank security company with black and green livery would take anything up to £100,000 across the pavement in one massive holdall. It was my ambition many years ago to rob one of these special security trucks and when I set my mind to something, I am normally successful. In short, I plotted on this 'Bank Van', as we called them, for months on end, because the logic behind their security was 'secrecy'! By that, I mean, the bank managers, cashiers, even the security company staff did not know what bank run they would be on until the morning they got to work. They would, as a rule, collect and deliver the money from these banks, once every six to eight weeks. Add to this the secrecy behind the collection times and dates and they were nigh on impossible to tie down to any logical pattern.

But this was a challenge for me and I knew that I could rob one of these juicy bank vans. I followed the pattern of the Bank Van for months and months and realised when it delivered money to a specific central London bank, its first port of call in the morning, it would collect money from another specific bank on the outskirts of the Capital later that same day. Another feature of their security was that they did not have two security guards on the pavement, like conventional security companies, but no less than four security guards – three in uniform and protective helmets and one in a pin-stripe suit like a bank manager. They would stand on the pavement and take one massive holdall across the pavement. They would not take the money across the pavement if they did not like the look of someone nearby. They would sit in their security truck and wait anything up to an hour until they felt the coast was clear. Put all these security features together and it would be a formidable task to get near, let alone rob one of these bank vans. But by now, you know me, I am a determined individual and I sat on a bench eating a bag of chips and when I saw the size of the green holdall float across the pavement before my very eyes, I pounced like a leopard, pulled down my facial disguise, retrieved my favourite Smith and Wesson revolver from my waistband and jumped in the middle of the four guards and bingo it was all mine. In the background, my two accomplices backed me up and off we went for the count out. To my surprise there was eleven thousand £5 notes, a grand total of £55,000.

That was the old days and now the self-imposed limit of £25,000 had to be revised, because the ATM cash canisters had to be filled to the brim. And if the cash canister had £10 notes, it could be anything up to £25,000. If the cash canister had £20 notes it could hold anything up to £40,000. If you could seize four or five of these boxes then it would be tantamount to a small lottery win.

CHAPTER 3:

SUPERMAN

My partner Harry said this South East London to clearing bank run was carrying up to 1.4 million pounds in ATM money and that was good enough incentive for me. But how were we going get inside this reinforced war wagon? The problem was the security guards driving the vehicle never stopped or got out of their fortified vehicle from the security depot to the clearing bank. The only possible way to successfully rob this fat turkey was to stop it in transit and either bust into it using a special made up ramming devise or cut into it using a chainsaw.

The security companies have got wise to this invasive surgery technique and adopted significant counter measures to prevent chainsaw robbers. One tactic they would employ was to laminate the metal panels of the security vans with wood. This meant the metal cutting blade of the chainsaw could not penetrate the interior of the security van. There was another way, however, that had been employed successfully by a well-liked and eminent South London robber who had the unusual nomenclature of 'Crackers'! Evidently, as robber folklore and parlance goes, 'Crackers' got his name for outlandish ideas of robbing security vans. In the earlier 1980s, he was the first robber to use a mobile crane to ram the back doors of a security van and retrieve its multi-thousand pound haul. He was also the first robber to successfully use the power of hydraulics.

I did have the privilege to meet this man once and I had high expectations of us working together and going for the big one. I admired Crackers and respected his natural talents in the noble art of armed robbery, but alas, I met this special person at the fag-end of his career and he is currently serving life imprisonment after being convicted of a series of armed robberies in southern England. Somehow, however, I believe we will not hear the last of Crackers as, during his case at a provincial Crown Court, the police produced a piece of tissue from one of the getaway vehicles and on the tissue was a significant amount of DNA profile belonging to Crackers. What is striking about the tissue is that the scenes of crime officer did not take any photographs of the tissue *in situ*. Plus, after the trial, there was found to be 56 grey fibres on the tissue that were similar to those of a police station cell blanket. Presently Crackers has lodged an appeal against conviction on the grounds that the police fabricated this powerful and compelling evidence against him in order to secure a conviction. I will take this opportunity to wish him well.

Crackers' use of hydraulics was not only evolutionary in the robbers' sphere, it was revolutionary. He rationalised, like the isolated tribes in Africa, if there was no crime they would stagnate and waste away. By that, he meant, crime dictates that one tribe employs the use of spears, the other tribe makes and develops the shield. One tribe acquires access to the gun the other tribe develops and secures the use of the cannon. The process carries on and on *ad nauseum* until we reach the insane levels of global destruction of today.

Likewise, the robber and security companies are in the same predicament. The 1960s armed robber would go through the front window screen of the armoured vehicle; the security companies would devise and fit toughened, laminated glass in order to thwart penetration.

Then in the 1970s and early 1980s there was the ramming phase, where robbers would devise all sorts of weird and wonderful ramming contraptions to bust into the back doors of security vehicles. To combat this the security companies adopted the use of inaccessible safes inside their vehicles. Then in the late 1980s we had the hi-jacking scenario where the robber would jump in the security van with the guards and drive the vehicle away. The companies came up with the revolving door system where only one person at a time could obtain access to the vehicle. This process of crime has led to a cat and mouse game with the security companies. Every time the professional robbers devise a new way to rob the security vans, the companies confront and combat it with evolutionary methods and remedies. The new weapon in the robber's armoury is hydraulics, their very own robber's Superman. With hydraulics anything is possible. It is like having two arms that can squash or prise open 20 tonnes of compact steel. It is phenomenal, awesome and frightening altogether. Down to Crackers' revolutionary ideas and thinking this would be the way forward and the way to nick the £1.4 million ATM money. It was only a matter of time and the South East London security van would go!

CHAPTER 4:

THE BERMONDSEY JOB

Humans are habit gravitating creatures and in the realm of crime and, more especially, professional armed robbery it may prove both advantageous and disastrous. Please let me explain. The security guards, driving their specialized armoured truck, have set routes to take during their day out on the road. Very rarely do they deviate from their precise company instructions, but when they do I am there to seize the opportunity. A short cut here, a traffic solving manoeuvre there and it could all lead to one thing – armed robber's vehicles blocking in the security van and getting to work on the exterior of the van.

From experience I have leant that it is of little value blocking in a security van and ordering the terrified guards to alight from their vehicle at gunpoint. All the guards do is scuttle into the rear of the secure van and cower until the emergency services arrive. The robbers leave empty handed and the super sleuths at the local Flying Squad accumulate and collate information on exactly who the perpetrators are. They have massive computer databases at their secret offices where the *modus operandi* of every known robber is kept. A detective's hunch, bolstered by the scientific measurement of computer technology, invariably means, after several successful armed robberies by a specific gang, a compelling pattern begins to emerge and a special operation is put in motion to nab the culprits.

Our first mission is to select a location to stop the van. Once this is done we work out how many and what type of vehicles are required. To stop and successfully block in a secure van, it is best to use vehicles bigger and more formidable than the security van itself. My idea was to use a well-tested method of stopping the security van. I had already been following this particular security van for several months so I knew its route and patterns like I knew the way around my school playground. I found the perfect place to stop the security van; a long, relatively busy, back road shortly after the van left its depot. We would strike our attack first thing on Monday morning as it left the depot at about 8 am. This way, sometimes after a long docile weekend, the security guards are still reliving what they were doing on the previous Sunday afternoon and not fully concentrating on the possibility of attack. They say the early bird catches the worm – with the likes of my firm and me on your case, we want to catch and devour the big fat turkey.

The plan was to have a large box truck parked up stationary along this long back street and let the security van driver indicate to overtake our large box truck. As soon as the security van overtakes our stationary vehicle, 50 yards in front of him would be our other vehicle, a large tipper lorry that would drive and box in the security vehicle head on. Meanwhile the box truck that the security van overtook would pull up right behind the rear of the security van. I have used this boxing in method several times in the past and it works a treat. The beauty about this method is the security van driver is not aware of any danger until it is too late – once he overtakes the stationary box truck it is too late. The reason for the large box truck is so that the security van driver cannot see the tipper truck facing him 50 yards further down the road. It works like poetry.

Once the security van is tightly in our grasp, we would then alight from our vehicles, two robbers in each vehicle, making four of the gang in all. My companion and me would then set to work on the security van while the other two robbers would watch our backs and deal with any senseless have-a-go heroes that fancied their chances. Additionally we would have a spotter on a radio transmitter outside the security depot to forewarn the robbers on the plot that the security van had left its depot and was due to meet us in the next five minutes. One of the overriding rules of putting together a successful major robbery is to keep things very simple and straightforward. Crackers knew the art of simplicity and that is why he was so efficient and effective at this dangerous trade.

I already had a regular team of very game and experienced robbers around me and they always liked my plans and ideas. They knew that if I were putting a piece of work together it would be based on military-like precision and expertise. I left no stone unturned and most important of all our escape route would have to be foolproof. By that, I mean, the escape route would have a failsafe mechanism where, if we were being pursued by the police or a have-a-go-hero away from the scene of the robbery, he or she would not be able to follow us as we could block off the road, or use a subway or railway crossing to halt our pursuers in their tracks.

The most disturbing threat to the armed robber during the commission of a robbery is the omnipresent threat of the Air Support Unit, or police helicopter. There are ways to combat and defeat the possibility of being pursued in the air but you need an element of luck and the right environment to do this. We will not go into that issue because we are positive robbers and any negative thinking must be expunged immediately.

The first professional armed robber on my list was Harry 'Hotshot' Forbes. Harry and I had been on numerous armed robberies together and we had developed a great rapport with each other. You could say he was my second-in-command, as he was the main person that I would bounce my ideas off. Harry got his nickname when he was once being pursued by an irate security van driver whom he had minutes earlier robbed. The security van began to chase his getaway vehicle and Harry ordered his getaway driver to stop the vehicle, he got out the vehicle knelt down upon one knee and let a salvo of shots go from his powerful 45 magnum at the security van driver, which promptly stopped the security van in its tracks and Harry and his companion got away. Thereafter because of the cool and calculated way Harry had dealt with the dangerous situation, we all alluded to him rather humorously as 'Hotshot' Harry. Harry is a diamond; he will stand and fight with you until the death.

My second choice was Billy 'The Warrior' Franks. Billy and I had met in the bowels of the British Prison system when we were both serving long sentences for armed robbery. Although we both came from diverse cultures, communities and backgrounds, we clicked together as soon as we met. Billy is short and squat with a powerful muscular frame. In prison he used to move several tons of metal a week in the gymnasium. Billy looked very intimidating and could have an awesome row. Once he took on the residents of a gypsy camp single-handed and decked their best men in the process. Conversely, however, I had become acquainted with the softer, more humane side of Billy. He was well read, watched hundreds upon hundreds of feature films and exhibited a healthy disdain for authority. He hated the police, the judiciary and the screws. He worshipped his family and friends and had even shown me the overriding value of life long friendship. Billy is a loyal and devoted companion. A true Viking of the modern era.

My third choice was my older brother Eugene Diamond. His name said it all, as the Latin root of Eugene is 'good'. In many respects, Eugene was a 'good diamond' and we had worked together in the past as a duo and with larger gangs. We all called him 'The Soldier' for his unswerving ability to adhere to instructions and follow them through to the *nth* degree. If there was one flaw in Eugene's character it was because he had a heart of gold. Eugene would put his life on the line during our robberies and then dive headlong into the wild London nightlife and literally squander his 'chunks of cash' on those around him. Several times he had to be overlooked in the organization of some robberies because my companions were concerned over his spending habits and because he was drawing too much attention to our special team and me. To sum up Eugene, he is strong, resolute but lacked drive and ambition. Eugene would jump into the lion's mouth like the rest of us. It was only when he went with his social clique that he let others and himself down.

On the night before the robbery, I had the arduous logistic task of putting all the vehicles in place for early the next morning. Like everything else in the robbery game there is an art to this also – as you don't want to put the vehicles being used in the correct place too early as some could be towed away, stolen or reported by traffic wardens, council workers or eagle-eyed neighbours. The answer lies in putting the vehicles near to the scene of the robbery and placing them in their correct position as late as possible. Obviously this theory goes out the window if you need to secure a specific parking place to be near the target. But that doesn't apply to this piece of work.

That night I put the two ramming trucks on a nearby industrial site and a stolen Ford Transit van, with a side loading facility, nearby as our first getaway vehicle. A black London taxi and large powerful saloon vehicle were put at the changeover point. The idea is to set all the getaway vehicles in their rightful positions in reverse order. For example, in the morning we drove to the stolen Transit van in the black cab and saloon, walked over the footbridge to the Transit van and pulled on the plot and got the large box van and tipper in place.

By now I was beginning to get increasingly excited, because once the action starts to roll, the whole mission and getaway process begins to fall into place like the collapse of a line of dominos. Bang, bang, bang and then you are home counting the luscious loot. I got into the tipper truck at 7:45 pm. with 'The Warrior' and started the vehicle, as I wanted the powerful V8 diesel engine warmed up before the security van arrived. I could see 'Hotshot' Harry and Eugene in the large box van 50 yards in front of me. We had our various disguises ready to smother our faces once the action began to start. I had a black balaclava rolled up on my head ready to slip over my face and my favourite black leather driving gloves purchased from Peter Jones in Sloane Square. 'Hotshot' Harry driving the large box truck had a dark blue crash helmet and a grey tunic- like uniform so that as he stood at the side of the security van, in the chaos and confusion, witnesses to the attack would believe he was a security guard and think there had been a road accident.

We had the white Transit van parked half on the kerb nearby, ready to whizz along a well placed side turning for our escape. Inside the van was the fifth member of the gang – our very own 'Superman spreader' – 62,000 lbs of total might ready to prise open the security vehicle. As I was sitting in the tipper my radio handset burst into life. The voice on the other end of the radio transmitter proclaimed, "The turkey has left the nest! I repeat the turkey has left the nest!" I quickly replied, "Message received!" The spotter would now jump into his nondescript Ford Escort and get as far away from the location as possible because it would be swarming with Old Bill in the next 15 minutes.

I flashed my headlights to 'Hotshot' Harry and Eugene in the large box truck. This was the signal that we were going to graft in the next five minutes. I noticed a thick plume of diesel smoke emit from the box truck's exhaust as the engine burst into life. Both engines of the trucks were running and ready. Eugene got out of the box truck and went to the Transit van to start up the mobile petrol driven generator, which powered 'Superman'. I then looked across to Billy and smiled at him, quoting Shakespeare I robustly exclaimed, "Come what, come what may / Time and hour runs through the roughest day!" Months of observation and hard work would come to fruition in the next few important minutes. This was my project, my baby, my destiny!

I looked ahead and I could just about see the familiar blue colour of the security van coming towards us. Quickly Billy and I pulled down our balaclavas. I had my Smith and Wesson 38 concealed in my shoulder holster. Billy had his favourite 45 magnum and Harry and Eugene were packing nine-millimetre Browning automatic pistols. From experience, it is very rarely that you have to brandish firearms in attacks such as these as onlookers are usually so amazed at what is going on that they do not get involved. The problem occurs when they do. That is when you need some firepower. All in all, however, almost all professional armed robbers would concur that shooting people for no reason at all is absolutely pointless and brings extra heat on the team. Thankfully, I had never had to shoot anyone before. I didn't intend to today either.

By now the blue security van had overtaken the large box truck and was making its way towards us. I applied pressure to the tippers accelerator and inched my way into the middle of the road. As soon as I noticed that the driver knew that something was wrong, I screamed the big diesel engine and forged forth until I was bumper to bumper with the security van. I looked down into the cab of the security van and I could see the look of utter fright and fear in the driver's eyes, already true to form his companion was scuttling into the rear of the van for safety.

Simultaneously, the large box truck with 'Hotshot' Harry at the wheel pulled directly behind the security van. He smiled inwardly as he came face to face with the stencilled sign on the back of the security van proclaiming that the crew did not have access to the contents of a locked safe in the van. Harry knew different. Once the security van had been well and truly boxed in, all the robbers got out of their vehicles and began to go to work. At a rough estimate we gave ourselves four long, time-consuming minutes to get the prize and flee. By the time I got out of the tipper and climbed on top of the security van roof, Eugene had started the generator and passed 'Superman' up to the roof to me. I had studied the roof of the security van as it passed a motorway footbridge so I knew what to expect. I inserted the specially toughened claws of the spreader underneath the lip of the security van's escape hatch and turned the hand throttle and watched as 'Superman' did his remarkable stuff. The escape hatch began to groan and grizzle as the 62,000 lbs of raw pressure was applied. I watched the lip of the escape hatch bend by about 4 inches. Then I reversed the hand throttle to close the claws and pushed the claws inside the hatch even further to acquire a better purchase. This time I opened the throttle full blast and the escape hatch popped open like a champagne cork. We were in!

As I looked inside the van both guards had fled to the front and were, quite understandably cowering in the cockpit of the van. 'The Warrior' then dropped into the van and ordered the terrified security guards to remain where they were and they would not be hurt.

Altogether, to reach this stage of the robbery had taken about 1½ minutes. Time is a precious commodity to the armed robber and the next few minutes would dictate whether it would be spent in a relative world of love and luxury or the spartan surroundings of a doleful prison. 'The Warrior' immediately started to pass through the escape hatch large blocks of cling filmed banknotes. Under close scrutiny, we could espy the familiar face of the Queen on the banknotes. We removed twenty-one of these blocks of money and sadly, because of the time constraints, we had to leave another seven behind. We put these blocks of money into several large holdalls and ran to our stolen Ford Transit van, not forgetting 'Superman', as he might be required for another mission in the future. We all got into the getaway van and drove about two miles to the next change over point.

This was a very precarious stage of the robbery, as we did not want anybody to see what vehicles we were changing into. A woman walking her dog, a Yorkshire terrier, looked up at us getting into the black cab and Ford Scorpio Cosworth and quick averted her eyes when she knew what was occurring. I heard her say, "Come on Reggie, hurry up, you will get cold!" As we left the anonymous cul-de-sac, 'The Warrior' pointed to the sky in the distance as we could see the police helicopter circling low, like a vulture over the scene of the robbery several miles away. We drove for about five more miles before we came to our flop. A self-contained unit that we had rented on an industrial estate. The spotter was already there to open the automatic metal shutters and let us in. It was only once we were all inside the flop that we felt safe. The robbery had gone smoothly as expected and there were no major dramas to discuss or deliberate over. In essence it was a supreme bit of work that no doubt would attain a focal point on the national TV Crimewatch programme.

CHAPTER 5:

THE COUNT OUT

It was 11:21 am. and my wife Stacey had just put out her second joint of the day. She had been trying to give the habit up for ages but her addiction was mutual. Cannabis softened the day. It took away all the sharp angles and made things much more sufferable. Especially on Monday mornings when the beginning of the week threw up all sorts of depressing and negative thoughts and feelings. She eased herself into the warm, aromatic bath and was listening to the morning show on the local radio station. Then she heard the 11:30 am. news bulletin. The news reader proclaimed, "A massive police dragnet is going on in Bermondsey and the surrounding dockland area of South East London today as a gang of armed robbers stopped a security van on a public road and escaped with a substantial amount of cash. The senior detective has warned that these are ruthless and dangerous men and should not be approached by members of the public!" The newsreader added, "There is a substantial reward on offer from the security company and if anyone has information about the perpetrators of the crime they may contact me on Crime Stoppers 0800 555111."

Upon hearing this Stacey bolted upright in the bath and burst into her characteristic endearing laughter. "The little rascal," she thought, "I bet that was Terry and his gang." She did not know anything about Terry's business save that he was a suave and debonair operator. Before she married Terry she had heard stories about him and his penchant for armed robbery but it was an area where she feared to tread. The less she knew the better.

Her usual mundane Monday, however, began to take on a new positive hue. She could not wait to see Terry and experience the thrill of being around a real man, a man that made her throb and tingle. It was only then that she realised in her cannabis-induced reverie that she was playing with herself in the bath. She knew it was wrong, more especially as it was only Monday morning, but what the heck, she surrendered herself to wave after wave of irrepressible pleasure and bliss. She couldn't wait to get her small sensuous hands on Terry's all exciting anatomy.

Meanwhile, in the self-contained unit, the count out began. The large blocks of cling-filmed banknotes were in £50,000 bundles of mixed denominations. There were twenty-one fifty-grand bundles making a total of £1,050,000. Eugene suggested cracking open a bottle of champagne to celebrate breaking our first million pound mark. But 'The Warrior' and I were against it as there would be plenty of time to celebrate and there was still loads of work to do. We still had to return 'Superman' and the tools to the safe house, burn all our clothing and other evidence, drop the Ford Scorpio and black taxi to a local scrap metal dealer who would crush the cars and hide our own money. After expenses were deducted, we shared the money out equally and gave the spotter £25,000 for his trouble. Upon leaving the Unit we all made plans to meet at The Tower Hotel at Tower Hill, London, the following Friday night to discuss the blag, any problems and celebrate big time.

The first policeman to arrive at the scene of the robbery was PC Mullen; he had only been in the force six months and thought he was an experienced server of the community. Training at Hendon Police College had taught him to preserve all the evidence at the scene of the crime. He reassured the security guards still inside the van and got them to seek a medical check-up by the ambulance crew that had arrived. PC Mullen then put the familiar blue and white tape around the crime scene to stop others from contaminating the area.

Shortly afterwards, an unmarked maroon Vauxhall Omega police car arrived and DS Herbert and DC Noel got out of the vehicle. Back at the Flying Squad office they referred to these powerful three litre police vehicles as 'battleships' for their ability to float around the streets of London and race to the scene of the latest armed blag. Inside the 'battleships' was enough firepower and ammunition to take on a small army. Apart from the service Glock 17 automatic pistols held in the secure glove compartment, it also carried body armour and two Heckler and Koch MP5 carbine machine guns held in a purpose built safe inside the vehicle.

As DS Herbert and DC Noel approached PC Mullen they flashed their Flying Squad warrant cards and surveyed the crime scene.

Immediately, both looked at each other and wondered the same thing. Was there any more money left on the security van? Quickly they extended the exclusion zone claiming that the robbers might have left an explosive device in the security van. All police and emergency personnel were to retreat up to 500 yards down the road. As soon as the coast was clear DS Herbert entered the security van via the passenger door and climbed into the back of the van. He could not believe his eyes when he saw seven fifty-grand bundles of banknotes still inside the van. Between them they removed four of the bundles and left three behind. They pulled their unmarked Omega up to the rear of the security van and quickly ferreted the blocks of banknotes to the boot of the car. DS Herbert then instructed DC Noel to take their booty to his luxurious flat in Chistlehurst. They would meet up later and share their swag with the DCI and two DIs back at the Flying Squad office at London Bridge.

CHAPTER 6:

OUT OF SIGHT, OUT OF MIND

The following Friday, 'The Warrior', Hotshot Harry, brother Eugene and myself all met up in the upstairs bar of the Tower Hotel. I like the panoramic view of Tower Bridge and the Tower of London from the bar as it conveys a sense of history, of continuity and change, of imperial power and national pride. I viewed myself as nothing more than my seafaring forefathers who had plundered the high seas around our globe and justified it in the name of the monarchy and religion. It was all the same to me. We were all robbers; only the cleverest robbers owned the banks.

After several bottles of Dom Perignon champagne, Stacey arrived with the other wives and girlfriends looking exquisitely tarty in their silk dresses and lip-splitting Versace trousers. Stacey had a knowing look in her eyes. She knew that we were celebrating something and it was not someone's birth or birthday. She pulled me aside and whispered, "I know it was you, you know!"

With a look of surprise, I countered with a smile, "What are you talking about?"

"You know," she said knowingly, "The robbery in the docklands!"

"That was nothing to do with me!" I smiled.

She said, "Well I'm warning you, make it your last job because the net will close in!"

Later that night, I sat there in bed and thought hard and long about what she had said. I knew that the life span of an active and prolific robber is very short. You have got to get in and out before it is too late. What bugged me most was Stacey was so right.

Only recently the New Dockland Yard's elite had mounted a successful operation against a very efficient and effective gang of armed robbers from the South London and Kent area. They had attempted to steal the Millennium Diamond from the Money Zone at the Millennium Dome in Greenwich, South London. The police had the robbers under tight observation for months and months and were lying in wait when the robbers struck using a JCB digger to smash into the complex and steal the biggest and most valuable diamond in the world. Alas, all the robbers were arrested and carted off to Cellmarsh Prison to await trial. I had an uncanny feeling that the specific attentions of this gang-busting police squad would soon be focusing upon me. I had to tread carefully so I decided to take and enjoy an extended vacation to the Canary Islands.

As the plane roared down the runway at Gatwick Airport and finally left the ground I looked out of the nearby window and saw the horizon disappear into the distance. Suddenly I felt my body being drained of all the pent-up stress and tension of the previous weeks. Something had been on my mind, an inner fear that the net was closing in and this was a timely departure from the badlands of South East London. It was like a rain-drenched overcoat being lifted from my shoulders. The mere fact that my wife Stacey and children did not leave the country with me was irrelevant. Naturally I would miss them but they could come to be with me at a later date. The most crucial point was that I was out of sight and out of mind. Time can be a great panacea for problems and I knew and felt what I was doing was right. Don't wait about, act immediately for tomorrow it could be too late.

The plane departed from Gatwick at 8 am and arrived at Queen Sofia Airport in the south of Tenerife approximately four hours later. As soon as I left the plane's exit door the sultry African heat hit me like a soft and wonderful pillow in the face. I love sunshine; as for me it is the very embodiment of goodness and brings the best out in me. I caught a white Mercedes taxi to a little village called Callao Salvaie about eight miles from Los Christianos, the capital of Tenerife nightlife. I did not know anyone on the island so I kept up my physical training during the morning, worshipped the sun and read during the afternoon and dined and rang home during the cool summery evenings. It was not the perfect situation or experience but a sixth sense warned me that it was the right thing to do.

By a pure stroke of luck, I was sitting around the pool one day when I heard the familiar twang of a Cockney voice in conversation with some young ladies. It was an old acquaintance of mine called Dave Old. The last time I had seen him was in 1986 when I was in Wandshearth Prison hospital with my leg hanging off after I was rammed on a motorbike during a failed armed robbery. We soon swapped pleasantries and he introduced me to his business friends on the island and we would hit the town together. I liked Dave as he too had foreseen nothing but grief and plenty of it back in Blighty and had taken the bold and daring step to pack up his belongings and flee to the Canary Islands. I admire individuals with gumption and Dave had plenty of it. He was polite, respectful and always immaculately dressed. He was a big strapping man in his mid 40s and had been part of the doorman scene in the 1970s. He had served several short prison sentences for handling stolen goods and quickly realised that prison was a mugs game.

I recall one evening we went to a special celebration night with some of his friends and it was like a fugitives paradise. Everyone at the function had been on the BBC Crimewatch TV programme. There were fugitives from Manchester, Liverpool, Birmingham and Bradford. We had a fabulous night at Bobby's Bar and hit the sack as dawn began to rise.

Then during one of my phone calls home I was told the inevitable. The Bermondsey docklands robbery was to be aired on the forthcoming BBC TV Crimewatch programme. Outwardly I was confident about this bit of work, as there was no significant evidence left behind at the scene of the crime. But inwardly, I was anxious and concerned, as I knew what the elite members of the Metropole Police Robbery Squad could get up to. It was not beyond them to yield to something called *noble cause corruption* where, if they really thought a specific robber and his team had committed a serious major robbery, they would manufacture evidence in an effort to secure a conviction. It had happened before and it will happen in the future but I was not about to become a sucker. Or so I thought.

Later that week I entered a little bar in down town Los Christianos and waited to watch the Crimewatch programme. The producers of the programme had staged a reconstruction of the Bermondsey docklands robbery using all the original vehicles used in the blag. The Flying Squad detective leading the manhunt for the robbers was DS Herbert. He wanted to know where the lorries used to ram the security van and the getaway vehicles had been parked prior to the robbery and claimed that there was a substantial reward for anyone with information about the robbers. As I looked at the programme and analysed its contents, a surge of pride swelled in my chest. What evidence had they got, absolutely nothing, save the perennial appeal to the legion of state paid and state registered police informants that lurk in the shadows of the so-called London underworld. They could go and fuck themselves too, they were not having me – or so I thought. I resolved to remain in Tenerife for several months and monitor things back in the UK. Time is a great healer. It always is and always will be. Shortly after the Crimewatch programme my wife Stacey and our three adolescent children joined me on the sun-blessed isle. We enjoyed months and months of quality time together and pushed the boundaries of loveliness to new and wondrous dizzy heights.

Then one day I rang my partner Harry and told him I was seriously thinking of returning home. He said that he thought it might not be a good idea and that I should reconsider it. I added that I wanted to be home with my family and not isolated on some sun-scorched island. Therefore, against better judgement, I flew back to the UK. I should have seen the signs.

CHAPTER 7:

THE AFRICAN WOMAN

I flew back to the UK and headed straight for my home address in Canvey Island, Essex. Almost immediately I wondered if the house was already under covert observation, with static cameras outside the property and intrusive surveillance devices inside the house. As a professional career criminal it is always best to expect the worst and that way you cannot do yourself or anybody else any harm. But in reality it's no way to live, always paranoid about what you can discuss with you wife and young family in the privacy of your own home. The Englishman is not king of his very own castle anymore. We live in a police state where civil liberties are being eroded on a piecemeal basis. If only we knew the extent of intrusive surveillance measures that are being adopted and employed in our little island. For many people, the UK is becoming nothing more than an open prison, forever tip-toeing through a minefield of automated car index recognition systems, CCTV and Gatso speed cameras. It is only right that criminals should be pursued and punished, but not at the expense of our natural civil rights.

Shortly after my arrival back home I met up with the rest of the firm and we sat down to discuss the future. Hotshot Harry said that he was bored and wanted to attack another security van, 'The Warrior' was up for another mission and brother Eugene was still splashing his money around the manor bringing on the heat. We decided to sort out another bit of work. This happened almost by accident. I was driving home to South Essex early one Saturday morning at about 5 a.m. when I saw a security van travelling in the opposite direction along the London bound A13. True to form, I made a mental note of the time, place and type of vehicle and the following week I was there in my nondescript run-around to get on his bottle and follow it to its destination. Once again it was an inter-depot run which meant it was carrying megabucks and we decided to prepare to rob it.

As usual I set about my standard methodical style of preparation and commitment. I was really excited about this project as we were going to stop the security truck and ram its back doors using a specially adapted crane. We were aware that some security vehicles use safes inside their vehicles but this one was so weighted down, as it went around a roundabout one day, the interior lights were on in the back of the van and we could see the familiar grey plastic sacks used by this security company. Even if the safes were full, this big fat turkey was still ripe for plucking.

In any event, we called this project 'Mother Goose' as it was going to lay the golden egg into our laps. I began to acquire all the vehicles that would be required for the robbery, for example, two robust lorries, a large van and several changeover vehicles. I always took personal control of this side of the project as I always knew what I wanted and I left no room for error. The idea was to leave the ramming vehicle to the last moment as it would have been difficult to park it up on a public road, or an industrial estate as other criminals or the gypsies in the area would steal any plant machinery left unattended for any length of time.

Then one day the most remarkable thing happened to me. I met up with Hotshot Harry in a quiet little Stratford pub one Friday afternoon. Gradually, bit-by-bit, we began to get increasingly inebriated mixing with several other friends and acquaintances enjoying the conviviality and merriment of comradeship. Then we moved onto another pub in the West Ham Park area of East London. I had only ever been inside this pub once before – one midweek dinnertime to meet someone. We were in the pub for about an hour, when I noticed a middle aged African woman dressed in green sitting on her own at the bar. I looked over to her and she smiled. I returned the smile and felt a compelling urge to walk over to her and talk to her. The next time I walked past her to use the toilets, I stopped and spoke to her and realised she was a deaf person. She could speak in a monotone voice but had to lip read what I was saying. What she told me blew my mind. She said, "You are in big trouble! You." She held her hand up straight in front of her in a tight fist gesture and said, "Pow, they are going to come from behind you." Then putting her hand on her back she added, "Blood, lots of blood, you why?" By now she had tears welling up in her eyes and was visibly crying. Folding her arms as if holding a baby she exclaimed, "You have baby! Money this big." and she held her index finger and thumb close together.

By now she was sobbing uncontrollably. Immediately the colour left my face, my pub smile had evaporated into a deadpan expression and I was gob smacked.

This woman who I had never met before had just told me what I was about to do. She described in detail the exact method of the attack on the security van and how I was going to be fatally shot and killed by armed police. She even knew it was me that was going to drive the ramming vehicle. How did she know all these things? It was scary, it was astonishing, it was otherworldly. I called Hotshot Harry over to listen to this amazing middle-aged, deaf woman and after listening to her he blurted, "Don't listen to her she is crazy!" I looked at Harry and thought 'God you are so shallow, this is not bollocks, this is a prediction'. I had to get out of the pub immediately and rationalize exactly what I had just heard. This was difficult as we had been on the razzle for the best part of six hours and trying to think straight when your body is in euphoric mode is hard to do. I pulled out a £20 note and left it on the bar. I reassured the African woman the best way I could by getting her to smile. I thanked her profusely and left the pub immediately driving home to Canvey Island in a mind-numbing stupor.

On the way home I pulled over into a lay-by on the motorway and sat there for what seemed like hours trying to fathom or comprehend exactly what had just happened to me. This was mad, it was surreal – was this really happening to me? As soon as I reached home I told my wife Stacey who knew nothing of my plans to rob the latest security van what had just happened. I decided there and then to halt all criminal exploits and escapades forthwith.

In simple and unadorned language, I had been warned by a supernatural entity. Someone was helping me. I have always believed in black and white issues, only now I realised there were in fact significant shades of grey and colours in between. Was this divine intervention or nothing but unalloyed humbug? Whatever it was, I was listening big time and it was time to hang up the six shots.

Later that week, I met up with the rest of the team and told them of my weird experience. 'The Warrior', who was fascinated with films about the psychic and supernatural world, immediately agreed that warnings, any warnings, must be adhered to otherwise we will pay the ultimate price. Hotshot Harry in the cold light of day had re-evaluated his initial opinion and reluctantly agreed that we had to disband the team. As for brother Eugene, he normally went with the flow and was too busy being a lovable social cat in and around the pubs of East London. We got rid of all the vehicles and alas resolved not to see each other for the next several months. As far as I was concerned the game was up. But the game was up on our terms not theirs. They were not having us – or so I thought?

In the following months, motivated by this strange experience, I went to see a well-respected female psychic in Canning Town, East London, where she warned me that I was going to be betrayed. I asked by who? She said she could not say, only that men are coming for me with guns and the person that betrays me will have a tattoo of 'Mum and Dad' on their arm. Thereafter everyone I met, I secretly checked their arms for this telltale sign of betrayal, the tattoo. There were times, of course, that I thought perhaps I was taking this all too far, and that perhaps my sanity was at stake. But as long as I did not commit any crime I was safe from persecution, or so I thought. I should have seen the signs!

CHAPTER 8:

THE HOMECOMING

Barely two months after I was warned by the psychic to stop my criminal antics, I heard that a good friend, and previous co-defendant of mine, was coming home from prison after serving seventeen soul-sapping years behind the cell door. We had been partners in crime, professional armed robbers, back in 1986 when we were deliberately rammed on our motorcycle by a car whilst making good our escape after attacking a security van delivering cash to a bank in North West London. We were both sentenced to very long prison sentences. I received sixteen years imprisonment and my co-defendant, John Wendall, was sentenced to a massive thirty-five years imprisonment for this offence and a catalogue of other offences.

Upon hearing that my co-defendant was finally coming home I was very pleased. Evidently he had been given nearly five years parole, but in my view he should have been home aeons ago. Despite this outward feeling of happiness at Wendall's release, deep down in my soul I felt unusually apprehensive and uneasy. I could not quite put my finger on it. All I knew was that I would help him on his release and then keep him at arms length, as the last time we were together it transformed into a veritable nightmare. I was so concerned about this gurgling malaise I spoke to my wife Stacey because, all things considered, did we really know this person? He had been stewing away in claustrophobic prison cell for the last seventeen years and we asked ourselves would he be the same person we knew, liked and loved as before? Only time would tell.

When he was finally released in April 2001, my wife and I invited Wendall and his wife to come to our home for a celebratory get together. We spent the whole night until the early hours of the next morning guzzling champagne and coming up to speed with each other's lives. It is customary amongst good friends and criminal associates to 'treat' those freshly home from prison. Normally the size of the *bung* or treat reflects the depth and strength of the friendship. Likewise, I offered Wendall some money or a £6000 car that I had on the driveway. He said that he required a car and so I told him to take it when he left. Despite Wendall having served such a long and cruel prison sentence I found him very sociable and humorous but with an underlying slice of bitterness. Nothing too pronounced but enough for it to register.

Over the coming weeks, Wendall and his wife became regular visitors to our Canvey Island home. Initially I encouraged this as I wanted to help him. Wendall needed guidance, support and assistance, but I soon realised that on a social level he was not my cup of tea. Quite understandably, Wendall wanted get out on the town and party, whereas my wife Stacey and I wanted to savour and enjoy the phenomenal delights of our newborn baby boy, Sonny.

More and more, Wendall would visit our address and more and more I would take him for long walks along the picturesque seafront of Canvey Island and listen to what he had to say. It was not long before I noticed that Wendall possessed a visceral bitterness and resentment about how his life had evolved and progressed. Putting things bluntly, here was a fifty-year old man that had served an outrageously long prison sentence and had compared and contrasted his social and economic status and standing against the young, stylish, wealthy drug dealers of East London and Essex. This made both his wife and him extremely jealous and resentful. They felt that their name and reputation was as good as, if not better than, anybody else's, and that they should be up there amongst the high flyers of the lucrative world of drugs.

On one of Wendall's visits to my house he tried to denounce and denigrate a well-known long term prisoner, who he had previously escaped with, as a grass and accused him of making a statement to the police when he was recaptured. This person is a very well liked and respected individual within criminal circles and I advised him to drop the issue and get on with enjoying some 'quality time' with his own family. Put succinctly, I told Wendall that he was in no position to start slagging off people and he should begin to enjoy life. With the benefit of hindsight, I should have seen the signs!

On another occasion Wendall dropped an outrageous bombshell when he asked me if I would be prepared to start committing armed robberies again. I looked at him as if he had recently emerged from a time travelling machine or he had been living with the dinosaurs for the past decade or more, as what he was saying to me was utterly prehistoric. Here was a fifty-year old man that had been home for two weeks since being released from a twenty-nine-year prison sentence asking me to start robbing again! From the very outset I made my position clear. I was not robbing, nor was he! Wendall appeared disappointed by my response but he knew I meant what I had said.

During another visit he brought up the robbery subject again only this time he adopted a different approach. He said that he was having it with an old friend of his called Danny Snakeshaft, who was skint and also wanted to commit an armed robbery. If I fancied it, would I be prepared to rob with him? Again I made it abundantly clear that I was not prepared to 'go back in time' and to start robbing again. It was then I told Wendall about my otherworldly experience with the African woman in the pub. He looked at me, as if to say "What a load of bollocks!" But I did not care, I did not know what I believed, all I knew was I was not going to commit armed robberies ever again. The way I viewed things, you do not ignore such mind-blowing warnings. If you do it would be at you own peril.

During another visit Wendall enquired, "What is the situation if you get arrested with a gun in your possession?" He asked if it was possible to be charged with 'intent to endanger life' as this would invoke the automatic *Two strikes and you're out* mandatory life sentence. I told him that I had heard about an old acquaintance of ours who had received a nine-year prison sentence for possession of a handgun despite having previous convictions for armed robbery. This was an odd question to ask me as the *Two Strike* statute had became law in 1996 and it would have been a very topical subject in the prison system where Wendall himself would have known the answer. Why was Wendall asking me this question when he already knew the answer? Was it that he wanted to know whether or not I possessed a firearm?

On another occasion, I was sitting in my comfortable house on a Saturday afternoon watching the sport on TV. Wendall came to our address stating that he wanted to see me urgently. We went for our usual walk to the seafront and he claimed that my brother Eugene—who is on remand in Wentonville Prison—was telling fellow prisoners that he was responsible for a major robbery in the Bermondsey area of South London. I asked how he had come by this information and he told me his friend Danny Snakeshaft was visiting someone at the jail and he had told him. Wendall then exclaimed, "Even I heard that you had a robbery in Bermondsey while I was in Full Shutton Prison!" Outraged, I denied any involvement in the robbery and tried to conclude the conversation, as it was none of his business anyway. He was beginning to annoy me, more especially when he said that I should have the hump with my brother because he could get me in serious trouble! I then asked Wendall what he thought I should do, as I was getting increasingly angry with him by now. I said, "What are you saying? That I should put one in his head because he is a fantasist and likes telling lies? You tell me what I should do?"

Wendall added, "Nah you can't do that he is your brother!" By now I was getting very annoyed as there I had been sitting in my house watching TV and this pest comes along with outrageous gossip–I should have seen the signs!

As these sporadic visits to my house became persistent–almost on a weekly basis–they always revolved around questions disguised as seeking advice, support and assistance. It is only now in retrospect, and under close examination and analysis, that I can see a pattern emerging. It appears that these were not Wendall's own questions and requests in order for him to get on in the world, but they were invariably structured to get me to admit to a crime or my agreement to commit a crime. I noticed that when the appropriate answers or feedback was not forthcoming, he would go away dissatisfied only to return as regular as clockwork with a new or fresh approach, as seen in the following request for a firearm.

Both the Wendalls came to my address claiming that a black drug dealer on their Rainham council estate had fired a pistol at their twenty-one year old son, Willy, over a dispute about him trying to chat up the black guy's pretty girlfriend. Wendall claimed he had confronted the black man and said, "The next time you take a look in the mirror, have a good look as you are looking at a dead man!"

I said to him, "Why did you say such a stupid thing like that? Because as sure as night follows day if anything occurs to the black man the first port of call by the police will be your address." It did not make sense to me! Wendall then asked me if I could get him a gun. Obviously Wendall knew that most criminals or former armed robbers have access to guns and I said to him, "What, do you want one right now?"

Wendall then replied, "Why have you got one?"

I repeated myself again and said, "Do you want one?"

He then added, "I thought that you had one, but I don't want it yet!"

Bemused and confused I could not make Wendall out. Wendall comes to my address with some pathetic story about his son being shot at, a sense of urgency then ensues and he wants a gun, then he does not want a gun. Bottom line, he really wants to know whether or not I have a gun at my address! I neither confirm nor denied this proposition, but left him with the notion that I had immediate access to a firearm. By the time Wendall comes to my address again I had forgotten all the palaver about the black man shooting at his son. More specifically, I had not totally forgotten about it, I simply did not want to bring it up. All I could foresee was trouble, big trouble and plenty of it: police, arrests, indictments and prison and lots of it. Wendall was not getting me involved in some nonsensical shooting incident over the amorous flirtations of his offspring.

In the short time Wendall had been home from prison both he and Snakeshaft appeared inseparable. In many respects, Wendall appeared to be hiding behind Snakeshaft by letting him do all the legwork while Wendall used his prison connections to promote and organize business transactions. It was a symbiotic relationship where they both needed each other to survive in the fast lane of drug dealing. There was, however, a darker side to their relationship, one that they tried unsuccessfully to smother and conceal, but one that would return to haunt them and me eventually.

The first chink in their façade occurred when Wendall came to my address and gave me his new mobile phone number. When I pointed out to him that he was quick in acquiring a new mobile phone as he had only been home from prison four weeks. He told me he had had to change his mobile number because his pal had been arrested with some drugs. Apparently, Wendall claimed that both he and Snakeshaft were due to collect some drugs from a former prison acquaintance, but the fellow never made it to the rendezvous point as he was arrested before he reached there. This fellow, Mickey Macitto and another person called Eddie Roberts were apprehended, arrested and charged, then they were carted off to the doleful confines of Wentonville Prison to await trial. When I heard this dreadful yarn I exclaimed, "Gosh, that guy is unlucky, he's not been out of prison long and now he is back inside!" What I did not know was Wendall had lied to me. Wendall and Snakeshaft had returned a consignment of drugs to Macitto who, upon driving away from the gym, was subsequently followed by the police and arrested less than three miles away. For some reason Wendall had hidden the truth from me about this episode. Why would he want to do that? I was to find out very soon!

The very first time I met Snakeshaft was at a penultimate football match of the season. A last gasp relegation match between West Ham United and Southampton at Upton Park. This was in late May 2001. Wendall had managed to get me a ticket and I met Wendall and Snakeshaft outside the ground. On being introduced to Snakeshaft, he proclaimed that he had a good tip for the big race of the day. We placed our bets on 'Golan' and during the half time period of the match Snakeshaft phoned Wendall from another part of the ground to say that the horse had indeed won at 11/1. We were to meet up again after the game at the nearby Ladbrokes Bookmakers to collect our winnings. Upon doing this we went for a celebratory drink to a pub of my choosing. Not only had the tip won but also West Ham at 3-0 to prevent relegation. At the pub Snakeshaft began to talk to me and appeared to be a cornucopia of gossip and information. He told me who had been nicked, who was out of prison, who was in Spain, who was doing well in criminal circles and who wasn't doing so well. After I left the pub I rang a friend on my way home and he said to me, "I don't like the sound of that fellow, he sounds like a 'cozzer' to me!" I decided to never visit that pub ever again.

During the weeks following my introduction to Snakeshaft and the win on the horse, he would provide Wendall with other tips, who would then inform me. I backed these horses placing £100 on them at a time. Then one day, when Wendall had come, and we were having drinks outside the front of my house in the sunshine, I asked Wendall to tell Snakeshaft to "drop me out of those donkey tips" that he had been putting my way as none of them had won since 'Golan' and I had done over a monkey. By now Wendall was getting progressively drunk but phoned Snakeshaft on his mobile phone saying, "The other fellow said if you don't drop him out with those horses, you are going!" (meaning Snakeshaft would get topped) and started to laugh. Snakeshaft cut him off and obviously did not view the conversation as funny. I was amazed at Wendell's perverse sense of humour, as I had not said that! It is only now, with the benefit of hindsight, I realize the perverse joke was not meant for Snakeshaft, it was meant for me! It was a private joke between them as they had plans for me and I was the one that was going.

CHAPTER 9:

THE SET-UP

While we were drinking outside my house in the bright summer sunshine, a woman, who had lived next door to my wife Stacey in Canning Town many years earlier, came up the drive pushing a pram. The woman had moved to Cornwall and was visiting relatives that lived nearby and had decided to pop around and see my wife. Inside the pram was a baby boy about the same age as our baby boy, Sonny. He was feeling unwell and appeared rather docile. Naturally I made this woman welcome, offering her drinks and making a fuss of both her and the baby. Wendall, however, in his inebriated state started to make fun of the baby and was sniggering. I felt that it was in bad taste and told him to stop. Not only was he abusing our hospitality, but making fun of a new guest to my home. In order to put a stop to it, I suggested that we finish our drinks and visit a local Chinese restaurant to have a meal.

It was during the meal that Wendall pulled me aside and asked me if I was prepared to run some 'parcels' to his former prison friends in the Midlands. I said that I was up for it providing it was not drugs, as I was still aware of the previous arrest of his mate Mickey Macitto. He said it would be a regular venture and that it involved counterfeit money. He wanted someone reliable and trustworthy to deliver some 'valuable printing presses' to his mates and once the counterfeit operation was up and going it would be a regular run. Wendall suggested he give me £500 for the first run and thereafter I could become a part of the operation and be paid in counterfeit money. I said I was prepared to do this providing he gave me a map of exactly where I had to deliver the 'presses' and he said that he would get back to me.

About a week later, on Monday 4th June 2001, Wendall phoned me on his mobile phone at 14:09 p.m. and asked to come and see me at my home. When he arrived he said he wanted me to collect the 'valuable printing presses' that evening and deliver them the next day. He gave me a map of Cambridgeshire and pointed out the rendezvous point at Tesco's superstore on the Ely turn off on the A14. I said that I was unable to collect the 'printing presses' that night as I had members of my wife's family, Danny and Tina, coming down from London to buy my jet ski and they were also staying for dinner.

I asked Wendall where were the 'printing presses' now?

He said, "Snakeshaft is bringing them from Brixton in South London."

I said, "Is Snakeshaft coming through Stratford?"

He replied, "Yes!" thinking that I was going to agree to collect them there.

I then added, "I will phone my friend Brian and ask him if he would be willing to collect them for me and I can collect them off him first thing in the morning!"

I could see Wendall's mind ticking and he then replied, "Alright then, I will leave you now and get back to you later on this evening!" Before Wendall departed I introduced him to my wife's relatives and also asked him if he wanted to stay for dinner but he declined. Later that night at 21:36 p.m. Wendall phoned me on his mobile phone and claimed that I could not collect the 'printing presses' that night as Snakeshaft felt "that there were too many Old Bill about!" Wendall added that he would phone me sometime the next day to collect and deliver the 'printing presses'.

CHAPTER 10:

THE ARREST

The next day, Tuesday 5th June 2001, I dropped my daughter Jade to school in the morning. Then I went for my daily jog along the seafront, showered, said goodbye to my wife Stacey and set off for London to see my friend nicknamed 'George Best'. Firstly though, I stopped off at the local florist on Canvey Island and ordered twelve red roses to be delivered to our address the following day, as it was our seventeenth wedding anniversary. I then stopped of at the local Safeway's superstore and bought some delicious cantaloupe melon for my lunch. I was already on my way to London when I noticed a voice mail message on my mobile phone. I phoned the voice mail number at 11:40 a.m. and listened to the message— it was Wendall who wanted me to contact him. Immediately I phoned him and asked him to leave a time and date on the voice mail in future to avoid any confusion. He said he'd been trying to contact me since 10:30 a.m. He asked me if I could meet him and we arranged to meet at Upminster underground train station. He then asked me where I was at the present time and I said that I was nearly there as I was on the A127 that passes the Upminster turn off.

Unbeknown to me, at 10:53 hours, a police radio message had been circulated over the airwaves for several Armed Response Vehicles (ARVs) to attend an urgent briefing about an "impending job". To compound the sense of urgency, one ARV Trojan 211 activated its blue lights and siren to reach the rendezvous point at Bornchurch Police Station as quickly as possible.

I met Wendall at Upminster train station and picked him up in my new black BMW 328ci I had bought several days before and that no one knew I had. He asked me to pick up the 'printing presses' and deliver them to Cambridgeshire that afternoon. I asked Wendall where they were now and he said Snakeshaft was bringing them from Brixton. I said to him to give me Snakeshaft's address and I would go and collect them and he could go! For whatever reason, Wendall was reluctant to give me Snakeshaft's address, which I viewed as odd—as if it was top secret and I could not be trusted. I then suggested to Wendall he give me his mobile number and I would phone him. Wendall then said he had left Snakeshaft's phone number in his car that was parked in a pay-and-display car park some quarter of a mile away. He also added that his wife Carol was in the car waiting for him. Again I thought this was odd—that his car was so far away from the meet, but I did not give it too much significance.

By now, at 11:20 a.m, a resolute phalanx of very senior and rank and file policemen and women were gathering for a briefing at Bornchurch Police Station. They included, the Borough Commander, two detective inspectors, one police inspector, one police sergeant, thirteen ARV police officers and a detective inspector and constable from SO11, the intelligence branch of New Dockland Yard. Also, at the same time, five undercover surveillance police officers, in three unmarked police vehicles, were deployed around Snakeshaft's home address in nearby Bornchurch—all obviously geared up and waiting for something definite to occur.

Wendall and I drove around to the pay-and-display car park. While I waited inside my vehicle Wendall went to his car to retrieve Snakeshaft's phone number. This was at about 12 p.m. I phoned Snakeshaft at 12:05 hours in the presence of Wendall and the conversation went as follows:

Diamond: Hello Dan.
Snakeshaft: Who's that?
Diamond: It's me Terry, I've got to see you haven't I?
Snakeshaft: Yeah!
Diamond: Where shall I meet you, at your house or somewhere else?
Snakeshaft: Can you meet me at my house, but can you give me 25 minutes as I have had to stop off somewhere!
Diamond: Alright, no problem!
Snakeshaft: I will phone you when I get back home!

Almost simultaneously, shortly after 12 pm the police inspector from the elite SO11 intelligence squad began the briefing at Bornchurch Police Station. What was said was confidential and has never been revealed to my legal representatives. But five ARV vehicles were deployed to a rendezvous point not far away from Snakeshaft's home address. These consisted of three Vauxhall Omega area cars, one Vauxhall Vectra control car and a Dog Section van with two armed police officers and two dogs inside.

After the above phone call to Snakeshaft I took the final instructions from Wendall and then told him to go. But strangely, Wendall refused to go saying that he would take me to Snakeshaft's house himself. I followed Wendall's silver Vauxhall Vectra, the one I gave to him on his release from prison, to nearby Bornchurch. On the way there Wendall dropped his wife off at a park gate close to Snakeshaft's house. We then drove a little further in convoy to a road I assume is near Snakeshaft's address. Feeling rather cynical I noticed the name of the road we pulled down, 'St Nicholas Road', and immediately I associated it with 'Old Nick', a synonym for the devil. In fact we both park in a turning off St Nicholas Road called Eyhurst Close. I had never been to Snakeshaft's address before so I didn't know where he lived. In fact, I only ever met Snakeshaft once before and that was at the West Ham football match.

Wendall and I exit our vehicles and walk together over the park and through a different gate than the one his wife entered. While over the park I share my delicious cantaloupe melon with him, little I knowing that would be the last treat my taste buds would be getting for a long, long time. At 12:27 hours, my mobile phone rings, it is Snakeshaft saying he is indoors now and for me to come around. As we exit the park, Wendall is leading the way. We walk down Barren Drive and I still don't know where Snakeshaft lives. We actually walk past Snakeshaft's house so that Wendall is able to look down the side of Snakeshaft's house to see if his white Ford Escort is there. Then Wendall proclaims, "He's in!" – which we already know – and we have to walk backwards to the front door. While Wendall knocks on the front door I stand on the front porch area looking away from the house at the houses opposite. I then have this preternatural feeling that I am being observed. As I am assimilating these strange thoughts and feelings, according to the police observation log, Snakeshaft opens the front door and at 12:33 we enter the hallway. We say hello to each other and then I said, "Where's the parcel as I want to get on my way?" Snakeshaft then asks where I am parked, as he states he will bring the parcel around to my car. I tell him that I am parked just off St Nicholas Road. I then ask for the £500 promised and Snakeshaft pulls out a wad of banknotes and gives me £500 in used £20 notes. I am a little concerned that Snakeshaft will not let me carry the parcel or examine it. More specifically, Snakeshaft wants to walk the parcel around to my car – does he want to see what car I am driving?

It is now 12:36 hours and, going by the official surveillance log, as I leave Snakeshaft's house with Wendall we walk 'empty-handed' back to our vehicles. Exactly one minute later at 12:37 hours, Snakeshaft emerges from his house carrying a blue bag with the 'valuable printing presses' inside. He walks around to Eyhurst Close and places the heavy 'blue bag' inside the passenger footwell of my vehicle. He taps on the roof of my vehicle and walks back the way he came and climbs into Wendall's Vauxhall Vectra that is registered to him. Meanwhile, I lean over the central console of my vehicle and partially open the blue bag using a drawstring. I want to check the bag for drugs, because I am still suspicious as to why they would not let me carry or check the contents of the bag inside the house. I look inside the 'blue bag' and I can see a yellow cloth or towelling material. I put my hand inside the bag and I felt something hard and metallic. Happy that I cannot feel any drugs such as pills, powder or bush (cannabis) I pull the drawstring and set off on my journey.

Little did I know, at 12:37 hours, the same time as Snakeshaft is leaving his house, at the behest of the Detective Inspector controlling the operation inside Trojan One, a Police Sergeant instructs the other ARVs to "stop the vehicle coming away from the premises, as it is believed to have a weapon in it." Somehow the ARVs are aware that there is a 'machine pistol' in my car and I believe that I am carrying 'valuable printing presses'. Who is telling the police this information, as they cannot be psychic, is it Wendall ... Snakeshaft ... or the both of them working together as a team? Something is not right!

At about 12:40 hours I pulled away from Eyhurst Close and set off on my way. I'm about 15 minutes into the journey, approximately three miles away from Snakeshaft's address, when the Detective Inspector controller of the operation in Trojan One authorizes the other ARVs to carry out a non-compliant stop procedure, as it now believed there is a submachine pistol in the body shell of my car! Strangely, the Detective Inspector then plays no further part in the arrest or allegedly the case for that matter.

I am driving along Wood Lane in Dagenham when I come to a set of traffic lights at a junction that ironically is called 'The Fiddlers'. The traffic lights are red and there is a car in front of me also stationary. I look into my rear view mirror and I can see two marked Vauxhall Omega police cars directly behind me, but even more disturbing the policeman in the passenger side of the lead car, Trojan 211, is wearing body armour and staring intently at me. So much so, I say to myself, "Are they for me?" My eyes are drawn down to the 'blue bag' in the passenger footwell. I look into the rear view mirror again and I can see the piercing evil eyes of the 'cozzer' burning into me. I can literally feel the intensity of his power of concentration as if he is really psyched-up for something. As the traffic lights change to green, the car in front of me begins to pull away and at the same time an unmarked black Honda police car comes up the inside of me and half-heartedly pulls across my path leaving me an appreciable gap to squeeze through. Again I look into my rear view mirror and 'evil eyes' is already out of the lead ARV with his MP5 carbine machine gun trained at the driver's side of my vehicle. For a spilt second I consider slamming the accelerator to the floor and going for the gap but sensibly I say to myself, "I've got nothing to worry about as I have only got 'printing presses' on board!" It is not the end of the world, or so I thought!

Even before 'evil-eyes' has time to bark his orders at me, "Armed police show me your hands!" I already have my hands out of the driver's door window. Another ARV officer then comes to the driver's door and orders me out of the vehicle. He then escorts me to the back of my vehicle where another armed police officer takes over and begins to handcuff my hands behind my back. As he is doing this I notice that his hands are trembling considerably. My mind was racing, I am thinking, "God, what is happening here? This is not some potluck, routine vehicle check. This is heavy shit!" As I am being led away to a waiting police car I look up into the clear blue summer sky and wonder when would be the next time that I would see my beautiful newborn baby boy again. Something is definitely not right here! The only way out of this is with the power of truth!

To compound my suspicions, as I am being handcuffed at the rear of my vehicle another police officer runs past and blurts out, "Who fucking parked that like that?"–alluding to the unmarked black Honda which was supposed to conduct a non compliant stop. A stage-managed gap had been left for me to power through only for the trigger happy 'evil eyes' to mow me down if I went for it. I can visualize the headlines now, "Dangerous villain shot dead in police road block...police find loaded Uzi submachine gun and 376 rounds of ammunition in the victims car!" There would have been a low profile inquiry into the incident and my wife would have been a widow always wondering to what extent were Wendall and Snakeshaft's role in the police trap.

Again, while at the rear of my vehicle, another plainclothes detective runs past me proclaiming they are from the Cranham Crime Squad and that they are looking for drugs. This was all bollocks, as minutes earlier it had been circulated over the police airwaves that there was a submachine pistol in the car. I am then chaperoned to the driver's door of my vehicle by a member of the same Crime Squad while another member of the squad goes straight to the passenger footwell of the BMW. I am ordered to watch as the detective searches the 'blue bag' and the following dialogue takes place.

DC Cole:	Alright, I am DC Cole from the Crime Squad at Cranham and I want you to watch carefully as the officers search your car.
Diamond:	Yeah, yeah! (I am thinking this is like a pantomime.)
DC Cole:	We've got reason to believe you've got a gun in here. Have you?
Diamond:	A gun–no way!
DC Cole:	Is that your bag?
Diamond:	What?
DC Cole:	Is that your bag in the passenger footwell?
Diamond:	No, I just picked it up for someone.
DC Cole:	What is in it?
Diamond:	Don't know I never looked.
DC Cole to DC Logan:	What have we got?
DC Logan:	A gun.
Diamond:	I don't know nothing about a gun!
DC Cole:	Right, listen to me, I am arresting you for possession of a firearm, a gun.

He then alleges he cautioned me and I made no reply.

The above dialogue is DC Cole's version of events that are basically true. It is true that I may have said I never looked in the 'blue bag', as in fact I did not check the contents of the bag thoroughly. The whole police operation was a grade A farce. It stunk of a set-up from the very beginning. My mind was racing as I expected 'valuable printing presses' to be in the 'blue bag' and not a gun. I had undeniably been set-up, but who was responsible. Was it Snakeshaft? Was it Wendall? Nah, my pal Wendall would not do that, he was good stuff! Or was he? All the dark anxieties and concerns over the release of Wendall began to haunt me. I was going over the events that occurred earlier that day. On the whole, Snakeshaft appeared to play the part well. But Wendall did look perturbed by something. Anyone who knows Wendall knows that its hard for him to conceal his thoughts and feelings. Why wouldn't Wendall tell me where Snakeshaft lived? Why did Wendall want to be at the collection point when he did not need to be there? He did not add up. As for Snakeshaft I hardly knew him and it was highly probable that he was behind all this as he insisted on knowing where my car was parked to see what car I was driving and, more specifically, he was personally responsible for putting the blue bag inside my car. One of them had set me up, or was it the pair of them? Only the endless forces of time would expose and excavate the plain unvarnished truth.

CHAPTER 11:

BORNCHURCH POLICE STATION

At the scene of the arrest in Wood Lane, Dagenham, I was searched and a large quantity of cash taken from me. At the police station I told the desk sergeant that the £180 in £10 notes and a £50 note was my money and the £500 in £20 notes was the money that 'the man' gave to me. The desk sergeant then ordered a member of the Cranham Crime Squad, DC Lark, to put the money into separate bags for evidential reasons. I was then escorted to a police medical room where swabs were taken from my arms, hands and face for firearm residue. After that I was taken to the police cells to ponder over the nightmare ordeal of the set-up. Was it Wendall? Was it Snakeshaft? Or was it both of them?

At 14:00 hours all the senior police officers in the case, along with the ARV police officers, attended a debriefing at Havering Police Station, no doubt to celebrate a successful police operation. More like a successful set-up but things were not to go to plan!

Firstly, remarkably, the police were claiming that they did not know who I was and I was not about to assist them because as far as I was concerned a firearm had been planted in my car and they would send armed police officers to search my address where I had young children residing. As far as I was concerned British armed police did not have the best record for entering premises with firearms at the ready. One child was fatally shot while sleeping in his bed in the 1980s and another naked adult had been shot recently and killed during a bungled house arrest in Hastings, Sussex. I saw it as my duty as a husband and father not to divulge my name and address until I had seen a legal representative. More alarmingly, I noticed that the hands of one of the ARV police officers who had arrested me were shaking like a leaf. Why?

Meanwhile in keeping with the strange machinations of the case, at 21:45 hours that evening my cell door was opened and in walked two Flying Squad detectives DS Herbert and DC Noel. They claimed, "due to the serious nature of the offence, we are taking over the case." Personally, I did not care who was taking over the case, it could have been Sherlock Holmes and his eminent sidekick, Watson. I would still have refused to divulge my name and address. They asked me if I would allow them to take my fingerprints. I agreed to this request and they took them immediately and sent them off to the fingerprint branch SO3 at New Dockland Yard for comparison. Apparently, a positive match had been made at 00:10 hours that same evening.

The very next morning, Wednesday 6th June 2001, with my identity now known, I was taken from the police cell and rearrested for being unlawfully at large from prison. Apparently there had been a warrant out for my arrest since 1996 due to the revocation of my parole licence.

Later that morning the police handed a pre-interview disclosure sheet to my solicitor, Mr Hugo Wiseman, that said:

> On Tuesday 5th June 2001, as a result of information received, the driver of a black BMW, registration number …, was stopped by armed, uniformed police officers. The vehicle was stopped at Wood Lane at the junction with Whalebone Lane, south Romford. There was no other person in the vehicle.
>
> Once handcuffed the driver was spoken to by DC Cole who is attached to Havering Police Station, while other officers searched the vehicle. In the passenger foot well of the vehicle DC Logan found a blue bag. Inside this bag was a cream coloured towel inside which was a firearm and other items as shown on the custody record.
>
> To summarize, Mr Diamond states he picked up the bag for someone but didn't know what was in the bag. He was then taken to Bornchurch Police Station.
>
> No other persons have been arrested.
>
> Police do not confirm or deny that Mr Diamond or any other person(s) were the subject of a surveillance operation.

After receiving the above disclosure sheet and discussing it with my solicitor we both noticed two salient points, one was the police were acting on "information received" and the second was "no other persons have been arrested." In the old days it was customary for me to say "no comment" to all police questions, but things had radically changed since the days of the defendant's right to silence. Now it could be held against you! I knew I had been set up and I knew I had to say something straight away in my defence, otherwise I would be accused later, at a trial, of making things up as I went along. After discussing the situation with my solicitor, Hugo Wiseman, he suggested that I make 'a prepared defence statement' in response to the pre-interview disclosure sheet and then say "no comment" in any police taped interviews later. In a prepared defence statement I said:

This was the weekend just gone. I met some people I knew. They asked me if I would run a parcel up to the Midlands for them. I asked them if it was drugs because if so I wouldn't do it. They said that it was valuable printing presses. They offered me £500 and I agreed. On Monday night (the day before my arrest) a bloke came around my house. He gave me a map of Cambridgeshire and pointed out where I was to take the parcel. By Tesco's superstore on the A14 Ely turn off and meet a man in a 'N' reg light blue BMW called Alex.

Next day I went to an address in Essex. A man there gave me the £500 and brought the bag out which he placed in my car that was parked around the corner. He walked away and I looked in the bag and saw a towel. I put my hand in and felt something metallic. I believed it was the printing presses. I was concerned it might be drugs. I drove off and shortly afterwards I was stopped by the police. I cannot supply the details of the people involved. I realize these are dangerous villains and I fear for my life and that of my wife and children. I had no knowledge whatsoever that I was carrying a gun. I would not have undertaken such a serious enterprise. I know that it would be helpful if I named the people involved but it would be the end of my life and that of my family. Please believe me this is true. I have not given my address because I am terrified that armed police officers will go to my house where I have young children.

This was signed by me and countersigned by my solicitor.

Upon reading this out during the taped police interview I was asked to elaborate on the 'prepared defence statement' which I would not in fear of bringing harm to my family and my life. I decided to tell the truth, but without divulging either the names of the people involved or the location of the house where I collected the 'blue bag'. Unbeknown to me, however, Snakeshaft's house in Barren Drive had been under observation in order to see what vehicle I arrived and left in! The Flying Squad officers knew everything. They knew about the house, the people involved–Wendall and Snakeshaft–and yet they had not arrested anyone as yet. They half-heartedly pressurized me to name names and locations but I would not, even though the police knew about the others involved. Put concisely, the 'prepared defence statement' had blown apart the whole set-up operation. The Flying Squad had to decide what to do? They decided to arrest the person who was seen putting the 'blue bag' into my car and let Wendall walk away. The overriding idea was that I was to get arrested, bang to rights, with the Uzi in the car, say "no comment" during the police interviews and trundle off to HMP Suckerville for a doleful decade more while the most toad-spotted plotters sidled off to collect their ill-gotten reward money.

The set-up plan began to go wrong almost immediately as someone had called in the Flying Squad to take over the case, which meant that the original Cranham Crime Squad–or 'Pantomime Squad' as I called them – were pushed out of the case. It transpired, against their wishes, the Flying Squad had to arrest one or both of the setter-uppers. To arrest Wendall would have meant they would have had to revoke his parole licence which amounted to nearly five years back in prison. Therefore, only after my interview, they decided it had to be Snakeshaft.

To use a hunting metaphor, all the hounds had chased the badger while the foxes had sidled off into the urban undergrowth. Similarly, some might say that some foxes were running with the hounds in the guise of the Cranham Crime Squad. Either way the Flying Squad were in a dilemma and they had to arrest Snakeshaft. The fashion of Snakeshaft's arrest was also quite striking. A resolute cohort of *unarmed* Flying Squad officers, including an eminent acting Detective Chief Inspector decided to visit Snakeshaft's address and arrest him at 19:40 hours on the 6th June, some 31 hours after my initial arrest. Apparently, he was sitting indoors eating his tea when the Flying Squad knocked on his front door. Despite already knowing about my arrest, he obviously felt that he was safe and that he was with the winning team. Amazingly, he was taken to Upney Police Station un-handcuffed and interviewed with a legal advisor present. Not surprisingly he made a 'no comment' interview, as these were not the usual 'legalized gangsters' that he was used to dealing with.

The Machiavellian plot thickens, however, as after my police taped interview on the 6th June, while being escorted back to the police cells, the following conversation took place.

DS Herbert: That was a good battle, wasn't it?

Diamond: What do you mean a good battle, that was the truth!

DS Herbert: You know that we nearly had you a couple of times.

Diamond: What do you mean a couple of times?

DS Herbert: You know that robbery in the docklands last year, it was a tasty bit of work!

Diamond: That was nothing to do with me!

DS Herbert: I was the officer in charge of that case, did you watch it on Crimewatch?

Diamond: No I did not! Is that what this is all about? I suppose this set-up is down to you?

DS Herbert: No, no, this isn't our case. We have taken it over from another squad. We know that you have it with some good people. In fact, if I was not a policeman, I would most probably be in your shoes.

Diamond: What are you saying?

DS Herbert: I have a kind of mutual respect for you.

Diamond: Listen, that was nothing to do with me. I am here because I have been set-up. I never knew that I had a gun in the car!

DS Herbert: I can help you, you know.

Diamond: What do you mean?

DS Herbert: If you give us some information.

Diamond: I have already told you, I cannot tell you who put the gun in my car because my family and me would be in danger!

DS Herbert: You know that we have photographs?

Diamond: Photographs, then you know that I have been set-up then?

DS Herbert: That is a matter for the court now!

Diamond: Yeah, this is a fucking liberty! You know that I have been set-up and you are fucking loving it!

DS Herbert then closed the cell door.

As we can see, the thick stew of intrigue and corruption begins to congeal. The new squad that has taken over the case from the 'pantomime squad' also suspect me of committing a major armed robbery on their patch and, lo and behold, DS Herbert of the Flying Squad is the principal officer in the investigation of the case! All this information, and the police say they did not know of my identity when they originally arrested me during the authorized non-compliant stop! The arresting officers were compelled to act dim so as not to compromise the source of their information from their informants. The likely scenario is that I had been under surveillance as a 'target criminal' in a joint operation between Essex Police and the Flying Squad in response to their suspicions that I was an active robber and had committed the Bermondsey Docklands robbery. And when I was set-up by the 'pantomime squad' they came in and took over the case as I was 'their man' and the Cranham Crime Squad had compromised an active Flying Squad surveillance operation. No doubt, the Flying Squad, especially DS Herbert was livid and in his frustration set about creating a connection between the Bermondsey robbery and the set-up palaver. For if DS Herbert could secure a conviction in the Uzi case and somehow invoke the *Two Strikes* automatic life sentence statute, it would save a lot of face for him back at the office. But how would he and the 'legalized gangsters' set about doing it?

The following day after my arrest, Wednesday 6th June 2001, I was charged with three offences. These were: being in unlawful possession of an Uzi firearm, which if found guilty carried a maximum sentence of ten years imprisonment; being in possession of ammunition, maximum sentence seven years imprisonment; and being a prohibited person in possession of the said weapon, maximum sentence five years imprisonment. On being charged the desk sergeant asked if I had any comment to make and was eager to enter 'no comment' on the charge sheet, but I interrupted him by saying, "I swear that I have never seen that gun before in my life and I had no knowledge of it in my car!" I was then returned to the police cells to await the slow and methodical wheels of justice to turn me into another convicted prisoner. But I was determined to expose the depraved scumbags that had done this to me and fight and fight until my dying breath.

CHAPTER 12:

THE INNOCENT MAN

After two days in Bornchurch Police Station, on Thursday 7th June 2001, I was taken by sweatbox to Bow Magistrates Court and after the facts of the case were read out to the court, the elderly female Magistrate gave me a contemptuous stare and remanded me in custody for four weeks. From there I was taken to that barbaric relic of a jail, Wentonville Prison in North London.

Fortunately for me, my brother Eugene was already in the jail awaiting trial on a preposterous charge of 'interfering with a witness'. He was later cleared by a perceptive jury at a Crown Court. I was placed on A wing in a cell with a half-caste prisoner serving four years for severely bashing up a gay man in his flat and robbing him. Straight away I was on my guard about talking to cell mates. In cases where the suspect is innocent the police, more especially the 'legalized gangsters' that were behind my arrest, usually seek to bolster their case by including a trumped up cell confession. They usually colour the confession with some facts that only the police and defendant know to give the whole charade an air of credibility. Whatever the case, being well versed in the Machiavellian tactics of the 'legalized gangsters', I was taking no chances at all and decided to convey only the basic details of the case to my cell mate.

My brother Eugene, who was on G wing, sent me over a much-needed 'survival kit' of writing implements, toiletries, foodstuffs and a radio. The clientele at the jail was very cosmopolitan, a veritable assortment of all colours, creeds, faiths and nationalities. The prisoners called A wing 'Beirut' and in many respects it was doing Beirut a disservice. Many of the prisoners were poor, unclean, either suffering from mental illness or drug abuse and were in for petty and pointless crimes and I felt and looked distinctly out of place. Despite many years in British penal institutions I was walking about in shock. I should not have been there. I began to view the brutal world of imprisonment through the prism of an innocent man. This was totally new to me. I had previously been morally and legally guilty of the crimes that I was in prison for, only this time it was radically different. Bemused and bewildered I inched my way through those first few days with a large uncomfortable lump in my throat. I was hoping, as soon as the dust had settled, that I could get some feedback from Wendall, Snakeshaft and my legal representatives about the case. I wanted to speak to Wendall to find out exactly what was going on? Was it Snakeshaft who had set me up? At this stage, I still viewed Wendall as a loyal and devoted friend. Little did I know that I should have seen the signs … !

After the first day at Wentonville Prison, I managed to borrow some phone cards and telephone my wife and direct family on the prison payphone. I have got to confess, I felt sick, as I had been well and truly stitched up. All I needed was a pink ribbon and bow on my head and I would have looked the part.

After two days at the prison, the first breakthrough occurred when a mutual friend of Wendall and Snakeshaft came to my cell and said that he had just seen 'Snaksie' on a prison visit. The screws had said that they would not put him on A wing with me as there was "A threat on his and his family's life!" Errrr …, that is exactly what I was saying in my police interview? Even more absurd, the acquaintance, who had been arrested with Wendall and Snakeshaft in the past, proclaimed, "Snakeshaft is good stuff you know! He hasn't done anything wrong."

I said, "How can you come out with a statement like that when you know nothing about my case!" Little did I know that Snakeshaft had been up to visit this person at Wentonville Prison several times before he and I were arrested. Apparently, this person had been arrested with two firearms and there were suggestions that Snakeshaft and the same police who arrested me were involved.

Scarcely had the prison doors clanged shut behind Snakeshaft and he started having regular covert police visits. But before I had time to speak to this dubious character, the jack-booted, black-attired security screws came for me and escorted me to the Segregation Unit. I was told that I had been made 'a potential category A prisoner' and because of 'previous firearm offences' I would not be remaining at Wentonville Prison. Well, the Cranham Crime Squad could not have me quizzing their number one police informant, could they?

Apparently, Snakeshaft had been remanded in custody for a week to give the Flying Squad and the Crown Prosecution Services enough time to disclose covert video evidence of Snakeshaft placing the blue bag, containing the Uzi submachine pistol, in my BMW. A week later there was no video evidence and he was refused bail. Was this because it would have shown Wendall in the video chaperoning me to Snakeshaft's address and this would mean that he would have to be arrested! Whatever the case, I was transferred to Cellmarsh Top Security Prison in South East London. In contrast to the doleful and dilapidated environ of Wentonville Prison, I had a clean kennel with in-cell sanitation and some sensible people to talk to. I had regular access to the payphones and immediately started to phone my family, friends and acquaintances in order to get some feedback on this guy Snakeshaft. The feedback I received was mixed. In all fairness, some people vouched for the guy saying, "He stood up for us," and "There was nothing wrong with him." Whereas others were more critical and cynical proclaiming that he had been going around East London and Essex saying that he had a 'top cozzer' who could provide information about surveillance and bugging techniques on target criminals, more especially on those involved in the importation of drugs. Another source recounted the time Snakeshaft was given a routine police check while driving his car which contained a large consignment of drugs only to be sent on his way five minutes later. One well-respected East London face was even taking Snakeshaft's children to West Ham United football matches until the bubble burst.

More disturbing for me, I was not only being kept apart from Snakeshaft, but due to the sudden elusiveness of my so-called, long-standing friend Wendall in the hour of need, I was going around chasing ghosts. I had so many questions to ask and yet no one to put them to. I felt cut adrift and isolated. Like a chainsaw upon my mind, I wanted to ask where this monstrous weapon had come from? Who provided it? And most significantly, why oh why, had such a close friend done this sick and terrible thing to me?

Consumed by the case it became an obsession. As soon as I woke up in the mornings, like a house brick in the face, it assaulted and ravaged my vulnerable mind. I felt a bit like a lunatic in the cell at the bottom of a long corridor, where other internees would declare, "Don't go down there, there is a mad man and all he does is ramble on and on about his fucking case!" More sympathetic prisoners, like Howard Prosser, Chris Pearman and Brian Richardson, encouraged and advised me to, "take a deep breath as it will all come out in the wash!" But the cold reality remained, here I was in the factory of silent screams, set-up, washed-up and all but eaten-up by the ruthless legal and penal machinery; seeking the very oxygen of hope and faith from legal advisers and loved ones who painfully empathized with my plight.

Like a demented mathematician, I tried to solve the Uzi enigma by working out the answer in reverse. We had the final result, the weapon placed in my vehicle, but not how we had reached there. Of course, the answers were there, like the perfidious motives of the police informant and his elusive accomplice, but with limited intelligence and substance, I could not unravel the mind-soothing formula. The only weapons I possessed to fend off the rigours of insanity were the soul-saving telephone calls to my wife Stacey. I had to eradicate any doubt, for doubt, any doubt, about the eventual establishment of my innocence was the overriding enemy. Like a moral lighthouse in a tempestuous storm, I had to confront and endure its fear and ferocity, for tomorrow, who knows, the sun may shine once again for this sucker.

After weeks and weeks of mental torture and anguish, on 5th July 2001, I was produced at Bow Magistrates Court for the second hearing. After a lengthy consultation with my female solicitor I was advised strongly to keep my cool and to say as little as possible to Snakeshaft in the dock, as we strongly suspected him of being a state paid police informant. When I first laid my eyes on Snakeshaft at the court, I knew the slag had done me! Years and years of observing body language and posture came in handy. Snakeshaft not only looked like a man who had been tumbled, his furtive eyes, nervous disposition and attendant loss of weight said it all. I could smell it on him, the distinctive malodorous whiff of a grade A slag! Why does humanity produce such evil and vile specimens? Micro scientists should isolate the DNA strand that causes such treachery and banish it to oblivion.

Down in the court cells I was double handcuffed and escorted to the court by a flotilla of prison screws. The Securicor screws slipped Snakeshaft in the dock after me so that he was nearer the door should I decide to steam into him. As the preliminary hearing got under way, I said to Snakeshaft, "You've got a lot of questions to answer." He replied rather unconvincingly, "I've done nothing wrong!" A wrong move, as I never said that he had done anything wrong, and already he was denying wrongdoing. The Crown asked for another four weeks remand in custody, as there was a logjam of firearms to be processed at the police forensic laboratory and the unfired Uzi did not warrant prioritisation. The dreaded 'Yardies' were the real hotshots in the summer of 2001 as they were giving the police forensic experts plenty of overtime.

During the third court appearance on the 2nd August 2001 I was ready for Snakeshaft, as somehow I had to get him to open up about the case. As I emerged from the category A holding cells at Bow Magistrates Court I spotted Snakeshaft with several Securicor jailers around him. They were waiting for me to get double handcuffed by the prison screws and then escort me to the court. The following conversation took place:

Diamond: Haven't you got bail yet?
Snakeshaft: He looked at me in amazement and declared,
               I have tried three times and I cannot apply anymore!
Diamond: Apparently they could not find the court file?
Snakeshaft: Yeah!
Diamond: Look you know that I have been set-up.
Snakeshaft: Yeah, but why are you saying that I have done it. 'The Crook' and Max down the gym are going around saying that it is me?
Diamond: Listen, I have not said it is you! I said it is one of two people (I then point my hand at him and an empty space and then added). One of you two have set me up! Do you think it was the little fellow then (meaning Wendall)?
Snakeshaft: Well it wasn't me!
Diamond: What are you saying then?
Snakeshaft: I was nicked 36 hours after you?
Diamond: Yeah, that is odd!

Snakeshaft then looked at me as if he is unable to talk in front of the screws and then declared, "We have got to get together for a legal conference!" I agreed.

The conversation continued for a little longer but the key factor was that Snakeshaft agreed that I had been set-up. Obviously Snakeshaft knew a lot more than he was revealing. He had lost more weight and his concentration upon questions was intense, in fact too intense, because when he denied setting me up and I had come up with the Wendall angle he looked very uncomfortable and asked for a legal conference. A sure method to stop the difficult questioning.

In the court, the stern looking female stipendiary magistrate committed the case to Southpark Crown Court for trial. A Pleas and Directions Hearing was set for another four weeks and we were both remanded in custody. As soon as I was returned to my cell, in the bowels of the courthouse, I spoke to my female legal representative and we wrote down a verbatim account of the conversation that I had had with Snakeshaft. Years and years of interaction with the police and legal representatives had taught me to log down any conservations, more especially when there could be a conflict of interest later on.

One of the eternal dilemmas facing any victim of an innocent crime, and more especially a set-up, is he or she is invariably the last one to be told any useful news or information regarding the case. For it stands to reason the police involved in the set-up have a vested interest in one overriding thing – a conviction. As the compelling maxim proclaims, "Knowledge is power!" Therefore, the police are ultra-reluctant to furnish their victim with any information at all. If the police had arrested me under normal circumstances and conditions, they and the Crown Prosecution Service, would literally throw the evidence at me. But when someone has been set-up and foul play is suspected, it is a case of providing the defence with the bare minimum of disclosure. One tends to rely, therefore, on news, rumours and gossip that is drip-fed or filtered through an intricate network of prosecutors, police, legal advisors, friends, enemies and associates situated at the coalface of fact and fiction.

A significant point in the case occurred while Snakeshaft was held in Wentonville Prison. My brother Eugene, and other associates that were in the jail at the time, were instructed by me to watch his behaviour and monitor his visits. On the whole Snakeshaft was under immense pressure at Wentonville, but was it the usual pressure and stress of being swagged away from one's family and loved ones or was it something more sinister? Was it the corrosive virus and anxiety of prison paranoia? The fear that a life-changing secret could emerge at any moment and render him a target for every prisoner's revenge at being grassed. Snakeshaft was not a happy prisoner, he felt out of place among the normal prisoners as he felt that he should not be there. Everyday he shuffled around slack-jawed and defeated and it was noticed. That is, until he came off the prison payphone on Friday 20th July 2001 looking sprightly and significantly rejuvenated. By all accounts, all the other prisoners noticed it. Did he know something they did not? Of course he did, as his buddies SO11 took him out of the cauldron of reality for seven days in police custody. The only problem was the custody record at Bornchurch Police Station showed Snakeshaft as being logged in the station on Monday 23rd July, so where had he been over the weekend? No doubt with his family, one of the perks of working for the State.

What we do know for certain is on 23rd July 2001 Snakeshaft was interviewed by DC Logan (the detective that searched the blue bag in my vehicle on the day of my arrest) and another police officer about the Macitto drug case. During the interview Snakeshaft is asked to comment on video surveillance while it is being replayed back to him. He names Macitto and another person but remarkably skirts around the issue of how he came to meet Macitto through Wendall. In fact, despite helping the police with their inquiries, he avoids naming Wendall during the interview at all. Why?

Apparently, after the long dubious week in police custody, Snakeshaft is then placed in Wormhood Shrubs. This is not normal practice, as Wormhood Shrubs does not come under the catchment area of Southpark Crown Court. Then the prisoners at Wentonville Prison found a list of telephone numbers hidden in the laundry room on the landing where Snakeshaft was allocated. The phone numbers were of Bornchurch Police Station!

The whole criminal and legal pattern of the case was contrary to normal procedure. I was supposed to be on the 'fast track' legal procedure where trials are encouraged to meet certain deadlines such as 'Custody Time Limits', but this case was perverse. Every time we went to court, the CPS employed a 'child' of a prosecutor who, as my counsel put it, "knew nothing" and therefore could not provide, let alone discuss, the most basic of information.

More disgustingly, I had been receiving anonymous hate mail in the form of greeting cards that were addressed to 'gimpy leg'. One card started with the line, "I hope that you are feeling sick sitting in there…". The next one was more localized as it declared, "Stop telling untrue lies about Snaksie." Whoever was sending these infantile cards were sick themselves and possessed a distorted view of life. The term "untrue lies" is in itself the truth. The contents of the anonymous cards were based upon certain events that had occurred during an earlier prison sentence and whoever wrote them was not in possession of the full facts. Indeed, they were relating the facts second hand. But who had recently come out of prison and wanted to regurgitate prison politics and make it a burning issue? It all pointed to one person, or couple! Strangely enough, the hate mail stopped after rumours began circulating that Snakeshaft was going to turn Queen's Evidence.

What gave me cause for concern was I had written a lengthy profile of the two protagonists involved in the case, putting forth reasons why they would want to set me up. I handed them to my solicitors and whether by fate, coincidence or luck, I received another anonymous hate mail card three days later. At the same time Wendall wanted to speak to my wife through a middleman. Apparently, he wanted to ask my wife Stacey some questions; not to explain his inexplicable behaviour after my arrest, when he enquired whether or not I was charged with 'intent' which would trigger the *Two Strikes* automatic life sentence palaver, but to ask what my friends thought about the situation?

Undeniably there was an element of *Schadenfreude* in Wendall's behaviour, as he was not acting as a true friend should and would. It was obvious that I had been set-up. Even Snakeshaft had admitted it at court and yet Wendall's allegiance was towards his louche friend Snakeshaft. It was this, more than anything else that made me believe that Wendall was the real mastermind behind the set-up. If he had orchestrated everything this would mean that he was a police informer too. Wendall had festered away in British prisons for seventeen years and at some point, possibly in the latter stages of his unconscionable incarceration, he had transmogrified into a veritable monster. Resentment and jealousy had coursed through his veins, no doubt compounded by the perpetual encouragement of his scrofulous spouse, aptly nicknamed 'Lady MacBeth', who had heard how I had become successful on all levels of life, that is marital, parental, social, economical and criminal. It seared a palpable hole right through their hearts and instead of redirecting all this negative energy and thought into constructive practices to enjoy a better quality of life and existence it was focussed upon me. In the warped way that jealousy works, they chose to bring about the destruction and downfall of a happy and loving family who had just had another newborn baby son–probably another source of jealousy.

Anybody who has known or been a victim of unadulterated jealousy and resentment and its all pervasive forces of evil will tell you that it is one of the most destructively nauseating human traits that can exist. As an observer of it at work in this case, jealousy crucifies the person to such an extent that he or she is willing to suffer, providing the focus of their perverse attention is suffering too. In this way, I believe, Wendall was caught up in this sad state of affairs, where his distorted and deformed view of life has rendered him mentally sick. Jealousy can be the product of self-induced malicious thoughts and feelings but, alas, it works better when it is supported or bolstered by others who agree that their jealousy is justified and legitimised. From malevolent thoughts and feelings of ill will emerges a perverse plan of perceived injustice and revenge. This calcifies into direct action. Because jealousy is such an insidious human trait, by that I mean it is treachery by stealth, and the action follows along the same path. It is not open for all to see. It is done in the seedy corners of the mind and the action is exhibited in the same way, as seen in the set-up of this case. Once the action of ill-will and harm has been carried out the perpetuators are usually so pleased with their distorted plan of action that they fail to see others are able to witness their perverse gloating, then the plan and action begins to crumble. The perpetrators are exposed. As a victim of unalloyed jealousy in this nightmarish case, my heart bleeds for all those victims of jealousy over the centuries that never knew their perpetrators as I do. Those of us that are familiar with the Shakespearean tragedy of Othello are fully conscious of the fatal flaw of jealousy. In the play, Iago misleads Othello into believing that his virtuous wife Desdemona is unfaithful. Othello succumbs to the evil forces of jealousy and murders his beloved wife. Alas, Iago's revenge is complete. He is blissfully happy, as he could not bear to see two people so in love. In the same way, Wendall has blamed me for the abject failure of his life and he wanted to see my family and me suffer to the point of utter despair.

As is the wont in this case, for some reason, my next court appearance was changed from Southpark to Basilstone Crown Court. On 31st August 2001, I appeared in front of His Honour Justice Ferguson for a Pleas and Directions Hearing. It should have been a straightforward hearing but the prosecution was not ready to proceed due to Snakeshaft's inclusion on the indictment of the Macitto drug case at Knaresbrook Crown Court. The case was, therefore, adjourned so that the Uzi case could be linked up with the drug case.

Several interesting events occurred at the hearing. The first was that I had a heated altercation with the Judge because he had authorized, but had not notified the defendant, that I was to be double handcuffed to a prison officer in the dock. Vehemently I proclaimed that this type of extra-judicial punishment was an outright injustice as the wearing of handcuffs in a modern secure courtroom was not only a Victorian anachronism, but it also undermined my innocence as the handcuffs were 'symbols of guilt'!

I explained to the Judge, *pace*, that I was an innocent man and asked him to justify and explain the reasons for such drastic treatment. The Judge warned me to control my behaviour otherwise I would be removed from the dock. Reluctantly, I agreed to calm down as I wanted to listen to the hearing, but it was an excessive security measure which portrayed me as an extremely violent and thus guilty prisoner, when *de facto*, I was a genuine victim of injustice and abuse of state power.

While all this courtroom drama was unfolding the now physically deteriorating Snakeshaft had sidled into the dock behind me unnoticed and without handcuffs. Before I had sufficient time to shoot some pre-planned questions at him, he was swiftly taken away to the vipers nest whence he came.

On the level of suckerism, however, perhaps the most noteworthy utterance of the hearing emanated from the prosecutor who announced that a third person, on police bail, was due to be charged and included on the indictment of this case. I was gob smacked. Wendall was to be firmly ensconced in the dock with the victim and his very distraught and emaciated accomplice. As a presumptuous prosecutor would no doubt proclaim if the case went to trial, "We will be like rats fighting on a sinking ship!"

By now, the Uzi case had gone from being a straightforward arrest of a suspect possessing a lethal firearm, to another suspect arrested 31 hours later for placing a firearm in my car, to the proposed arrest of the third person, Wendall, who had walked away from the scene unscathed. It all pointed to Snakeshaft. Somehow he had to have already named Wendall in a statement or debrief. But why was he not already arrested and charged? The prosecutor specifically said in open court that this was going to be done in three weeks time on the 19th September 2001 when Wendall's police bail was due to expire. The case did not make sense or contain any logic, not unless Wendall was working with the police. If the police operation to apprehend and arrest me with the Uzi was a straightforward above-board exercise, why did they not arrest all the suspects at Snakeshaft's premises? Why did they want to arrest me away from the house? Why did they allow two suspects to slip away into the urban undergrowth and focus upon one individual?

To adopt or embrace a snooker metaphor, the set-up was a straightforward, run-of-the-mill pot! The object ball (me) was teetering precariously over the pocket and all the set-uppers had to do was hit the cue ball with sufficient force to pot the ball. But as the ball was struck, on the way down to the object ball, the cue ball clipped another ball and it went crashing in off! Commonly known as a 'foul'! Neither the set-uppers nor their senior police handler had expected such a disastrous reaction to a simplistic action. The pre-planned, sober shot had gone completely wrong, as things often do in life. They did not expect such mind-boggling complications and consequences. Now they had to extricate themselves from this cat's cradle of deceit and treachery or be exposed!

Meanwhile, back in the brutal world of reality, the pace and development of the case was fluid. We learned, after four months in prison custody, that on the 1st September 2001 Macitto was reclassified as a top security category A prisoner. This meant that he was reallocated to Cellmarsh Prison where we were able to compare and contrast the merits and shortcomings of our respective cases. Space and time do not permit me to regurgitate our discussions here, but rightly or wrongly, Macitto felt that Snakeshaft was perhaps innocently involved in his arrest due to a covert police operation called 'Salieri', the subject and focus of which was Snakeshaft.

Alternatively, Macitto exhibited significant reservations about Wendall whose Vauxhall Vectra was spotted adjacent to my BMW by the surveillance team when Snakeshaft placed the blue bag containing the Uzi in my vehicle. At the very least, Macitto proclaimed, "Wendall should have been charged with being knowingly concerned in the supply of a firearm!" This alone would have resulted in the revocation of his lengthy parole licence and the immediate return to prison. I must admit, no one likes to see anyone go to prison, but the way Wendall had extricated himself out of this arrest, we had better call him 'Houdini'.

To summarize the Macitto case; we learned that Wendall and Snakeshaft visited Macitto at a Dagenham gymnasium. Snakeshaft enticed Macitto outside the gymnasium to the car park where he placed approximately half a kilo of amphetamine sulphate in Macitto's car which was being covertly videoed by a surveillance team who were originally watching Wendall and Snakeshaft. Macitto then drove several miles to meet his friend in another car park with the surveillance team in tow. The police witnessed a transaction between them and arrested them on the spot. By coincidence, the arresting police officer is DC Cole of the Cranham Crime Squad, the same arresting officer in the Uzi case.

The overarching question remains, however, how did the police know the small parcel wrapped in a plastic carrier bag, no bigger than a medium sized dictionary, was drugs? In my view, they must have had inside information that it was drugs, as not only was Snakeshaft the subject and focus of the operation, but Snakeshaft was the *sine non qua* of the operation. A cunning, covert operation where the target was in cahoots with the surveillance team, ordered to flush out, entice, create and develop serious organized crime in order to secure economic profit and *carte blanche* for his own criminal activities and survival.

Put succinctly, Wendall and Snakeshaft felt that they were above the law, because in reality they were the law, going around selecting unsuspecting victims with all the cold calculation and chilling indifference of a professional hit man.

Another significant aspect of the case was that Wendall and Snakeshaft had the same solicitor, who was also a former Flying Squad police officer. Then in September 2001, Snakeshaft sacked this former Robbery Squad legal advisor and employed another solicitor. The rumour that Snakeshaft was about to go Queen's Evidence was gathering momentum at this stage, more especially with him changing solicitors. The theory goes that these two scumbags had to have separate solicitors, as sooner or later there would be an embarrassing conflict of interests.

At about this time also, I was receiving unconfirmed gossip and rumours that Snakeshaft was either out on bail or in protective police custody. The source of this information came from people who I had long suspected of having a secret relationship with the police. In many respects, this case was a revelation for me. It was transparent to see that in the East End of London, or anywhere for that matter, there was an intricate sub-culture of state registered and state paid police informers, who occasionally pulled together when one of their own was in trouble – more especially, a priceless and valued police informer like Snakeshaft and his tyro accomplice Wendall.

In spite of being a moral and upstanding villain, at times I felt as if I was not only against the police, CPS and the judicial system as a whole, but also police-cultivated lawyers, fellow villains with dubious pasts and not least my immoral and evil co-defendants and some of their equally venomous family members. It was like a low budget Hollywood sci-fi movie, where the alien species – the state paid informers – invaded planet Earth in order to overrun the human species and the only way to recognize these informers was through their green eyes or 666 stencilled upon their scalps. In essence, I felt as if the good villains were being out-numbered by the ever increasing and multiplying informers. They were being recruited like conscription during a crisis of war. There was even a famous list of police informers that was circulated around the East End of London by a disgruntled CPS worker which, although I did not get a chance to see it, contained the name of at least one person whom I knew.

A former armed robber friend of mine, who had fallen on hard times due to the debilitating ravages of heroin, was arrested for shop-lifting at a well-known cathedral of retail therapy in Essex. When the suspect was questioned about the crime, the detective, who knew of the suspect's robbing pedigree and exploits, sought to recruit him as a state paid police informer. He told him that, "It pays good money" and tried earnestly to convert the person. The detective was unsuccessful, hence this story. The days are gone when a policeman uses detective training or his own gut instinct to solve a crime.

Nowadays there is an almost infantile dependence and reliance upon information and intelligence. This opens up massive grey areas in policing where a crime can be unlawfully constructed and activated – as in my case – where the over-zealous police handler and his trusted drug, gambling, alcohol dependent or recently paroled informer work together to create and develop crime that otherwise would not be committed. If that is the situation here, which I believe to be the case, where do the likes of Wendall and Snakeshaft and their perverse type of criminal behaviour rank in the legal world? Because what happened to me was unlawful and it would be absurd if they were allowed to get away with it. Hence this story!

CHAPTER 13:

WENDALL'S POLICE INTERVIEW

Alas, what a day today, the 11th September 2001! On the day that well-organized international terrorists hijacked four civilian airliners and crashed them into the Pentagon and the World Trade Centre in America I received a solicitor's visit and was furnished with primary disclosure material, notice of further evidence and unused material that may undermine the case for the prosecution.

On this day, when thousands of people lost their lives, we learned the most powerful symbol of American prestige and wealth – the World Trade Centre – were not the only things to crumble and disintegrate as, at long last, I took possession of a printed copy of Wendall's taped police interview conducted on the 24th July 2001 at Wilford Police Station, some seven weeks after my initial arrest and four days after Snakeshaft was taken out of Wentonville Prison and taken into police custody for seven days.

From the written account we learned several relevant things. Not only was Wendall using the same legal services as Snakeshaft at that time but he also adopted and embraced the self-same interview tactics as Snakeshaft by offering 'no reply' to all the questions put to him. Admittedly, this type of blank reply to police questions is considered laudable within criminal circles when it is called for, but in this case it has a more sinister tone as seen when a member of the Flying Squad remarkably puts to Wendall:

DC Noel: I put it to you that you are the person who has set this up. You have set up Terence Diamond in cahoots with Daniel Snakeshaft, you knew exactly what was going on. Is there anything you'd like to say about that?

Wendall: No reply.
DC Noel: Do you deny any knowledge of that?
Wendall: No reply.

Do you believe this! At long last we have some groundbreaking progress. DC Noel actually puts the blame for the set-up squarely upon Wendall and even suggests Snakeshaft had played an active part in the sordid enterprise. I am absolutely buzzing on the strength of this marvellous revelation and now I can fully understand and appreciate why it was stated at the last court hearing that Wendall was to be charged and placed upon the indictment for the next court hearing at Knaresbrook Crown Court on September 25th 2001.

Long overdue as it is, this is without parallel, a seminal moment and event in the case for me. I have been churning this nightmare ordeal over and over in my mind like a turbo-charged cement mixer for the past three months and now at long last we have a significant sanity-saving breakthrough.

More to the point – which carries little probative weight with my female solicitor – the above extract has originated from an official source. Indeed it has derived from DC Noel, the second in command in the case behind his partner DS Herbert. What is interesting is the precise and unwavering import of the extract as it leaves little or no scope for ambiguity or obfuscation. The pinpoint strike of "I put it to you …" is very clinical in its delivery and has all the accusative content and potency of the fencing term 'touché'! Admittedly, this influential and productive police interview is not tantamount to Wendall or Snakeshaft's guilt in the set-up, but unquestionably it marks a sea change in the case as it has, once again, come from the lion's mouth.

This new groundbreaking development, coupled with the heart-thumping power of belief that justice will prevail, has now blossomed into relief. Paradoxically, who would believe that a non-cooperative, former armed robber would be actually rooting for the Flying Squad? Similarly, who would believe that a resolute and unequivocal opponent of police informers and all that they stand for would be hoping that one, in the shape of Snakeshaft, would inform against his partner in the set-up, the equally bad guy Wendall?!

This whole case is not about direct opposites, it is about role reversal. One minute the bad guys have the good guy sweating in the hot seat and the next minute the good guy has exposed the bone-deep treachery of the bad guys. Likewise, one minute the elite Flying Squad are hunting down dangerous criminals and the next minute they are, absurd as it seems, covering their own arses by alluding to their quarry's innocence. Whoever thought up this crass, ill-conceived idea to set me up deserves not only the pejorative accolade of 'wanker of the week', but without doubt 'mong of the millennium', because fancy setting someone up and getting nicked, exposed and imprisoned for it yourself. This has got to be the ultimate accolade in folly and failure and should signify that it is high time for the clumsy conspirators to consider retirement from the criminal underworld and its attendant activities.

CHAPTER 14:

SEPTEMBER 2001

As the weeks passed, my concentration was focussed upon the 19th September. This was the day when Wendall was supposed to surrender himself to the police station to either renew his bail or be charged with the Uzi offence. But like everything else in this Byzantine case, the date came and went like a passing shower without incident.

On the 25th September I appeared at Knaresbrook Crown Court for the rearranged Pleas and Directions Hearing in front of Her Honour Judge Webster. When I was produced from Cellmarsh Prison, however, for some absurd reason, Snakeshaft was not produced at the court and the Crown expected me to put in a plea without my co-defendant being present. Not only was this extremely odd, but it is unethical as it puts the defendant at a disadvantage as he or she does not know how the case is panning out. I refused to submit a plea until my dubious co-defendant was present.

More surprisingly, we found out through an unconnected barrister that Snakeshaft had appeared at the same court a day earlier and it was held behind closed doors or *in camera*. Any inquiry by my legal team to find out from Crown counsel and the court's listing office as to Snakeshaft's previous or next court appearance was being met with a remarkable lack of knowledge and indifference. This made my barrister James Goodwyn incandescent with rage, as even the basic courtesy of acknowledgement of future events was not forthcoming. Matters deteriorated even further when my counsel asked the presiding Judge to order the prosecution to produce Snakeshaft at the next hearing but she would not.

This was unadulterated madness. Here I was on the 'fast track' judicial system and the Judge would not aid in the smooth running of justice. Obviously, Her Honour Judge Webster knew something we did not. Later the same day, I submitted my one and only bail application on the basis that the Flying Squad had put in a formal interview that I had been set-up by a third party, Wendall. The prosecution claimed the police had not accused Wendall of setting me up but merely setting the transaction up. To clarify matters, my counsel read the passage out to the court in its full context, along with the preceding paragraph that obviously pointed to a set-up in order to arrest me. The bail application was refused.

Prior to this second abandoned Pleas and Directions Hearing, in conjunction with the Criminal, Procedure and Investigation Act of 1996, the defence were encouraged to submit a 'defence case statement' to the court in order to trigger secondary disclosure material from the prosecution. In simplistic terms, this basically means that if the defence outlines its defence case to the prosecution they are duty bound to provide the defence with additional material. The sort of material we asked for were KRIS reports, CAD reports, observation logs, audio and video evidence, briefing and debriefing notes and, of course, the crucial telephonic billing between all the defendants in the case. Generally these are run-of-the-mill documents that should be disclosed by a 'defence case statement'.

The prosecution may withhold such material, however, should it consider it as 'sensitive material' and ask the trial Judge not to disclose it under the Public Immunity Interest Act or PII. To explain the complexities of PII and its procedures and practices would take up another book. Safe to say, from a defendant's point of view, the PII non-disclosure procedure is the most unfair and unsatisfactory aspect of English law. A prosecutor may ask for a PII hearing in secret, state its case to the trial Judge and in exceptional cases – which this was turning out to be–not even notify the defence that a PII hearing has been heard. Therefore, in a case, such as this, where I claim that two well-known criminals have colluded with a senior police handler or controller to set me up, the prosecution may seek to conceal the identity of the police informers from the defence. Whether this will occur in this case is a moot point. It would be in the public interest to prevent a miscarriage of justice to disclose whether or not the two most toad-spotted scumbags were indeed police informers because they actively partook in the placing of a bag containing an Uzi submachine gun in my vehicle.

CHAPTER 15:

OCTOBER 2001

On the 2nd October 2001, once again I appeared at Knaresbrook Crown Court for a Pleas and Directions Hearing that, in many respects, turned out to be an action packed occasion. Presiding over the hearing was His Honour Judge Wanlip who appeared much more in control of events than Judge Webster had been the previous week. The three charges on the indictment were put to me, whereupon I pleaded 'Not Guilty' to all three counts. They were: count one, possessing an automatic weapon; count two, possessing a firearm when prohibited for life; and, count three, having a loaded firearm in a public place.

A provisional trial date was set for 21st January 2002, which was some three and half months away. This is quite a considerable wait, but it was extended by an extra three weeks in order that I could secure the eloquent services of my barrister James Goodwyn.

With regard to the directions we outlined that we would like access to all the unused material we had asked for the previous week. More importantly, we wanted to know if Wendall was likely to be joined on the indictment and whether or not Snakeshaft was going to turn Queen's Evidence. We also wanted to include a further three police officers on the court witness production list. These would include Chief Superintendent Linley, who oversaw the whole pantomime, Detective Inspector Helliman, the suspected senior-police handler and Detective Inspector Fisher of SO11, the briefing and debriefing specialist. I was very pleased that we were calling these senior police officers as it put them on notice that not even the top brass were to be spared in this atrocious set-up. His Honour Judge Wanlip ordered the prosecution to comply with these requests by 4 p.m. on the 24th October 2001.

We also learned that Snakeshaft had appeared at the same court, again a day earlier, and that the hearing was held *in camera*. Apparently,

Snakeshaft had pleaded guilty to all three counts, which were similar to those I faced. The overall picture was becoming much clearer now. I believed that Snakeshaft was unable to plead 'Not Guilty to the charges because the Flying Squad had evidence that he and Wendall had set me up. The only way out for Snakeshaft was to plead guilty, get his case severed from mine and have his paternalistic handler or controller provide the Judge with a *text* of his treacherous *curriculum vitae* in order to receive a nominal sentence. Outwardly, I was annoyed that the scumbag had 'slipped the net' as it would be harder for me to prove to a jury that I had been set-up, as it looked like Snakeshaft had pleaded guilty because I had asked for the weapon. Inwardly, however, I was pleased, as a pre-planned police-crook operation to set me up had gone disastrously wrong. So much so, that even their own long-term valued and valuable police informant had to plead guilty to supplying an Uzi submachine gun to an unsuspecting sucker. There would be no back-slapping, champagne celebrations down the favourite police watering hole tonight! More likely, an embarrassing column in the Police Monthly Magazine, expounding the supreme folly of the super-sleuth who thought up this wretched scheme to set me up.

At the Pleas and Directions Hearing of Snakeshaft, no one was allowed inside the courtroom while the hearing was in progress. This unconventional court procedure combined with the information that the direct family of Snakeshaft had moved out of their house in Bornchurch and the sudden appearance of graffiti on a wall in Canning Town proclaiming that *"Danny Snakeshaft is a super grass"* in large blue letters all pointed to his defection to the prosecution camp. To be perfectly frank, I was not too bothered by this news, as all through this nightmare ordeal I have had supreme faith, no matter what slimy strokes the Judge, the prosecution, the police, my co-defendants or my own lawyers try to do, I am going home to my family. The bastards were not going to send me back to prison for umpteen years on the strength of an egregious set-up, no way! More positively, if Snakeshaft decided to give evidence for the Crown it may do them more harm than good! We will have to wait and see.

CHAPTER 16:

CAN I TRUST ANYONE?

Perhaps a word should be mentioned here about the legal representation I have employed to take on the resourceful might and machinations of the CPS and the elite Flying Squad. For years and years whenever the need occurred, I have used the legal services of a well-known law firm in deepest East London. For personal reasons, namely the way that they handled a close friend's appeal against a life sentence, I decided to opt for a female solicitor who came highly recommended from my brother Eugene. On the positive side, she was a born and bred East London solicitor whose quasi-perception and experience of criminal law and practice by far exceeded her fragrant years.

Despite umpteen aborted attempts to furnish me with a basic folder in which to carry my case papers, she exuded an acute sense of alertness and circumspection around this far from normal case. I say not 'normal' as there appeared to be a fundamental fault line running through the case and it all started and ended with the perverse working relationship between the senior police handler and the set-uppers.

I explained all the details about the case and emphatically expressed my anxiety and concern about the bizarre way I was apprehended and arrested. From the very outset, she played the role of a 'devil's advocate', challenging my assumptions about Wendall and Snakeshaft and even went so far as to say that what I was saying about Snakeshaft did not make sense, as he had been arrested and the police also had no reason to arrest Wendall. This was partially true, as it was Snakeshaft that placed the blue bag in my vehicle and not Wendall. But we all know how professionally inquisitive the police are, especially the experienced police detectives. Surely they would want to know who the other person was at Snakeshaft's address? Perhaps they knew who he was already from a Police National Computer check of the details of the silver Vauxhall Vectra parked adjacent to my vehicle, that was registered in Wendall's name and address. If the surveillance team knew of Wendall's identity and antecedents for shooting people, armed robbery, kidnap and the small fact that he was out of prison on nearly five years parole, why did they not arrest him? Every policeman worth his salt would want Wendall on his CV as he is a veritable premiership scalp. My solicitor's arguments were built on sand and nothing could convince me otherwise.

During my very first legal visit at Cellmarsh Prison I pointed out to my solicitor the vital importance of obtaining the mobile telephone evidence – the itemized billing of all three central characters involved in this case. She told me that the police would most probably secure this evidence, but I insisted upon making some effort to acquire the evidence ourselves. In short, I filled out a BT Cellnet form asking for the itemized billing of my mobile phone that was in police possession. This would allow me to obtain the correct phone numbers of the rats and show exactly how I was set-up. Several weeks later I asked if the BT Cellnet form had gone off to them. She checked the case file in front of me and it was still in there. Admittedly, the form being left to snooze in the folder could have been an oversight but it did not do my confidence any good.

Then, after Snakeshaft had spent seven days in police custody without legal representation and several telephone calls between her and Snakeshaft's solicitor, the former SO8 operative, she claimed that she fancied Snakeshaft was a police informant all along and even supported my long-standing assumption of a set-up. This was complete bollocks, as she had even tried to get me to panic about the possibility of 'holding my hands up' and pleading guilty to possession–an absolute offence in English law–lack of knowledge of a prohibited weapon in my car is not a defence.

To compound matters there was a significant groundswell of distrust and disaffection directed at this particular firm of solicitors in Cellmarsh Prison. I met an amicable black guy, out of East London, in the jail who was awaiting trial for murder. He told me he had sacked this firm of solicitors because when he asked them to carry out an autopsy upon the deceased, the solicitor proclaimed that the body was too decomposed for an autopsy. In actual fact, a co-defendant had given the same instructions to his solicitor and the autopsy was carried out faultlessly. Apparently, the location of a mysterious flat, where it was alleged the offence took place, was pivotal to the prosecution case and this solicitor was subtly urging the client to divulge its location. The client was deeply suspicious and sacked the firm and went on to be acquitted. The co-defendant received seven years for a minor offence.

So, this episode, along with the clash of minds over the 'absolute offence' palaver, was the start of lingering doubts and uneasiness over my legal representatives. The problem did not appear to go away. I gave a junior clerk some very sensitive material regarding the possibility that Wendall was responsible for the set-up. Then, Wendall wanted to organize a meet with a female member of my family, through a respectable middle-man to ask her some questions. After months of elusive behaviour, Wendall now wanted to contact my family with a witness present to ask us some questions? It may have been a remarkable coincidence, or it may have been much more sinister, but I would have to take some action to protect the integrity of the defence case and defence witnesses who were prepared to give evidence for me against Wendall, whom we all suspected of being a rat.

More disturbingly, we had all noticed how the female solicitor flirted *ad nauseum* with the principal Flying Squad officer in the case at the Magistrate's Court. At the last high court hearing, my family and friends observed this and became very concerned, more especially when she was seen to be talking with two Flying Squad officers. Upon being noticed, the whispering trio felt uncomfortable and all three of them sidled around a corner to carry on with their conversation. When she emerged thirty minutes later, my family asked if she had found out any more news or information, as we were being kept in the dark about many things. She proclaimed that she could not extract any information because the other officer was present.

It was with some sadness, but absolutely necessary, that I sacked the solicitor. Basically, I said that I felt there was a security leak at her office and I could not jeopardize the safety of my defence witnesses who were due to make very sensitive statements in the coming weeks. When I first broached the subject about parting company she appeared to be expecting it. I said it was not due to prison gossip or rumours, but purely in the interest of maintaining confidentiality in my case. My eloquent barrister tried to talk me out of this, but when he saw how determined I was about the issue, he decided not to pursue or push the matter any further.

More remarkably, after I had parted with her legal services, her final words to me were that Snakeshaft had said, "The reasons why the Uzi was being purchased was for a specific job!" How long had she known this information? Why had she not mentioned it before? It confirmed and reaffirmed the position that she had not been totally frank in her handling of this case. In many respects she seemed to embody, or symbolize, the busy-bee that flies from flower to flower extracting pollen while simultaneously fertilizing the plant. This two-way tradecraft of swapping gen and gossip with the enemy is unacceptable at any level, more especially when you were fighting for your life like I was.

My new, hand-picked, solicitor was Andrew Conrad–linked to a well-respected firm of East London solicitors. I had known Andrew from an earlier case where he had represented me for a driving offence. Since those early days, however, Andrew had come of age. He was young, vibrant and enthusiastic. I sensed that he liked a case with a *soupçon* of police skulduggery and corruption. At this time in his legal career he had just finished representing a client in a major cocaine smuggling case and the prospect of visiting new clients facing low life crimes and exploits did not appeal to him.

The Uzi set-up was tailor made for him, as it had all the ingredients of a Shakespearean tragi-comedy. The case had a lethal firearm of dubious provenance, a former armed robber who propounded his innocence, police informants, a bungled police operation, the Flying Squad, a damage limitation exercise, an elite surveillance squad that didn't use video equipment, the involvement of the secretive Special Investigation Services of New Dockland Yard, a co-defendant who may go QE, sacked defence lawyers, the gangsters of language and intransigence at the CPS and last, but not least, a failed plan to shoot and kill the suspect while in possession of a planted weapon. Taken altogether this was humanity at its most base and reprehensible and ideal for someone of Andrew's inquisitive mind.

CHAPTER 17:

SHOOT TO KILL THEORY

In my opinion, the burning question or issue that certain police officers wanted to shoot and kill me at the scene of the arrest is not without foundation. Whether rightly or wrongly, I honestly believe that there was a closely guarded internal conspiracy to shoot and kill me not only to protect and safeguard the police informers, but also to 'take out' an erstwhile career criminal for personal reasons and as a deterrent to other potential villains. I base these powerful presumptions upon several seminal observations during the arrest.

The first observation that the set-up squad, or 'Pantomime Squad', was not aware of my identity is total hogwash. We learned that Wendall and Snakeshaft tried to set me up the night before by asking me to collect the pseudo 'printing presses', but I had been unable to collect them because I had some relatives coming to my address to buy my jet ski who were also staying for dinner. When I suggested that a friend of mine would collect them for me, Wendall claimed that he would get back to me later. Indeed, he did contact me by mobile phone later that night and declared, "Snakeshaft said that there are too many Old Bill about to do it tonight!" Even the 'Pantomime Squad' did not want a person of minor criminal significance to collect the printing presses as they wanted a veritable 'face' and they were prepared to wait until the next day to corner and trap me, with the vital help of Wendall and Snakeshaft if they were successful.

Secondly, we learned from the police statements, at the pre-arrest briefing, that 'evil eyes', the police marksman – who was first out of the leading ARV – received a personal and individual briefing from a Detective Constable linked to SO11. The inference being, why should 'evil eyes' require an entirely separate briefing when DI Fisher was to officially address the entire meeting moments later. I believe, given the slightest opportunity, 'evil eyes' was recruited and encouraged to take me out!

Thirdly, when PS Gladstone, who was in Trojan 1 alongside the controller of the operation DI Helliman, delivered the order to carry out the non-compliant stop, the lead vehicle which contained 'evil eyes' opted to carry it out once they had passed a bus stop so as not to endanger the public should they have to open fire. Despite forcibly stopping the suspect's car in a public place with many witnesses about, this would have justified and legitimised the use of their weapons, as they were already fully aware that there was a lethal firearm in the body shell of my vehicle. It transpires, the more independent witnesses to this pre-planned execution the better.

Fourthly, the most predominant feature of the conspiracy to kill theory is the method the police used in the non-compliant stop. As I was in the traffic waiting for the car in front of me to pull away at the traffic lights, an unmarked (black Honda) police vehicle pulled across my path. Not in a resolute, you're-not-going-anywhere, decisive fashion but, instead it was an insipid, half-hearted manoeuvre, which left the BMW that I was driving an appreciable gap to power around the unmarked vehicle and achieve a possible escape. I refused to take this pre-planned opportunity to flee, however, as I only had valuable 'printing presses' on board, not the crown jewels. We learned that if I had taken the opportunity to flee, my driver's door would have been entirely exposed to the line of fire from 'evil eyes' who was already out of the lead ARV and ready to let rip with his MP5 carbine machine gun.

More disturbingly, why did the ARVs directly behind my vehicle not activate their siren and blue lights, or flash their headlights, to indicate that they wanted me to stop and alight from my vehicle? Was the lead ARV Trojan 211 fitted with an in-car camera, especially knowing that it would be involved in a delicate armed operation? The upshot is, this was a non-compliant stop by stealth. There was nothing overt about this operation as it had a hidden agenda – to force me into making a wrong move so that 'evil eyes' could take me out. Thankfully, by the grace of God, or Allah, this did not happen and I am here to tell my story.

Fifthly, there was some evidence to suggest that some of the police marksmen knew who I was because when PC Morley put the handcuffs on me at the scene of the arrest, not only were his hands trembling with fear, or anticipation of a possible shooting, but he also declared in his statement, "I handcuffed the male due to the firearms information I had received and the person possibly becoming violent in the circumstances."

There is no disputing that I have previous convictions for violence against the police and armed robbery, but were these police officers aware of that? Why were PC Morley's hands shaking so perceptibly? Did he know who I was and was he expecting violence? More pertinently, did PC Morley know that I was to be shot given the slightest opportunity?

Finally, and most importantly, when I exited the BMW and was handcuffed at the rear of the vehicle by PC Morley, one unnamed police officer, running past me to the front of my vehicle, blurted out, "Who fucking parked that like that?" Thus he alluded to the way the unmarked black Honda police car had half-heartedly pulled across my path. It was obvious that this particular police officer was not privy to the secret agenda of execution. Because if we consider all the facts, not all the police were *au fait* with the underlying plan to shoot me We are talking about a murder here! The fewer who know or are aware of the plan the better. At the most, I believe, three or four of them were party to it. At a calculated guess, I would say the conspirators were DI Helliman, PC Blackmore or 'evil eyes', PC Morley, DC Curtis the SO11 operative and the driver of the black Honda, DC Logan.

Taken in isolation, these are very serious allegations and accusations to make, but such conspiracies are prevalent in any police force and, by extension, society where seemingly accountable specialized police squads are able to act and behave like unaccountable legalized gangsters. This is made all the more commonplace by the increasing Americanisation of contemporary criminal activities in the UK, where the growing phenomena of unreported drug transactions allows vast amounts of cash, and also power and influence, to fall into the hands of dishonest and depraved detectives.

It is this symbiotic relationship between the police and criminal, handler and informant, rat-catcher and rat that has led to this surreal nightmare. Admittedly, some critics may crow that being unlawfully set-up is part and parcel of being a professional criminal, but when two wrongs begin to make a right in the British justice system, it can lead to disastrous consequences for society in general.

Obviously, there are some who would assert that how could I have been so naïve to allow this to happen to me? Firstly, when you are not looking for betrayal and treachery you are not expecting it, more especially from a close friend. And secondly, when I first heard that Wendall was being released from prison, especially after receiving nearly five years parole, I did feel a little apprehensive and concerned as to how my friend would react to me after serving seventeen years in the bowels of the British penal system. I did discuss this extensively with my family, as we were anxious not only about his physical, psychological and mental condition, but also about what type of mindset he would adopt and embrace when interacting with us. Would it be one of genuine affection and mutual respect or would it be one of inveterate jealousy and simmering resentment and evil. For there was a strong and significant possibility that Wendall would espouse the latter.

CHAPTER 18:

THE UZI SUBMACHINE GUN

In the light of recent developments, such as the elusive nature of Snakeshaft in court, his *in camera* court appearances, the Judge refusing to order a co-defendant to be produced at court, sacked solicitors and a negative bail application in spite of the police claiming, during an interview, that Wendall had set me up, it transpires – bottom line – not only are Wendall and Snakeshaft in cahoots to set me up, but the terrible triumvirate of the Judge, CPS and the police are in cahoots to railroad this case into a conviction. Like the deadly force of an express train bearing down upon its destination they desperately want to imprison me for umpteen years. You can forget justice, fairness, truth and neutrality, for this is personal. To them my burgeoning previous criminal convictions make me a true premiership scalp and they think that they can taste the three points of victory. Yet, despite these disturbing reservations, I feel supremely confident and optimistic, like a blind man who has faith amidst the darkness of his existence.

In our new, post-World Trade Centre, Manichean cosmos, it remains perfectly clear that the terrible triumvirate are not on the side of the angels. The cosmic struggle between good and evil, light and darkness and even faith and despair is mirrored by the underdog of the individual versus the omnipotent State in this case. A veritable David and Goliath scenario where on paper the police evidence looks and sounds rock solid. But in reality – as is its wont – it reveals a case of extreme doubt and misrepresentation built on a foundation of melting ice. If the defence can explore and expose this structural weakness their case will fail and dissolve very quickly.

It goes without saying, the Uzi submachine gun is at the epicentre of the case and therefore the role of forensic science should play an important part in the forthcoming trial. For example, Michael Kemble, a forensic scientist specializing in the examination of firearms and related items stated that he took possession of a black Israeli-made Uzi submachine pistol, wooden shoulder stock, suppressor-silencer and a magazine containing twenty-nine rounds of 9 millimetre ammunition.

Interestingly, in Kemble's analysis and conclusions–that we may come back to later – he asserts, "The original gun might have been partially deactivated" and later replaced with a smooth-bored barrel. More specifically, the purpose of his report was to establish that the gun worked faultlessly in both fully and semi-automatic modes of fire, which he concludes the gun did.

Similarly, David Sturges, a forensic scientist, whose field of expertise is the DNA examination of biological evidence, took possession of the gun for his own unique tests. Sturges, we learn, swabbed all the above components of the weapon for blood, saliva or skin cells left through physical contact with the weapon and then compared this with a DNA profile of the suspect taken shortly after I was charged at Bornchurch Police Station. The profile tests were unsuccessful, meaning – as was to be expected – that there was no DNA link between the firearm and me.

This was of grave importance to me as I feared that the original 'Pantomime Squad' would plant my DNA on the weapon. I say this because I had lost a pair of expensive sunglasses at Bornchurch Police Station while I was outside my cell in the interview room. I was worried, despite reporting them missing when I returned to the cell, that they would be rigorously rubbed against the seized items to be forensically examined. You may think this is highly improbable and an exercise in paranoia, but if the 'Pantomime Squad' would go to such lengths to set me up, then surely they would complete the task with a smidgeon of DNA or firearm residue linking the suspect to the gun, á la Barry George in the Jill Dando case.

Perhaps the sole reason why they did not do this was because they already had me 'bang-to-rights' with the weapon inside my vehicle. As far as the 'Pantomime Squad' were concerned this was an open and shut case, as 'possession' of anything illegal, more especially a firearm or drugs, is an 'absolute offence' and lack of knowledge of it is not a defence in English law. Therefore, in the 'Pantomime Squad's' eyes, any type of forensic fit-up, such as, fibre, fingerprints or DNA were superfluous to requirements. The suspect was nicked in 'possession' and essentially English law dictated that I could not escape a conviction. The 'Pantomime Squad' apprehended a sucker, arrested a sucker, charged a sucker and my god, I felt like a sucker!

Over the months since I was apprehended and arrested in the set-up, people who had heard about my case, some that I did not even know, were supplying me with a constant source of gossip, rumour, fact and fiction. It started off with the information that Snakeshaft received police visits at Wentonville Prison, then the news that he was putting it around the East End he had access to a 'top cozzer', then the fact that he was taken out of prison into police protective custody for seven days. He was then transferred to Wormhood Shrubs, then a list of phone numbers were found hidden in the laundry room at Wentonville Prison that corresponded with Bornchurch Police Station, then a rumour circulated that Snakeshaft had been attacked while in prison. He was then rumoured to be in police protective custody again, then he was on bail, then someone spotted him parked in a car in Beckton, East London and he looked bashed up. Police audiotapes of Snakeshaft naming Mickey Macitto in the earlier drugs case were then being circulated around the East End. Then in large letters the words, "Danny Snakeshaft is a Super Grass" were painted on a wall in Canning Town, then rumours continued that he had been arrested along with two corrupt detectives in a police-on-police swoop. So it was not a complete shock to me when the latest rumour was that Snakeshaft had in fact turned Queen's Evidence and was prepared to give evidence for the Crown. It all made sense in my view, as he had been caught by me, 'bang-to-rights' setting me up and any street credibility he had quickly evaporated.

It seemed a natural progression for him to seek a safe haven in the open and loving arms of the law. No one can abide snitches, grasses, Judas', sneaks, squealers or stool pigeons, but in the pantheon of police informers, the worst of the worse must be the police informer who actively takes part in the set-up of a major crime where the victim is not only likely to be convicted and sent to prison for a decade or more, but knows there is a strong possibility – as in my case – that the unsuspecting victim may be shot and killed by police marksmen. These type of perfidious police informing specialists, who covertly manufacture and construct crime and traps for their victims are at the nadir of the human species, and they must be excavated and exposed, and lanced like a festering boil so that everyone can open their nostrils and smell how they stink.

CHAPTER 19:

THE NEW SOLICITOR

On the 22nd and 23rd October 2001 I had an extended solicitors visit from my new legal advisor, Andrew Conrad. My initial impression of him was excellent. Andrew appeared to contain and exhibit a genuine concern and anxiety about this case, even to the extent where he could already foresee a potential miscarriage of justice should we—God forbid—fail in our legal endeavours.

Without any prompting or encouragement, Andrew had already started on a very detailed chronological schedule of events in the case. More importantly, he came up with some fresh and novel ideas, especially the use of an independent firearms expert, video evidence of the scene where Snakeshaft planted the 'blue bag' in my vehicle, the use of road maps of the same area and a police expert to examine and decipher the codes used in the KRIS and CAD reports.

Despite being already five months into this case, Andrew claimed that he hadn't a clue which way the prosecution would fight this case. Andrew's initial impression of Snakeshaft was that he is a police informer and that Wendall's role before and after the arrest points to him being heavily involved in the set-up. Andrew stated, as I do to, that the set-up was not a viable plan without the input of Wendall. Additionally, DC Noel put the set-up squarely upon Wendall's shoulders when he claimed in the interview of 24th July 2001 at Wilford Police Station that Wendall was responsible for the set-up.

During the legal conference Andrew expressed deep concern about what went on inside Snakeshaft's address when I went inside to collect the 'printing presses'. He claimed any detective worth his salt would have had a video camera or listening device inside the premises recording all the events. Andrew added, however, that this high tech equipment would most likely be illegal and therefore inadmissible as evidence in a court of law. Although it could be used in secret PII hearings to deny the defence access to potential sensitive material. I am of the opinion, however, that if this high tech recording evidence does exist the police are reluctant to use it as it not only points to a *bona fide* set-up from the outset, but it also exposes the extent of Wendall's role in the sad affair.

To summarize the case at this stage, Andrew believes that the prosecution cannot rebut or disprove anything that I have said in my 'prepared defence statement' or interview. Therefore, the prosecution cannot prove beyond reasonable doubt that I was aware there was an Uzi submachine pistol in my vehicle. It would therefore be wholly unsafe to leave it to the jury to decide upon this issue without evidence to the contrary.

In short, it would be wrong for the Judge to let the jury extrapolate unknown evidence that is not there. The issue in question is of *fact* and not *conjecture*. How are the police and prosecution therefore going to prove that I knew there was an Uzi submachine gun in my vehicle? Andrew claims that they need Snakeshaft to go QE or require legal listening devices with verbal evidence to the contrary. All in all, it is the 24th October tomorrow and the prosecution have until 4 p.m. to comply with the Judge's order to supply us with the secondary material we asked for. If it has not arrived by the end of the week Andrew is going to list the case to be heard at a Mention Hearing at the same court. Andrew wants to keep the pressure up otherwise the prosecution will surprise us with the material minutes before the trial, which will give us no time to authenticate the evidential value of the material.

As expected the crunch day for the secondary disclosure material came and went without a murmur. Andrew phoned the CPS and they claimed that the case officer, DS Herbert, had not even bothered to sift through the material to organize what was disclosable and what was sensitive material. There I am sitting in my cold concrete cubicle in Cellmarsh Prison, a victim of a flagrant set-up and those with a vested interest in denying me access to prove that I was set-up, are not playing by the rules of law that are plain to see, read and understand in the bible of English law, *The Archbold's*. In my opinion, the CPS are acting like 'legalized gangsters' themselves, claiming that the case worker is never available on the phone, blatantly ignoring receipt of official correspondence and then refusing to obey a high court ruling to furnish the defence with the material. I felt so helpless and wondered what it must have been like for the Birmingham Six, the Guildford Four, the Carl Bridgewater Four and many others who were victims of police malfeasance and corruption in the 1970s and 1980s. But at least they had each other to talk to and share their common problems and anxieties. I felt like staging a protest inside the jail to highlight my case, such as, a hunger strike or a roof top protest but access to the roof at Cellmarsh, a modern jail is very difficult and I always have felt self-starvation is self-defeating as it not only debilitates one's physical strength, but it blurs and distorts the focus and concentration on the case itself. Patience is not a glamorous human trait, but I had to sit there and watch the police and CPS dictate events until the eventual trial.

One consolation, however, Andrew was informed by the CPS, over the phone, that Snakeshaft had indeed pleaded guilty and his case was adjourned for sentence and that it had been "decided that John Wendall will not be prosecuted as there is insufficient evidence at this time." Did this mean that the CPS were going to prosecute Wendall once they had acquired the evidence? Or that he was still working for his police handler and needed more time? Or that he was not going to be prosecuted full stop? How much more evidence did they need? Wendall was seen walking away from an alleged transaction involving an Uzi submachine gun, loaded magazine, shoulder stock, silencer and 376 rounds of ammunition. He was on nearly five years parole for serious firearm offences and the police were aware of his existence and identity on the day of the alleged crime. What was stopping them from arresting and charging him? Why did they not nick him? Or was he, along with his venal police handler, the mastermind of this despicable set-up? I leave it to you the reader to work it out yourself, but these are the unadulterated facts of the case.

In any event, my solicitor sought the courts assistance in resolving the prosecution's failure to comply with the previous court order to produce the secondary disclosure material. On 29th October 2001 at Knaresbrook Crown Court in front of His Honour Judge Bond the Judge ordered that all the telephone records we had been asking for be served to the defence by 7th December 2001 and he also ordered that the defence provide further particulars of the secondary material we had asked for earlier. He ordered that the defence had seven days to provide the particulars and the prosecution had seven days to reply. This was a ludicrous request as the CPS were fully aware of what material we wanted and it seemed utterly pointless to have to do it all over again. Nonetheless, we complied with the order as it was to our advantage and we waited yet again for a response.

CHAPTER 20:

WENDALL'S SECOND ARREST

In keeping with the bizarre nature of the case, on the 2nd November 2001, *unarmed* Flying Squad officers decided to visit Wendall's address and arrest him. During a search of his address they took a quantity of legal papers and correspondence and several small wraps of white powder that were sent off for analysis. Then, strangely, when Wendall reached Havering Police Station they shut down the front office as a security measure and deployed armed police around the Police Station until Wendall appeared at the nearby Magistrate's Court the following day.

At court Wendall was remanded in custody to Cellmarsh Prison where he was made an exceptional risk category A prisoner–the highest prison security classification in existence. From a layman's point of view, the dangerousness of the prisoner looks conclusive, but from a professional villains viewpoint, the arrest of a former armed robber on parole for serious firearm offences without armed police is at variance with the later excessive security measures and precautions at the police station and prison. In my view, it quite clearly points to an administrative smokescreen to camouflage Wendall's working relationship with the police. A police spokesperson even apologized in the local newspaper for the closure of the police station and any inconvenience caused. The two actions and reactions are not compatible. Like creosote and custard they just don't go together.

Due to the fact that Wendall was classified as an exceptional category A prisoner he was held in the High Secure Unit at Cellmarsh Prison. As a standard risk category A prisoner I was placed on normal location on the house block, therefore we had no way of seeing or speaking to each other. Not that I wanted to see the scumbag, as in my view he was as bad, if not worse than Snakeshaft, a perfidious state-paid, state-registered police informer, but it was a matter of how I was going to prove it. It was my word against Wendall's. Most of the prisoners that I spoke to on the house block, some that knew me from outside, from prison and new acquaintances, had read my case papers, listened to my endless mantras about the case and could see quite transparently that I was set-up and Snakeshaft was a rat and that Wendall had walked away from the planting of the 'blue bag' in my vehicle. But it was not conclusive proof that he was involved in the set-up, it was the build up to the set-up, that was not in the official case papers, and Wendall's strange *Schadenfreude* behaviour after my arrest, that was the real damaging evidence against him.

Thus, in a devious and desperate attempt to deflect my heartfelt claim that Wendall was a police informer, Wendall started his own counter-accusations and recriminations, accusing me of being a grass– based upon the fact that I made a 'prepared defence statement' not naming names nor locations in it. Wendall's arguments were purely for propagandist and disinformation purposes as he was focusing upon the *person* and not the *facts*. As one sagacious prisoner enthused, "Wendall has shit himself and he is blaming you for farting!" Wendall's scowling and splenetic accusations were hurtful as the label of a 'grass' in prison is the easiest name to get and the hardest to get rid of, but I had the supreme knowledge of faith and truth on my side that possessed almost religious-like qualities and substance. I was unstoppable.

The salient reason for Wendall to discredit me was plain for all to see. The 'prepared defence statement' I had made when I was arrested had blown apart the set-up operation. It had exposed a visible fault line running through the set-up by 'the three men of sin' – Wendall, Snakeshaft and their senior police handler DI Helliman. If the plan to shoot me failed, I was to get arrested and stay *schtumm* by giving a 'no comment' interview, but they did not anticipate nor expect what occurred. It meant the external and elite Flying Squad had to probe and investigate my claims, which would mean serious trouble for the confident conspirators. Alas, now as I write, they are both nicked, one has already pleaded guilty and the other is hanging on by his finger tips to his worthless name and reputation in the criminal underworld. What Wendall had done to me was unforgivable. It was quintessential evil and his just reward would be utter and complete exposure. This was not character *assassination* this was character *realization*. I saw it as my duty and destiny to strip away the paper veil of Wendall's criminal respectability and esteem and lay bare the visceral bitterness and resentment that had ossified into marrow-deep jealousy and malevolence towards me and others. Although the nightmare ordeal is not over yet, there is a long way to its conclusion, but things could have been far worse, in my opinion. I could have been interred in the loamy soil of a cemetery, or permanently crippled by police bullets or, at the very least, sitting here in Cellmarsh Prison without a hope in hell of winning this case, while the laughing hyenas of iniquity sought out their next unsuspecting victim.

Not surprisingly, this case had become a moral crusade for me to unmask the treachery and wickedness of these arch plotters. It is imperative that they are not allowed to do what they did to me to anyone else again, as next time the unsuspecting victim might not be so lucky to be able to speak out about it.

Meanwhile, in spite of the groundbreaking news that Wendall had been arrested, charged and remanded in custody for the Uzi set-up, two more of Snakeshaft's victims, Mark Knight and Arthur Weal, were languishing inside Wentonville Prison for the possession of MDMA, used to make ecstasy pills. Apparently, Snakeshaft had asked them to look after a bag containing the drug in a lock-up shop in Loughton, Essex, but the National Crime Squad raided the premises and arrested them. Again it was a classic case of Snakeshaft planting incriminating articles inside someone's property. Another unconfirmed rumour soon gathered pace from these quarters that Snakeshaft had been an active police informer for as long as sixteen years. This would coincide with when Snakeshaft was released from a four-year prison sentence back in 1985. Moreover, a quick glance at Snakeshaft's antecedents revealed he has had no criminal convictions since 1983, a remarkable feat for someone making a significant living from petty crime.

On the 12th November 2001, Wendall reappeared at Thamesmead Magistrates Court for committal proceedings. At the hearing Wendall was served with two 'undated statements' made by Snakeshaft purporting to go QE. As things stood, these 'undated statements' had no evidential weight and therefore the prosecution asked for an adjournment for three weeks in order to get them dated. The alleged reason for the delay was that Snakeshaft was bartering with his captors over the conditions of his prosecution witness status. Snakeshaft wanted a new identity and a safe house in a new location in which to live. The adjournment was granted.

CHAPTER 21:

SNAKESHAFT SHOWS HIS COLOURS

In spite of months and months of innuendo, rumour and gossip that Wendall's accomplice was about to turn QE, this was the proof we required. According to English law, in order for Snakeshaft to turn QE he had to make a full and frank confession about all his past crimes and misdemeanours. Apparently, for legal reasons, super grasses have to do this so that their evidence can be taken as the absolute truth and show that they have nothing to hide.

To summarize the statement of Snakeshaft, consisting of ten pages, he claims that he has been a low-level thief and toe-rag all his life. He spent his life in snooker halls, betting shops and mixing with villains who were out of his depth. He meets an older local hoodlum called John Wendall and in 1982 is asked to drive a van full of stolen cigarettes away from a burglary. Snakeshaft is arrested and claims that he kept *schtumm*, but deep in the subtext of the statement we know that he 'comes his lot' and is recruited to become a police informer. Several weeks after Snakeshaft's arrest for the stolen cigarettes, after intense police surveillance and observations, Wendall and his associates are all nicked. A member of the police squad that arrest Wendall *et al*, is none other than the suspected senior police handler in this case, DI Helliman.

In 1983, Wendall and the others have a long trial and are all found guilty. They receive outrageously long sentences, Wendall receiving the longest of ten years imprisonment for burglary. Snakeshaft pleads guilty from the outset and receives four years imprisonment and is out on his first parole after 18 months inside. Thus the malodorous metamorphose from embryonic thief to an adult police informer is complete. Snakeshaft has been on the police pay role as long as sixteen years and all that time he was visiting his buddy Wendall while he was in prison.

Also in the statement, Snakeshaft mentions about being arrested while transporting a van full of cannabis in June 2000. Along with three other defendants Snakeshaft has a trial and he is acquitted, but in my opinion the police handlers who organized his defence save Snakeshaft. The owners of the contraband are not happy, as they can smell a rat. They give the debt for the cannabis to a local henchman and he puts pressure upon the scumbag to cough up the dough. He states this is the reason why he gets involved with me. All complete and utter bollocks! I have only ever met him once before, at a football match where he sat in another part of the stadium.

Regarding the Uzi palaver, Snakeshaft claims Wendall asked him to acquire the Uzi for Terry Diamond. By coincidence, Snakeshaft meets a black guy at an East London gymnasium. Snakeshaft overhears the black guy talking about a 'yogga' (slang for a firearm). Snakeshaft asks him to get him an Uzi and a deal is struck. Snakeshaft meets the black guy on Monday 4th June 2001 and the black guy states that it is not ready and he can collect it tomorrow. The next day–the day of my arrest–Snakeshaft meets the black guy on Hackney Marshes. He is then told to follow him to an unknown flat in Islington where Snakeshaft does not inspect the Uzi in the 'blue bag'. Amazingly, Snakeshaft then leaves the flat without paying for the weapon from the black guy that he has only met once or twice. The level of trust in this inter-racial deal is incomprehensible. Snakeshaft then drives to his house in Bornchurch, Essex.

There he claims Wendall and Diamond come to his house after several phone calls from them. Snakeshaft leaves Wendall downstairs and takes Diamond upstairs to a bedroom. It is alleged Diamond removes the Uzi from the blue bag and puts all its different parts together, the shoulder stock, silencer and magazine. Diamond then puts the Uzi in a firing position and proclaims, "This will do a good job, as the Bermondsey job!" (Classic 1970s police verbal, alluding to a major armed robbery of a security van in the docklands area of South East London.) Diamond then dismantles the weapon and orders Snakeshaft to look after the weapon for several days. Snakeshaft refuses. Diamond then orders Snakeshaft to bring the blue bag to Diamond's car that is parked around the corner to his house. Snakeshaft claims that he expects Diamond's fingerprints to be all over the gun, as he was not wearing any gloves. He alleges that Diamond then pays him £2500 in cash for the weapon and

Snakeshaft drives to the gym to pay the black guy.

The very next day Wendall hears that Diamond is nicked and meets Snakeshaft. He claims that Wendall is annoyed and takes Snakeshaft's mobile phone chip out of his phone and destroys it. After his arrest he then claims my brother Eugene threatened him inside Wentonville Prison and ordered him to say the police instructed him to set-up Diamond. Snakeshaft concludes that he has not got the "pull on" to set this up, he is just a runner. He takes orders from the likes of Wendall and Diamond but does not give them himself.

Basically that is the gist of the statement. The prosecution later declared that the statement was made on the 19th October 2001, but I suggest the material used, in the compiling of the statement, was collated as long ago as July 2001 when Snakeshaft was taken into police custody from Wentonville Prison for the seven days. There is some evidence to support this presumption, as when the detectives are debriefing Snakeshaft they would need his criminal antecedents and history to compile the statement. We know that this document was printed at 10:38 hours on 23rd July 2001, three days after Snakeshaft was removed from prison custody.

Secondly, and more strikingly, when the DNA and fingerprint evidence is received from the police forensic laboratory on 1st August 2001, it has come back negative. The suspect Diamond has not touched the weapon. Snakeshaft is lying. This is a massive blow to the 'Pantomime Squad'. Snakeshaft has lied to them so as not to offend them. Like the little boy who lies to his father that he did not see his mother kiss the milkman, he tells the father what he wants to hear and not what actually happened. The same willingness to please theory applies to Snakeshaft. He tells his paternalistic senior police handler what he wants to hear as not to let the side down, but the forensic evidence does not support his claim. In fact it refutes it.

Thirdly, during Snakeshaft's seven day sojourn in police custody the Flying Squad visit Wendall's address and hand deliver a typed letter dated 22nd July 2001, with the message to contact them over an outstanding matter. Two days later, the 24th July 2001, Wendall walks voluntarily into Wilford Police Station with his solicitor. The civility involved in this gentleman's agreement is risible. Remember, we are talking here about a dangerous armed robber on epochs of parole, an Uzi submachine gun with 376 rounds of ammunition and the elite Flying Squad, what is going on? At the Police Station Wendall is formally arrested for the procurement of an Uzi firearm. He flatly denies knowledge of the offence in a 'prepared defence statement' proclaiming, "I have never possessed any Ouzi firearm, I have no knowledge of any Ouzi firearm" (sic). Remarkably DC Noel of the Flying Squad then puts to Wendall, in unequivocal terms, that he is responsible for setting up Diamond along with Snakeshaft. The overarching question is why would the Flying Squad who took over the case put such a damning question to Wendall if they did not have the evidence that Wendall and Snakeshaft had indeed set up Diamond? Obviously something significant occurred during that notorious week in July 2001 to cause the Flying Squad to act and to pull him in for questioning. Let us not delude ourselves here, logical deductive reasoning dictates that Snakeshaft had 'come his lot' about the set-up and had implicated Wendall's role in the conspiracy.

Finally, the malevolent mastermind of this rapidly becoming farce had to leave Snakeshaft's statement undated so as not to compromise the duplicitous role of Wendall in the criminal world. For if the statement was made and dated when the police first had access to this information it would have dictated that Wendall would have had to be officially charged and returned to prison as a parole violator as early as July and not November 2001. Instead they left the statement undated so Wendall could go about his clandestine activities for another five months before circumstances dictated that he had to be nicked. The Byzantine twists and turns in this case indicate that short-term tactics often compromise long-term strategy and this is the Achilles' heel in the whole case. It is my view that the conniving police and CPS were unable to present the case against Diamond without exposing, to some extent, the role of the police informers.

Because the case had not gone as planned from the very beginning it was being conducted on a piecemeal basis, having to contend with and negotiate the individual interests and concerns of two or maybe three police squads involved. Naturally the Cranham Crime Squad desired a conviction at all costs, even if it meant the sacrifice of two police informers, one of whom had brought them so much success in the past. The Flying Squad also wanted a conviction but were snookered by the fact that they were aware of the perverse mechanics of the case and they had to be careful that it did not result in a miscarriage of justice. Because if it did and it came out later, as it surely would, that the Flying Squad were aware the case was a set-up by police informers they could be placing their bright careers in the Metropole Police Force at risk. Sandwiched in between all this were the overriding interests and concerns of the Special Investigation Services (SIS) of New Dockland Yard. Although cloaked in secrecy, it is believed that this special police unit was responsible for the gathering and collation of intelligence and evidence against highly organized criminal gangs and organizations. At the time of writing this, the cloak and dagger secrecy surrounding this special squad is oppressive but my solicitors have been told that behind the scenes they are definitely involved in this case. All in all, it looked like there was no doughty captain at the helm of this floundering ship, and now it had hit a veritable storm the crew were doing all sorts of desperate things, through sheer defiance to keep the wretched craft afloat.

CHAPTER 22:

CUSTODY TIME LIMITS

On 21st November 2001, I was produced at Knaresbrook Crown Court in front of His Honour Justice Smithson for a prosecution application to extend Custody Time Limits. Basically this means the prosecution have to satisfy the Judge that it has fulfilled all its pre-trial duties and disclosures to the defence within a proscribed time limit. This is often alluded to in the legal world as the 'fast-track system' but, as seen in this protracted case, it was more like the 'hard-shoulder system'. Alternatively, if the Judge feels that the CPS have not acted 'with due diligence and expedition' it may bail and discharge the defendant. At the hearing, the prosecutor got off to a good start as he claimed he had only received the file at court that morning and he was no position to make the application. This was exactly our point. The Custody Time Limits were not due to expire until the following day and therefore the matter was adjourned to enable the Crown to make the application.

The following day the Crown wanted to extend the Custody Time Limits until the 29th January 2002 so as to cover the trial that was to start on the 21st January 2002. The defence argument was that the Custody Time Limits should not be extended because the Crown had wantonly disregarded and broken not one, but two high court orders to provide secondary disclosure material to the defence. Also, the inexplicable late arrest of Wendall some five months after the arrest of Diamond was both unsatisfactory and unacceptable as the defendant was being unfairly penalized due to the lack of diligence and promptness of action by the police and CPS. The defence thought we had a compelling argument, but the Judge ruled against us. He claimed the trial date of 21st January 2002 was the first available date available to all parties and he could not take into consideration the late arrest of Wendall as he was not legally a co-defendant of Diamond. His Honour Judge Smithson concluded, however, that if the prosecution sought to apply for the trial to be postponed beyond 21st January 2002, to incorporate a possible new defendant of Wendall, the Crown could expect to face a difficult application to further extend the Custody Time Limits of Diamond.

In plain, simple and unadorned language, I was well rumped! The CPS had blatantly broken two Orders of Court regarding disclosure material and the absurd late arrest of Wendall was tantamount to an abuse of process. This is another reason why the police decided to post-date Snakeshaft's QE statement, otherwise it would have been transparently clear that the police, for some incomprehensible reason, had not arrested and charged Wendall at the appropriate time. In spite of having a compelling and persuasive case, my solicitor and barrister claimed that it would take a brave Judge to rule in favour of the defence, especially knowing that there was a lethal Uzi submachine gun and 376 rounds of ammunition involved. It was frustrating for my family and me as the overriding issue was that I had been set-up by two depraved scumbags and it counted for nothing. I would have to sit back and be patient and wait for the eventual trial.

In spite of this setback, the Crown provided the defence with a new bundle of primary disclosure material regarding the arrest of Wendall. In the bundle were the run-of-the-mill documents concerning his arrest, such as: police custody record; property seized, which consisted of four mobile phones; case papers regarding this case; a copy of a letter sent to a prison friend trying to justify his role in the case and calling me a grass; phone books; and, documents regarding his latest fifty minute taped interview. More interestingly, there was mention of an untitled, undated and un-addressed handwritten letter that had not been sent but was reputedly meant for my wife. Apparently, Wendall had written the letter to my wife, Stacey, explaining that he had not set me up and yet he did not post it! Conveniently, the letter was found in a wardrobe in the bedroom when the Flying Squad arrested Wendall. We did not have a copy of this 'wardrobe letter' as the prosecution did not provide us with one. Why? My solicitor claims that it is highly unlikely that such a letter could be used as evidence as it is deemed a 'self-serving letter' and is inadmissible in a court of law. The CPS also neglected to provide us with a copy of Wendall's latest interview when he was arrested and charged on 2nd November 2001. Why? What was going on?

There was one other significant aspect; the Flying Squad claimed that they had put a warrant out for Wendall's arrest on the Police National Computer on the 19th June 2001, some two weeks after my arrest. One of Wendall's conditions of parole was that he had to live at a known address and visit his Probation Officer regularly. Later, Wendall told a friend of mine in Cellmarsh Prison that he did not want to go on his toes over this incident because of the parole situation. If that is the case, why did the police leave it until 24th July 2001 to formally arrest Wendall? It is the inaction of the police in Wendall's arrest that points to some collusion between the two parties. We learn proper police procedures and practices have not been carried out in this case and it does not bode well for Wendall's role in the set-up.

One of the prominent aspects to emerge from the Custody Time Limits hearing was that the prosecution were to have a conference about the case on the 29th November and any material not deemed sensitive was to be disclosed to the defence by the close of play on the 30th November 2001. Amazingly, we were told later that the prosecution's conference did go ahead on the 29th November, but remarkably the officer in charge of the case, DS Herbert of the Flying Squad, was not allowed to participate in it. This was because of the involvement of the Special Investigation Services based at New Dockland Yard. What was going on? Surely a conference where not even the Case Officer was allowed into it was absurd? Unless the material discussed was so sensitive that they did not even trust their own men. The case had so many cracks and crevices in which the CPS could hide the truth; it was rapidly becoming impossible to follow their game plan. The only consolation I had was that I was bang-on with my presumption, and it was Wendall who was the main informant who they were duty bound to protect. But they underestimated Terry Diamond.

CHAPTER 23:

DECEMBER 2001

The protracted saga revolving around Snakeshaft's 'undated statement' continued when Wendall appeared at his next court appearance on the 3rd December. Initially I felt that this was another police-constructed manoeuvre and the case against him would collapse at the next hearing because how long does it take for the CPS to get a statement dated, not four weeks surely. But three days later on 6th December 2001 the legendary 'undated statement' was dated and Wendall was committed to stand trial alongside me at Thamesmead Crown Court.

On the 7th December, the very next day, my case was listed at Knaresbrook Crown Court for a Mention hearing, but because of the security implications surrounding Wendall's arrest, the trial could only be heard at the Old Bailey or Thamesmead Crown Court. Therefore, His Honour Judge Bond transferred my case to Thamesmead Crown Court to be joined with Wendall's case. Much more disturbing for me, the presiding Judge extended the previous court order for the phone billings by four months to incorporate the four mobile phones that were taken from Wendall's address when he was arrested for the second time in November 2001. This was ludicrous, as it would mean that my trial date of 21st January 2002 could not be met. Even more disturbing was the delay would be caused by the police trying to get the phone billings of four mobile phones that, in my view, were not central to the case. I pointed this out to my solicitor and told him once again the mobile phone billings that we required were recorded on the last ten calls dialled and received on my mobile phone of which we had a copy in the unused material supplied by the prosecution. I had told my solicitor about this in October two months earlier but he had failed to act on this information.

On 7th December 2001, Mickey Macitto and his co-defendant appeared at Knaresbrook Crown Court and pleaded guilty to possession of a class B drug, 869 grams of amphetamine sulphate. Macitto received 21 months imprisonment and was immediately removed from the category A prisoner status at Cellmarsh Prison. I asked Macitto why he did not fight the case knowing what we did about Snakeshaft. He claimed that even if he fought the Snakeshaft issue of placing the drugs in his car, it was the later transaction in the car park between him and his co-defendant that would have been hard to explain to a jury. Admittedly, he did have a valid point. Moreover, the low-grade drugs that were involved and the time he had already spent in prison custody meant that it was far better for him to go with the grain than against it. Pleading guilty had its shortcomings, however, as not only would it mean another conviction on his record and allow the Drug Trafficking Act to seize his vehicle, cash and other items of clothing from his home address, but by pleading guilty it made Wendall and Snakeshaft right and they would no doubt be collecting their reward monies. There is no disputing, if Macitto had fought the case it would have helped me in my endeavours to extract more information about Wendall and Snakeshaft from the CPS, but obviously he felt that he had chosen the right path. Only time would tell if that was the case!

In the meantime, the conference between the crown prosecutor, the CPS case officer and DI Fisher of SIS had triggered the production of the long awaited secondary disclosure material. This included scene of crime photographs of the black BMW, the blue bag in the vehicle, snaps of the Uzi submachine gun laid out with all its component parts, a map of Cambridgeshire and a hand written telephone number on a piece of paper. This was Snakeshaft's mobile phone number that Wendall had given to me at 12 p.m. on the day of my arrest. In the photograph, however, the police had strategically placed my mobile phone over the number to obscure several numbers on it. A cheap move that made me even more determined to acquire the telephone billing of that number.

There was also a printed copy of the observation log that referred to the events outside Snakeshaft's address on the day of my arrest. And, most importantly, there was a copy of four Computer Assisted Messages (CADS) between the police vehicles and the incident room. In one of the CAD messages, a police sergeant, Paul Tuna makes an emergency

999 call to the New Dockland Yard incident room at 12:23 hours, ten minutes before I walk into Snakeshaft's house, where he asked to speak to the control room inspector about an armed operation in Bornchurch, Essex. The significance of this 999 call had not yet become evident, but with a name like PS Tuna it definitely sounded fishy.

Also in the CAD messages was the revelation of another ARV with the call sign Trojan 231 that was parked in Coburn Avenue, Bornchurch. We had no reference to this ARV in the case papers. We needed to explore and evaluate the role of this police vehicle as it took the Trojan armed response vehicles up to five. What became transparent was that this was no Sunday afternoon crowd control operation and yet they still let two potential suspects to an alleged firearm transaction walk away from the scene.

There is some evidence to suggest that Wendall was still working for the police after my arrest in order to set-up associates or, at the very minimum, to pass on potential criminal information. For instance, a week after my arrest an associate of mine met up with Wendall to discuss the bizarre nature of my arrest. After the initial conversation, Wendall asked this associate of mine if he 'wanted to go to work?' , meaning to commit an armed robbery with Wendall. The associate, who was not an active robber anyway, knowing the bizarre circumstances of my arrest declined the offer claiming that he felt he was under police observation. He said this so that Wendall would not pursue the matter. My friend found it strange that Wendall would be looking to 'go to work' so shortly after my suspicious arrest. Once again things were not adding up, or rather they *were* adding up – the rat!

A month after my arrest in July 2001, Wendall contacted a well-connected black guy from Brixton whom we had both met in prison. The black guy told me in Cellmarsh Prison that Wendall wanted a kilo of 'Charlie', but, for personal reasons, the black guy did not want to get involved with Wendall.

The most disturbing and damaging scenario occurred when I learned that Wendall had travelled to Holland in August 2001. Being on parole and not allowed to travel abroad without Home Office approval, you would think that Wendall would want to keep quiet about the trip, but it was common knowledge amongst the criminal fraternity. More germane, Wendall went to Amsterdam to see a Dutch drug dealer who he had become friends with in Flankland Prison. The Dutchman became very suspicious of Wendall's motives to organize a drug deal as the Dutchman was fully aware of the Macitto arrest and that Wendall was also on police bail for the procurement of an Uzi firearm. Later the Dutchman told an English colleague that he felt Wendall was either setting him up or was going to rip him off. Acting upon natural insight and intuition, the quivery Dutchman refrained from any transactions with Wendall who returned to England empty handed.

The pattern appeared to be that the senior police controller or handler of Wendall was able to keep Wendall out of prison, on police bail for the Uzi offence, provided that he could keep supplying bodies and information about drug deals and other crimes. The senior police handler, believed to be DI Helliman, could only keep the Flying Squad from his door provided Wendall was coming up with results. By coincidence, Wendall acquired the pejorative nickname 'The Pest' as he appeared to want his fingers in every pie. This, combined with the extraordinary news about my arrest and the message I had sent out from Cellmarsh Prison for others to be careful when having anything to do with Wendall, made most people with any brains dubious about Wendall's over-zealous desire to organize drug deals. This may point to the inexplicable delay in Wendall's arrest and arraignment for the Uzi offence. The rat was willing to set-up and sell friends and associates in order to obtain freedom and acquire economic gain. This is not the first, nor the last time, this has happened, but it serves to reveal the lengths the police and scumbags will go to in order to obtain their devious aims and ambitions.

Some critics may find this nightmare story hard to believe and I would always encourage people to be critical, but please believe me, I am not writing my account of these events for fun. This is reality at its most painful. Looking out of a cell window in Cellmarsh Prison facing a long sentence as an innocent man is no joke – it is a living nightmare that I would not wish on anyone!

CHAPTER 24:

NEW DEVELOPMENTS

Shortly before the Christmas period of 2001 my solicitor had contacted the CPS by phone. They said that the case was now being transferred from the CPS based at East London to a new female CPS operative located near the Old Bailey in Central London. My solicitor was instructed that all correspondence had to be addressed to this female special case lawyer. My solicitor quickly sent the new female prosecutor a letter asking why the case had been placed under her control and remit. Once again, for the umpteenth time, the letter went unanswered. *Plus ça change.*

It was not long before the festive period would be upon us and although I had spent many other Christmas periods and New Years behind the cell door, this one was markedly different in that I should not have been there. If I had been apprehended and arrested for a crime where I was legally and morally guilty, then the pain and anguish of brutal separation from my beautiful family would have been much more bearable. Instead, however, I did what I have always done in such testing situations, I dug deep into my inner resolve and gained strength from adversity. I treated everyday as an ordinary day and focussed intently upon the legal battle and challenge ahead. I was utterly and unequivocally determined that these pair of slags, who harboured and expressed a distorted view of life, were not going to take me away from my family for countless years. Not only was I going to prove that I was set-up, but I was going to tell my story to the world. I wanted to exhume and expose the dark side of humanity, as expressed by Wendall and Snakeshaft, so that the world could see the perverse power of jealousy and resentment in its most quintessential form.

More poetically, I wanted to express in this book, in the most articulate way possible, how a treacherous and evil plan had gone disastrously wrong. To an enormous degree, the writing of this book in

Cellmarsh Prison – not the most conducive milieu to carry out a literary exercise – has had a cathartic effect for me. It has sublimated the negative human traits of inner-rage and revenge into a positive and constructive method of communication and understanding. The old adage that in order to beat your enemy you need to understand them applies here. I have sat for hours and hours chewing relentlessly upon the bilious bubblegum of why a so-called friend who had come through a nightmare prison sentence with me, would want to see my loving family and me completely and utterly destroyed. Admittedly, it is not that difficult to get one immoral and iniquitous person in your life who wishes to inflict upon you maximum harm or suffering, but here I had three or more people who ruthlessly conspired to send me to my grave, destroy my beautiful family and sit back and enjoy every moment of it with such perverse delight that it becomes totally horrific. These were the type of unholy and depraved individuals that I was dealing with. What possessed them to embark upon such a sinister and vile venture?

Quite simply, Wendall's fatal flaw was his deeply ingrained and irradiated jealousy. I had broken him out of a prison van and he had ended up, by his own volition, with a 35-year prison sentence. I had pleaded guilty, nearly lost my leg during our arrest for the Kensal Rise robbery and received sixteen years imprisonment. While in prison, I submerged myself in the constructive sphere of education while Wendall sat in prison cells and talked bollocks. On my release, I had put my family first and did not show Wendall as much attention as he would have liked. Constantly in Wendall's ear was the Lady Macbeth of East London, his wife Carol, urging him on to seek revenge on his release. I had it all, the loving, loyal and devoted wife, three healthy adolescent children, a beautiful new born baby boy, a new house, car and a contented smile that stretched for ear to ear. He was a bald, pot-bellied, fifty-year old villain, long past his sell-by-date, with a wife whose colourful past was legendary. We had nothing in common, save that he wanted what I had achieved in life. He was the very personification of failure whilst I was the living embodiment of contentment and success. Wendall had one plan for me and that was total destruction.

As for his alter ego and side-kick, Snakeshaft, from what I had learned about him, he possessed an equally rich vein of jealousy in that he abhorred and detested the fact that he was employed to run around for very rich and successful drug barons. Snakeshaft counted the large chunks of cash for others and then extracted his thin slither of notes before passing the cash onto its owners, and this crucified him. Snakeshaft felt that he was due more than he was getting. Coming up to the wrong side of forty he was going nowhere fast, save sucking up to his paternalistic senior police handlers, where they no doubt cut up the reward monies between them.

Accordingly, Snakeshaft viewed me as fair game. I represented all that he was not, a well-respected East London villain that radiated all the trappings of success and happiness. The unholy marriage between Wendall and Snakeshaft was compounded by their ferocious jealousy of others and they became the Ian Brady and Myra Hindley of the East End where their evil was limitless. If left to run unchecked, who knows what heinous crimes they would have wrought on others. Their fatal flaw of jealousy was exacerbated by a woeful dearth of brains. Snakeshaft had been a successful state-registered and state-paid police informer for sixteen years until he recruited the more dominant partner of Wendall. Where Snakeshaft had been stealthy, furtive and insidious in his vile tradecraft of informing, Wendall was bold, blasé and ambitious. It was a lethal mixture of traits destined for failure, an experience that Wendall was wholly unfamiliar with. Where Snakeshaft would provide his senior police handlers and controllers with globules of underworld gen and gossip, silently watching those on the periphery of his social and criminal circle getting mysteriously swagged and banged away for countless years, Wendall was a clumsy novice at the game. Eager to impress his state paymasters that had practically airlifted him out of a top security prison on the pretence of parole, he steamed into his newfound trade with all the grace and finesse of a Russian-speaking KGB agent at a CIA annual conference. Wendall's amateurish tactics lacked the long-standing status and experience of Snakeshaft. On the day of my arrest Snakeshaft played the part exceedingly well, but it was Wendall who exhibited a tranche of guilt. Not a lot, but enough in retrospect to provide evidence against him later on during my own video-like memory playback of events. Wendall had failed yet again. He was useless as a criminal. He was useless as an informer because ten weeks after he had been released from prison I had tumbled him. Alas, the only thing Wendall was good at was serving time in British prisons, a fitting epithet for a king rat.

One of the reasons why the senior police handler wanted to set me up was that I was undeniably a premiership scalp in a league of second-rate crooks who had attained success in the lucrative world of drug dealing. I was real juicy meat on the bone, not a nibble around a spare rib. I had been home from prison for six glorious family-loving years and he and the Flying Squad had suspected me of committing a major armed robbery on a security van on their patch in South East London. In their view, if they could not get me one way, they would get me another way. Like how the Americans had used Pakistan as a condom to get into Afghanistan, the 'cozzer' had used Wendall to get into me to set me up. But when I would not agree to Wendall's plans to commit robberies or supply him with a gun, they hatched the plan together to plant the Uzi in my car and arrest me. One way or another I was going! But fundamental errors and mistakes had been made. In Snakeshaft's official debrief process and QE statement he never mentioned procuring, possessing or supplying any type of firearm before, yet this time, the very first time that he has supplied a firearm for anyone in his life, it is an Israeli-made Uzi submachine gun with a shoulder stock, loaded magazine, silencer and 376 rounds of ammunition. Not bad for a novice 'gun-runner'. One massive question the jury will have to face is, did Snakeshaft receive the Uzi from the relatively unknown and untraceable black man or, as in my view, did a corrupt 'cozzer' obtain the weapon from a secret armoury? We are aware that the senior police handler has been suspended from duty before, but at present the CPS are reluctant to confirm or deny this issue. The plot thickens!

CHAPTER 25:

THE PLEAD GUILTY LETTERS

The pounding New Year hangovers endured by the legal profession had not even subsided when I was due to make another court appearance. On 2nd January 2002 I was supposed to be produced at Thamesmead Crown Court for a prosecution application to join my case with that of Wendall's, but for some strange reason, I was not produced at court! Wendall was produced alone and the joinder application did not take place.

My solicitor, who was present at court, informed me that there was some suggestion that Wendall wanted to plead guilty to the three counts on the indictment; namely, the procurement of a firearm, possession of ammunition and being a prohibited person from possessing a firearm. But the prosecution had cut off this escape route for Wendall by claiming that both Wendall and I were to face a new count. This was under Section 16 of the Firearms Act, the possession of a firearm with intent to endanger life. The 'intent' aspect of the count would mean that it would activate the automatic *Two Strikes* life sentence policy if found guilty. Apparently, my brief informed me, Wendall was livid at court as he could not plead guilty and slip out of the case like the other scumbag Snakeshaft. This meant that Wendall had to come face-to-face with me at the next hearing!

Evidently the crux of the 'intent' count was based upon the fabricated comments that it is alleged I made in Snakeshaft's house, i.e. "This will do a good job, as the Bermondsey job!" This was taken to mean that the Uzi was being purchased for future robberies and as a result would place the public in danger.

On a personal level, the farce was getting even more farcical. The evidence to pursue the 'intent' count against me was tenuous in the extreme. As for Wendall the evidence against him for this additional count was practically non-existent, as Snakeshaft claimed that he was not even in the room when this comment was made! The only rational explanation for the 'intent' count was scare tactics in possibly forcing me to hold my hands up to the lesser charges and avoid a mandatory life sentence. To support this assumption, the prosecution had not even provided the defence with the indictment. Life sentence or not, I wouldn't plead to a parking ticket in this case, let alone possession of a planted firearm. I would fight to the death even if it meant dying in prison fighting to clear my name, the rats were not having me, no way! At this hearing, His Honour Judge Atkinson QC set a new provisional trial date of 9th April 2002. This was because the Flying Squad said all the telephone evidence would not be ready until the 7th April 2002. Whatever happened to the 'fast-track' legal system?

Before the next proposed court appearance at Thamesmead Crown Court on 11th January 2002, quite astonishingly, I received two risible handwritten letters from Wendall passed to me through the prison grapevine. To appreciate the full import of these letters and to do them justice, I believe that I should show them to the reader in their full entirety. The first handwritten letter I received on Tuesday 8th January. It stated:

> *You must be aware by now that we have been charged with possession with intent to endanger life. An automatic life sentence for both of us if found guilty.*
>
> *When we next appear at court, very shortly, to plead and so on. We can either argue, call each other names and get nothing sorted out and thus both end up with life sentences. Or get together in the same cell and sort this mess out, then sort out our personal problems at a later date. The way I see things, and I am sure that you agree, is that we should both plead guilty to at least one, or most likely, all three of the original charges and get the Pross (sic) to drop the intent charge. I'm not sure if they will stand it because they may badly want to life us both off. If that's the case then obviously there will be no deal. However if their evidence for intent is slim, they will go for the deal. I don't believe that they will accept just one of us pleading, because it would still mean a trial and the third man having to give his evidence. At*

least if we plead to those three counts we will have a release date, and will probably get 7 yrs max. You realise as well as I, if we get lifed off then I will definitely never be coming home again, and you will certainly end up serving double figures. Its your decision.

I received the second handwritten letter from Wendall 24 hours later at 4:30 p.m. on Wednesday 9th January 2002. It stated:

This note is in anticipation that you agree to plead guilty to the original three counts if the pros accepts to drop the intent charge.

I don't think the pros will accept as they want to life us off, but one way round it would be to get your solicitor, if you can phone him before Friday court date, to contact the grass solicitor and say to the grass solicitor that the pair of us are willing to plead to the three original charges if the pros drops the intent charge that way the grass won't have to give evidence which I know he will be double thankful for. The idea is to try and let your solicitor know before Friday so he can get in touch with the grass solicitor before Friday at court. What hopefully should happen is the grass solicitor should then put pressure on the prosecution to accept our deal. If for some reason your solicitor can't get hold of the grass solicitor by the latest Thursday then your solicitor and counsel at court Friday should speak to the grass solicitor and counsel – I believe the grass solicitor/counsel were both at court last week – and tell them what we intend to do and hopefully they will put pressure on the pros to accept our pleas.

I've already wrote a letter to my solicitor explaining the above but he is off sick until Friday court day but I've been told the office will fax him the letter at his home.

If my anticipation that you will plead is wrong then ignore this note.

When I first received these two handwritten letters the anger and revulsion welled-up inside me like a volcano. Here was a scumbag that had set me up, nearly got me ironed out by the police, grassed me off around the prisons and now had the effrontery to ask me to plead guilty so that it would make it easier for his vile accomplice. As one sagacious prisoner proclaimed when he read these sick letters, "I don't know what Wendall is on over in the High Secure Unit, but I wouldn't mind an ounce of it!"

Several issues emanate from these letters. Firstly, if Wendall could persuade me to plead guilty not only would Snakeshaft not have to give evidence in a public courtroom, but also the defence would not be allowed access to sensitive material that would, in my view, point to a police-crook set-up. Moreover, Wendall and Snakeshaft were most probably on a financial bonus if they could persuade me to plead guilty. It was at this stage that I really felt Wendall was suffering from some serious mental illness, most probably delusions of grandeur. More annoyingly, the contents of these letters made it look as if I had knowledge of the Uzi before it was discovered in my vehicle. Wendall really thought that he had it all worked out. Boy, was he in for a shock when we got to court!!!

Naturally I handed these preposterous letters to my solicitor and he pointed out that these were hardly the actions of a man who fought an unwinnable case in the 1980s with a revolver in one hand and a bag of stolen cash in the other hand. My solicitor viewed Wendall's scam as a last ditch attempt to prevent the truth from coming out. Far from the 'plead guilty' handwritten letters and additional *Two Strikes* count weakening my resolve, it made me stronger and stronger. I knew that Wendall desperately wanted to bury the truth but it was the truth, the unswerving ironclad truth, that pushed and pulled me through every minute of everyday, that was going to be my saviour in this case. The more Wendall and Snakeshaft contributed to the case, the more it revealed it as being all chinks and no armour.

In the interim, my solicitor contacted Wendall's legal advisor and related Wendall's madcap scheme to plead guilty and even he was confused by Wendall's actions as the 'intent to endanger life' count was unsustainable in English law, more particularly against Wendall. It transpires that Wendall was desperate to avoid a trial, because he could not afford to have one. A trial would reveal the true extent of his involvement in the set-up. On closer examination of the facts, Wendall was in a veritable corner with only one way to run. Wendall had to reveal his true colours and follow in the footsteps of his despicable accomplice, the most toad-spotted Snakeshaft. What would he do? Stand and fight or run with the foxes? Only time would tell, but it did not look good for him.

The date for the next hearing was set for 11ᵗʰ January 2002. I was eagerly looking forward to confronting the scumbag Wendall and putting it to him, face-to-face, that he had set me up! I had been chatting to solicitors, barristers, family, friends, fellow prisoners and even screws over the last seven months, telling them that I had been ruthlessly set up by Wendall and Snakeshaft and now it was time to confront and denounce my nemesis. Friends and legal advisors had given me advice not to talk to him, not to attack him in the dock because it would only make things worse, but as soon as the scumbag walked into the dock at Thamesmead Crown Court I could not contain myself. Wendall already knew what was coming as he had removed his glasses and favoured Mr Magoo the cartoon character. I went for him but was held back by several burly screws who were aware of the hostile atmosphere.

I blurted, "You dirty no-good slag, you set me up. The truth is coming out, you scumbag!"

Wendall replied, "They all know, you know!"

I added vehemently, "Know what, know the truth, you rat!"

I desperately wanted to keep calm but it was impossible. It was like trying to hold back the raging sea with hands full of clay. As the volcanic like verbal anger erupted inside me I could see my solicitor cringing in the seats at the side of the court trying to be as insignificant as possible.

Eventually the hearing went ahead with a human wall of Cellmarsh screws separating us. Wendall was arraigned for two counts and pleaded not guilty. Then the Crown stated that they would be in a position to provide all the phone evidence in an evidential format on 7ᵗʰ April 2002 two days before the proposed start of the trial. We objected to this as it left us only two days, over a weekend, to examine and analysis the evidence. As a result, the trial was set for Monday 13ᵗʰ May 2002. There was to be a separate hearing to discuss and argue the merits and short-comings of the 'intent' count and because of the postponement of the trial beyond its original date I would have to face another Custody Time Limits hearing and this was set for 28ᵗʰ January 2002.

Down in the bowels of the courthouse the slanging match between Wendall and I continued from cell to cell. To recount word for word what I said would be impossible because I completely lost it. I remember saying, "You are not a grass! You are a POLICE INFORMER! You, Snakeshaft and DI Helliman have set me up and the truth is coming out!" I recall saying, "Why are you pleading guilty?"

Wendall said, "Because of the Two Strikes!"

I continued, "But there is no evidence against you? You fought a case with a gun in one hand and a bag of cash in the other and now you want to plead guilty? You are a POLICE INFORMER!"

The loud hailer like verbal continued for about 15 minutes and then the senior prison officer who escorted me to court asked me to stop shouting as he could tell that Wendall was winding me up. He was right; Wendall was always good with his gob. He had a toxic tongue but now he used it to talk to his mates in blue and it had got him massive trouble. In my view Wendall had decamped to the other side and worse still he had been rumbled. Wendall, in effect, had burnt all his bridges and had sold his soul to the devil. He had not only betrayed himself and his family, but he was a true legend in prison folklore, the first prisoner to escape from a British prison in a helicopter. When he passes away his obituary should read, "Little man with towering inferiority complex was airlifted out of top security prison and then became an unsuccessful police informer and stool pigeon!" What a waste, what an unforgivable diabolical waste of a potentially good man!

In the nature versus nurture debate of police informers, some would say police informing is a hereditary human trait, it is born in them from the very beginning. Others would claim that some criminals can exhibit all the characteristics of a fine upstanding moral crook and then all of a sudden through a crisis or enforced circumstances turn turtle! The nurture or crisis aspect does seem more prevalent in modern society, but I believe that grassing is either in you or it is not. You have either got betrayal lurking inside you, lying dormant like an inchoate virus waiting to strike at an opportune time, or it doesn't exist at all. Like I said in my police interview, when the Flying Squad was asking me for the names of the people who planted the blue bag inside my vehicle, I would rather hang myself than divulge the names. It is plain and simply just not in me to volunteer information that may implicate and incriminate others.

CHAPTER 26:

THE HIGH SECURE UNIT (HSU)

On the 14th January 2002, three days after the volatile confrontation with Wendall at Thamesmead Crown Court, a screw accosted me on House Block Four at Cellmarsh Prison. He ordered me to pack my kit as I was being re-categorized to a High Risk category A prisoner and I would be transferred to the High Secure Unit, where Wendall was housed, in the afternoon.

Immediately I thought, what a coincidence, I had been a standard category A prisoner for the last seven months with no anti-social or control problems and now I was being placed in the same prison unit as the person who had helped put me there. I was not concerned about the physical aspect of being near Wendall as I was supremely confident that I would rip the scumbag's arms off and hit him with the wet ends. I was more concerned about the ulterior motives behind the reallocation. Wendall had already sent me two pathetic handwritten letters urging me to plead guilty. He had also asked to be put in the same cell as me in the bowels of the courthouse, where I was advised not to communicate with him for legal reasons and now, when that ploy had failed, they were putting me with him in the High Secure Unit?

In my view, there were two salient reasons for this. Firstly, the police wanted Wendall to be near me so he could claim at court that I said something incriminatory which could be used at the trial. Or secondly, the police wanted to monitor and eavesdrop on conversations that I would have with my solicitor and social visits. Some doubters may view this as a very cynical or paranoid assumption, but let me daub some colour on the canvas so to speak!

Cellmarsh is the flagship prison of the British penal system. It is an ultra modern high security jail built in the early 1990s and finally opened in April 1991. During my sojourn at Cellmarsh the prison population varied between 850-900 prisoners. Standard category A prisoners were dispersed amongst four prominent house blocks that also housed run-of-the-mill prisoners. The more quasi-dangerous clientele, the high risk, double A and exceptional risk, triple A prisoners, some of whom were perceived as a danger to the State, were incarcerated in the separate High Secure Unit.

The High Secure Unit is basically a prison within a prison. It has an additional high, grey, reinforced concrete wall around it similar to the exterior wall and its very own gate that is electronically operated from a central control room. The Unit itself contains four interlinked spurs or miniature wings that hold a maximum of twelve prisoners on each spur. It also has its own punishment or segregation unit. This was being used for a solitary Columbian female prisoner while I was there. How I detest that word or term 'Segregation Unit', as it implies that a prisoner is being segregated from others because he or she is in some way infected or contaminated with a social or medical disease or virus. The apposite term should be an 'Isolation Unit' as that is exactly what it is! Prisoners are put into isolation from others as punishment. The euphemistic term 'segregation' underplays the full impact or import of what is happening. The isolation of a prisoner is far more damaging than mere segregation. It is sensory deprivation in the extreme and may contribute to further dysfunctional human behaviour that requires even more drastic measures of enforced isolation, such as the use of the strongbox or psychotropic drugs.

The High Secure Unit, or HSU as it is known, is completely electronic. All the heavy metal doors are locked and unlocked by a central controller. Everywhere, apart from inside the cells, is under constant CCTV surveillance and observation. This includes the visits and all telephone calls where a screw is designated to listen to and tape all calls. The Unit also has two small exercise yards that are, in effect, large human aviaries with alarmed wire fences and canopies to prevent airborne escape. All in all, it represents and embodies a very clinical and oppressive atmosphere in which to live. So much so, that I alluded to it as, "A concrete mausoleum for the living dead!" Apparently, one foreign national who had left the HSU shortly before I arrived had been housed in the Unit for over two years while awaiting trial. During his trial, the defence barrister commented upon the physical and psychological deterioration of his client to the trial Judge who ordered the Prison Service to conduct full medical examinations of prisoners held at the Unit. These were to be carried out on all prisoners held in the Unit at three monthly intervals.

The supreme irony of the HSU is that it is more likely to contain a higher percentage of innocent prisoners than that of the mainstream prison. Suspected enemies of the State, such as the perceived Irish, Islamic and Taliban terrorist prisoners, are given high secure status because, more often than not, there isn't the evidence available for a conviction and one of the reasons to house them in these conditions is to acquire more evidence or intelligence for a conviction. Put bluntly, that is one of the reasons I believe I was transferred to the HSU, as I was getting uncomfortably close to finding out the real identity of the person who supplied the Uzi firearm to Snakeshaft. Indeed, was it the untraceable black guy with the unique nickname of 'The Porpoise' or was it, in my view, the informants' senior police handler?

On arrival at the HSU I asked to be allocated to a prison cell and spur where I was unable to communicate with Wendall. The last thing I wanted to do was get to trial and have Wendall proclaim, in the style of Snakeshaft, that I had admitted to some incriminating act or deed that the jury may be tempted to believe. This was not an unreasonable request given the circumstances of my arrest and I was allocated to cell 4 on spur 3 where I was greeted by an old social and prison friend Kevin Brown who was awaiting trial for a series of armed robberies in the Kent and Sussex areas. We exchanged pleasantries and Kevin relayed to me Wendall's version of events. The most remarkable being that Snakeshaft was not a grass and that he only turned QE when he was attacked in prison.

Wendall claimed he had gone to my address to speak to my wife while I was in prison and she would not open the front door (all bollocks). So he had written a personal letter, pleading his innocence about the set-up, which he had intended to post, but instead it was conveniently left to be found by the police in a plastic bag containing legal papers in the bottom of his wardrobe, at his home when he was arrested. At this time, the defence still had not received disclosure of the contents of this letter but Wendall was already laying the groundwork for its eventual revelation.

Wendall also claimed that he wanted to see my brother Eugene, but again it was all bollocks, my brother would not see him. Moreover, Kevin noted, Wendall never pointed his finger once at Snakeshaft for the set-up and Wendall always radiated the impression that he was going to plead guilty despite, on the face of it, there being minimal evidence against him. All in all, once Kevin had heard my account of events—not that he needed reassuring – his loyalty and allegiance was with me. This was expressed several days later when Kevin was ordered to move cells from my spur in the HSU to Wendall's spur. Kevin refused due to the conflict and was moved to a completely different spur nonetheless.

CHAPTER 27:

CUSTODY TIME LIMITS II

On 28th January 2002, I was produced at Thamesmead Crown Court to oppose the extension of Custody Time Limits that were due to expire the following day. The significant defence arguments were based upon the fact that the police, and by extension the Crown, had not acted with due diligence and expedition in the arrest of Wendall.

It is not disputed that Wendall was present on the 5th June 2001 when the 'blue bag' was planted in my vehicle. Therefore, to say that there was no evidence to arrest Wendall on that day is hogwash. In plain and simple terms, the police should have arrested all three suspects at the scene of the alleged transaction. The absurd delay in the arrest and arraignment of Wendall meant that the defendant was being unduly penalized by having to wait for his trial in prison custody for longer than was considered necessary. To postpone the trial date of Diamond because of the late arrest of Wendall was patently unfair and did not point to promptness of action by the CPS. The defence argued that the Custody Time Limits should not be extended.

In traditional schematic fashion, His Honour Judge Atkinson QC took it upon himself to point out that the fixed trial date of Diamond was always going to be delayed due to the defence requests for phone evidence and records. Namely the four mobile phones seized at Wendall's address when he was arrested for the second time on the 2nd November 2001. The defence argued that the production of phone evidence is not a sole matter of the defence, as it was the duty of the investigating officer, DS Herbert in this case, to seek any evidence that pointed towards and away from the accused. Phone evidence, being important evidence in any modern case, therefore dictated that the onus to supply this evidence was upon the Crown not the defence. The Judge begged to differ. The defence wanted to know what steps had been taken to secure the telephone evidence and despite the case officer, DS Herbert, DI Fisher of SIS and a senior member of the CPS being present at court, none of them, they claimed, were responsible for the request and accumulation of the telephone evidence.

In response to this legal stalemate, His Honour Judge Atkinson QC ruled, *"… in order to make a judicial decision as to whether there was good and sufficient cause to extend Custody Time Limits the matter requires an adjournment to enable both sides to have this matter fully investigated."* As a result, the Custody Time Limits were extended by an additional nine days until the 6th February 2002 for this to take place.

In my view, the Judge was having none of it. First of all he body-swerved the defence argument about the inexplicable late arrest of Wendall and then he adjourned the hearing so that it gave the police and CPS time to organize, rehearse and perfect their evidence at the next Custody Time Limits hearing. Before I was swagged away to the lugubrious confines of Cellmarsh HSU, my solicitor sidled over to me in the dock and whispered, "I think the Judge has fucked up, as the ruling he has just made was illegal." In essence, the Judge had to be *satisfied* that the CPS had acted with all due diligence and expedition to extend the Custody Time Limits. By definition, the Judge had extended the Custody Time Limits to hear further evidence concerning due diligence and expedition. By employing logical deduction, this meant that the Judge was *not* satisfied, as he had asked to hear more evidence.

Through a wilful desire to keep me incarcerated, it appeared that the Judge had made a massive legal blunder. In football terminology, whatever way we tried to get around the Judge he obstructed our path. With all the judicial power and might at his disposal, he was utterly determined not to let us pass him. But in an unforeseen act of folly and bias, we had nut-megged him! We had slipped right between his wide open legs and were on our way to the High Court at the Strand to argue that HHJ Atkinson QC had fucked-up and in the interest of English law and justice, the court would have to release me!

The very next day I spoke to my solicitor on the phone and he said that he had been in consultation with an eminent female QC and she had supported his supposition that as of midnight that night (29th January 2002), I was being held in prison illegally. All the next day I had my capacious head firmly ensconced in the Archbold's, the English bible of law and practice and, according to the text, it was there in black and white. The Judge had to be satisfied that there was good and sufficient cause for extending the Custody Time Limits and "…that the prosecution had acted with all due expedition." Outwardly I was elated. But inwardly I was profoundly sceptical, as I had experienced the weasel words of the High Court Judges before. They were, in my view, professional conspirators who crouched down in a huddle in a private room everyday of the week to rump the underdog. Only once in a while did they support the underdog and that was to foster the illusion that they were acting on behalf of the common people.

As an example, after numerous unsuccessful appeals, it took the Court of Appeal over sixteen years to release the Birmingham Six. It crucified the judiciary and establishment to release them, but they knew, eventually, justice had to be seen to be done, as the Birmingham Six had become a permanent pebble in the judicial shoe.

What made me believe that my case would be any different? For a start I was not asking for the gracious goodwill or the munificent mercy of the court. I was asking for the Judges to apply the letter of the law. The law that they had written, endorsed and imposed on the people of the land. But would they concede to this issue and release me? Was it worth exposing a visible fault line through the integrity and status of three High Court Judges to keep me, Terence Diamond, a former, but in their eyes, ruthlessly active armed robber, in custody? Would they be willing to compromise their judicial worth and esteem? We would have to wait and see. But first, before we did anything, we had to obtain the transcript of HHJ Atkinson QC's ruling that he passed on the 28th January 2002.

Since I have been incarcerated in the High Secure Unit at Cellmarsh Prison I have given great thought as to how Wendall was in communication with his state paymasters. Ideally this could have been done through his former SO8 legal advisor, or even his equally embittered spouse who had to have been in on the set-up. Not only was she present on the day of my arrest but, it was suspected, because of her toxic tongue, that she was responsible for the hate mail that I had received. Both of these methods of communication would be very dangerous, however, as all calls on the prison payphone were monitored and recorded as well as all social visits.

Then one day I was walking in the exercise yard with one of the defendants in the Millennium Dome diamond robbery. He told me that because he was on the periphery of the case – it was alleged that he supplied the getaway vehicles for the robbery – he was working as a cleaner in the HSU, and he was pulled aside by a screw while the other prisoners were banged up and taken into a nearby room. In the room was the police liaison officer of Cellmarsh Prison, a great big fellow, who asked the prisoner if he was prepared to turn QE on the Dome robbers and if he had heard anything else about other prisoner's cases. He told me, in order not to draw attention to himself, that some of the prisoners were giving information and they were invariably given cleaners jobs in the HSU which meant they were out of their cells while all the other prisoners were locked away. Of course, the prisoner refused the generous offer by the police liaison officer and told his co-defendants and me about it.

Not surprisingly, Wendall was the cleaner on spur 4. Moreover, the prisoner proclaimed, for a proper debrief, they occasionally took their informants on fictitious dentist and optician appointments. None of this surprised me as I had met my fair share of shifty scumbags throughout previous sentences, but it was gratifying to know from the horse's mouth, in not so many terms, that this was possibly how Wendall was communicating with his new friends in blue.

CHAPTER 28:

FEBRUARY 2002

On Wednesday 6th February 2002 I reappeared at Thamesmead Crown Court in front of His Honour, Judge Atkinson QC for the continuation of the extension of Time Limits hearing. By now the Judge had well and truly circumnavigated the late arrest argument of Wendall issue and wanted to hear evidence solely about the process and procedure by which the police were obtaining or had obtained the telephone evidence and records. Present at court were the case officer, DS Herbert of the Flying Squad, the phone evidence liaison officer DC Griffin, a crime analyst, Perry Wiles, who was with the Serious Organized Crime Group of New Dockland Yard and a senior official from the CPS, Mr Nadir. Out of all these officials, DC Griffin appeared to be the main man, as it was his duty to ask for and chase up the phone evidence with the Telephone Investigation Unit (TIU) of New Dockland Yard.

A prime example of DC Griffin's tardiness could be seen when we learned that although Wendall was arrested for the second time on the 2nd November 2002, this detective did not ask for subscriber checks on Wendall's four mobile phones until 11th December—some five weeks later. Worse still, this detective did not ask for the itemized billing of these four mobile phones until 30th January 2002 which was some twelve weeks after Wendall's arrest.

There was some investigation into the matter as to when the police actually asked for the phone records of those mobile phones seized at the time of my arrest in June 2001. The police confirmed that they could proceed with the case without the phone evidence—of course they could—and did not think it necessary to pursue this avenue of inquiry until the defence asked for the phone billing in early October 2001. In fact, the defence initially asked for all the phone evidence in a formal 'defence case statement' submitted to Knaresbrook Crown Court and the CPS on 24th September 2001. This official document appeared worthless as the police, prosecution counsel and CPS completely ignored it. I was getting increasingly annoyed and frustrated as the police were misleading the court into thinking they were actively seeking the phone evidence. But when counsel for the defence asked DC Griffin how many times he had phoned the Telephone Investigation Unit, to chase up his inquiries, he said several times – definitely twice and maybe more. When we asked if there was any log of these calls to the TIU he said "No" and the Judge intervened to prevent his embarrassment. Everyone in the court could see that this detective was ad-libbing, taking an inordinate time over answering the questions and making it up as he went along.

More significantly, the crime analyst, Peter Wiles, claimed that when he received the phone records from TIU he analysed them using a computer programme and then presented it to the case officer. Wiles claimed that the hard disk drive, which contained the landline itemized billing of Snakeshaft's address, had come back blank and he had sent it back to the TIU. To be honest I was not surprised, because how could the police provide the defence with the home phone records of their main police informant – that would reveal a working relationship between 'the three men of sin'. To provide the defence with this conclusive evidence would be suicidal. It was then that I realized just how important it was to obtain this phone evidence, but how was I going to obtain this data as I had been practically screaming for it since my original arrest.

Even more disturbing, the police were focussing upon two mobile phones taken from Snakeshaft's address on arrest and four mobile phones that were taken from Wendall's premises on arrest. Both Wendall and Snakeshaft knew, as well as the police, that these mobile phones would be of little value to me as these were not the mobile phones they were using on the day of the set-up. I knew all the details of the mobile phone evidence that I wanted as they were on the last ten calls dialled and received on my subscriber check document, in the unused legal papers that were in my possession. I knew that I could not go to trial without this evidence, as it would prove beyond doubt that a conspiracy to set me up had indeed occurred.

When the Judge finally gave his ruling, he claimed that it was the defence fault that the Custody Time Limits was extended in November 2001 because counsel for the defence could not meet the trial date in early January and therefore the trial date had to be delayed longer until the 21st January 2002. Secondly, the Judge stated the fact that as Wendall had been arrested in November there had to be a joint trial. To subject Wendall to a voluntary Bill of Indictment that would force Wendall to meet the 21st January deadline would be impractical, because it would leave Wendall little time to prepare for trial (as if he could face a trial anyway). In any event, the 21st January trial date was vacated as Wendall was a high security prisoner and he could only be tried at Thamesmead Crown Court or the Central Criminal Court. As a result, the Judge ruled, "…the 13th May 2002 was the first date available. Therefore, there is, as I find, good and sufficient cause in the postponement of the trial."

With regard to the responsibility of the police to obtain and secure the telephone evidence and billings the Judge declared, "There is no duty that I know of on the prosecution to produce, of their own volition, lengthy telephone billings over a number of mobile and land lines." This was absurd, as when the police asked for a search warrant from a Magistrate the first item they stated they were looking for was firearms and the second was mobile phones. To proclaim that the police and prosecution ought to seize phones and then not seek to obtain the data on them is nonsensical. What is the point of seizing mobile phones from suspects if the data inside them is not going to be formally retrieved and analysed.

All in all, the Custody Time Limits hearing was a farce. The Judge was so biased in favour of the prosecution it was nauseating in the extreme. As my family and friends looked down at me, from high up in the public gallery, they too could tell that we faced a Sisyphean task. As soon as we thought that the police witnesses were making significant mistakes and errors in their evidence, the witness would hesitate and look askance for help, whereupon the Judge or prosecutor would ride in to their rescue. It was like some unwritten code, where if a policeman was having difficulty with his evidence or a particular issue, he would feign confusion or ignorance and the Judge would clarify the issue for him.

In practice, they had refined this method of intervention and saviour over many thousands of hours in the courtroom. We must remember, this was their arena, their colisseum, their territory and I could see exactly what was happening as clearly as you can see unalloyed innocence in a newborn child. In my view, if the Judge would stoop to such unilateral levels of bias during a simple Custody Time Limits hearing, what was he capable of during the trial, when we would ask him to order the prosecution to divulge the police informing status of the most toad-spotted duo.

It transpires that I had been held in prison for seven months and the elite Flying Squad had not bothered to obtain the phone evidence because it did not enhance their case one iota. Nor did they arrest and charge Wendall at the appropriate time. In my opinion, I was being unfairly penalized and punished by the inaction and negligence of the Flying Squad. I knew that I had to make myself heard, because like a true nightmare I was screaming as loud as I could but no one could, or was willing to, hear me. I resolved to embrace and employ *per se*, the only weapons I had at hand, and they were my intellectual thoughts and feelings that could travel down my right arm and express themselves through the nib of a pen. Years ago I used to go to work with a sawn-off shotgun, now I was going to work with a sawn-off pen.

Since the very beginning of this case, I had badgered and urged my legal advisors, firstly the sacked female solicitor and then more recently my new solicitor, Andrew Conrad, to ask the police and CPS for the phone evidence. Whether I am cynical, paranoid or both, no-one appeared to be acting upon my requests! I remembered that when we first submitted the 'Defence Case Statement', back in September 2001, my female solicitor asked me to read it to see if there was anything that we needed to add to it. To my amazement, she had left the all-important request for the phone evidence off a very detailed and exhaustive list of requests. It was added at my request under the last alphabetical sequence of (L).

Then I recalled writing out the mobile phone numbers of all the relevant phones and giving them to my new solicitor on the 29th October, only to find that he did not take the list with him and I still have it in my possession. Then I realized the only way to get things done was to formally write to your solicitor and give them written instructions and if they do not act upon them at least you are covered. But covered when? After a conviction and swinging sentence at the Court of Appeal? Bollocks! I decided to write my own very detailed letter asking for all the relevant phone records that were obtainable from the unused case papers. I did not want to get to trial in May and have the CPS declare they were unaware of the significance of these new phone numbers and either oppose an adjournment due to late disclosure or seek another lengthy adjournment in order to cater for the new defence requests. I perceived it as my duty to forewarn the trial Judge, the CPS, the Flying Squad, my solicitor and two broadsheet newspapers (as insurance) that these were vital phone numbers in the case for the defence to prove there had been a well planned police-crook conspiracy to set me up. It was imperative that I did this as I could visualize serious trouble ahead.

In spite of the debacle at Thamesmead Crown Court we did not come away empty handed. After the Judge gave his lop-sided ruling and hearing evidence from the prevaricating, hesitating and ad-libbing police witnesses the Judge recalled the case officer DS Herbert back to the witness stand and gave him a stern warning that he had to get his act together as the defendant, he claimed, "had been in custody long enough and the trial would be starting on the 13th May 2002." More positively, the Judge, by way of pacifying the defence, ordered that the phone billings were public records and that the prosecution had to disclose all the phone evidence they already had and any new material within 48 hours of the police receiving it.

As a result of the court ruling, we began to receive heavily edited phone evidence in the crude form of raw data. Of particular interest was the fact that when we examined the itemized billing of Wendall's home phone number it was devoid of any data from 2nd-7th June 2001 – the crucial period of the investigation and my arrest? With regard to the two mobile phones that were seized at Snakeshaft's address, one came back completely devoid of data and the other had billing of about fifteen calls on the 6th June 2001, with one call completely blacked out.

I sat for hours and hours in my cell cross-referencing the phone numbers and calls that we had with each of the numbers from Wendall's address and phone books taken from his address on arrest. I was looking for clusters of calls that could show a definitive pattern, but with the phone records being incomplete and edited it was an impossible task. What was remarkable, however, I could prove that the phone data retrieved from my mobile phone, seized on the day of arrest, had been tampered with too. I had phoned a relative, Danny Fearon, on Monday 4th June (a day before my arrest) in order to give him instructions on how to get to Canvey Island. For some reason, his number – one that I had not called from that particular phone before – was missing from the phone billing. Someone had removed it on purpose! I could prove that I had indeed phoned and received calls from this number because it was on the last ten calls dialled and received on the subscriber check documents that were supplied by the phone company the day after I was arrested. Why would the police want to delete this number? There was only one explanation. Perhaps the police thought a phone number in my wallet under the heading of 'Danny' was Danny Snakeshaft's phone number and decided to erase this number from my phone record believing it could be damaging when, in reality, it was Danny Fearon's number. Either way, who knows, it was more mulch for the compost!

CHAPTER 29:

OTHERS HAVE NIGHTMARE CASES TOO!

As the days merged into weeks and the weeks into months the cogs in my mind kept churning away in an attempt to reach some definitive answers about this mind-plaguing nightmare. Occasionally I focussed upon how I had come to be arrested, what a sucker I was, or upon certain individuals such as Wendall, Snakeshaft and their venal police handler. I had surpassed the stage where I was in control of my thoughts and feelings. Naturally I shared these thoughts and feelings with other prisoners in the HSU who I considered to be 'sound people'. One of these prisoners was Billy Todd, a born and bred Bermondsey lad who, after serving a nine year sentence of imprisonment for car offences, decided that prison was a mug's game and to moved away from the badlands of Bermondsey to enjoy the economic fruits of the importation of cheap foreign vehicles to England. By utilizing his streetwise skills and acumen he became a very successful businessman, sporting designer clothes, a beautiful girlfriend, a luxury pad and a personal fleet of top of the range vehicles.

Similar to the progress in my life, Billy Todd's life was at the pinnacle of his existence. He was cruising along completely oblivious to the profound depths of jealousy and resentment that his personal wealth and success had created. This was all about to change, for, on a winter's day in February 2001, Billy was on his way to meet his girlfriend and in-laws at a trendy London restaurant when he received a call from some drug-induced, gun-carrying liberty-takers. Billy had refused to loan them a substantial amount of money several days earlier. They were in Billy's ex-wife's house threatening her and their two young daughters for a substantial amount of cash. The gun-totting thugs were refusing to leave the address until Billy gave them the money that they believed he had hidden in the house. Billy Todd knew these thugs and had mixed with them on a social and minor business level and now they viewed him as an easy target, someone to bully and abuse. Someone that could be violently coerced into parting with a substantial sum of cash in return for the safety of his ex-wife and children. As you can imagine, Billy was in a very awkward dilemma. Did he call the police and invoke the relentless shame and ignominy of being labelled 'a grass' or did he sort it out himself? Billy had to think very quickly as his ex-wife and children's lives were at stake. Billy told them to wait at the house and he would come and see them.

In the interim, Billy phoned several people and asked them to meet him at the house in Painbourne, Berkshire. On arrival, Billy led the way into the house where his friends produced guns and a gunfight took place. One of the drug-raddled, liberty-takers was shot and died immediately, another was seriously wounded and another fled to the Caribbean. Billy Todd had done what any right-thinking man, husband or father would do to protect his family. He was arrested several weeks later and refused to answer any questions put to him by the police because, as in my case, his life was in danger.

Later, at Crown Court, during a trial for murder, the wounded thug, in the style of Snakeshaft, became the main prosecution witness. Despite the police finding the thug's DNA on a spent 9 mm cartridge at outside the house, the thug denied possessing a gun and blamed Billy Todd for shooting him and the deceased. Alas, Bill was convicted and sentenced to life imprisonment with the Lord Chief Justice's recommendation that he should serve a minimum of 25 years. Billy Todd's conviction and sentence is without doubt a travesty of justice and one day I hope to help him prove it as such.

Two months after his trial and conviction in December 2001, Billy carried out a successful dramatic escape from Wintester Prison. He cut through the cell bars and fences and scaled the massive prison wall to attain freedom so that he could draw public and media attention to his case. But unfortunately he was recaptured after only seven days unlawfully at large. He was traced by his mobile phone after a so-called 'friend' gave the number to the police.

It was during our stay at Cellmarsh HSU that I spoke to Billy about my case and we quickly realized that we had a lot in common. For example, prior to our arrest, we were both supremely happy with our lives. We were contented with our family, lifestyle, health and economic situation that is until the great ogre of jealousy, in the form of erstwhile friends, had sidled into our lives. Their warped philosophy was, "We like what you have got, we are unable to achieve it, and so we are going to either take it from you or destroy you!" In a way it reminded me of a childhood experience when I had just come back from a bird nesting adventure. I met a school friend in the street who asked to see the nest and all the bird's eggs that I had collected inside it. As he looked at the bird's eggs, he smashed his fist into the nest smashing all the eggs and ran off as fast as he could to his house. For what appeared like aeons, I stood there transfixed, absolutely gob smacked at what I had just witnessed before I chased him to the sanctuary of his house. That was, sibling jealousy aside, my first real experience of jealousy and it has haunted me all my life to the extent where I am now sitting in the HSU of Cellmarsh Prison swapping tales of jealousy with Billy Todd.

One day I was talking with Billy on the exercise yard and he said that something was bothering him about the case. He said that when I met Wendall at Upminster train station, prior to collecting the printing presses, I had told Wendall to go so that I could go to meet Snakeshaft at his address alone. But Wendall would not give me Snakeshaft's address, so I asked for Snakeshaft's mobile number instead. Wendall said it was in his car that was parked in a nearby pay-and-display car park and we had to drive around to retrieve it from his wife who was waiting in the car. What bothered Billy was why Wendall did not recall Snakeshaft's mobile number from memory, because they were bosom-buddies and had phoned each other countless times day after day. Why did Wendall need an excuse to retrieve Snakeshaft's phone number? Did he want time alone to phone someone else? Did he ask his wife to phone someone else on her mobile phone? Why didn't Wendall have his mobile phone on him at Upminster train station? Things just didn't add up.

As the case progressed and we sensed that the set-up could not have taken place without the help and assistance of Wendall, we were aware that Snakeshaft had been working for the police for a very long time. As a direct result of defence requests, we were allowed access to the papers of the cannabis case in June 2000, where Snakeshaft and three others were arrested and tried. Apparently, there was a police operation codenamed 'Verga', the focus and subject of which was Snakeshaft. He was employed by some alleged cannabis smugglers to drive a van in convoy with his employers to collect and deliver the contraband. Needless to say, the collection was successful but the delivery was not. The two-vehicle convoy was stopped by a small army of armed police on the southbound carriageway of the M11 and all were arrested and charged with the importation of a controlled drug. Despite Snakeshaft being alone at the wheel of the van containing 103.5 kilos of cannabis resin he was eventually acquitted. If we conflate the facts of the cannabis case with the facts of the Mark Wright and Arthur Weal MDMA case, where Snakeshaft left the drug in their lock-up shop, also the Mickey Macitto drug case where Snakeshaft placed a parcel of amphetamine sulphate in Macitto's vehicle, and finally the Uzi case where Snakeshaft planted the 'blue bag' in my vehicle, we can all see a pattern emerging that states one thing – Snakeshaft has been a naughty boy for a very long time!

All throughout this nightmare ordeal my industrious solicitor has been writing very detailed letters to the CPS asking for information and material that is disclosable to the defence by law. Recently, the new special case lawyer who has taken over the prosecution case has answered a growing backlog of six letters composed over the last three months. In a letter dated 21st February 2002, the case lawyer answers thirty-two questions, mainly using succinct one-line answers. There appears to be, however, a subtle sea change in the style and substance to the replies of old, as usually we received the stock bureaucratic reply of "We neither confirm or deny that this is the case." The replies to the most recent questions have taken the upgraded tone and content of "This is subject to PII (Public Interest Immunity)." For instance, in one incisive question we state, "Additionally, we require contact sheets of officer's contact with this witness (Snakeshaft) relating to any meeting that took place whether before or after the commission of this offence." The answer was "This is sensitive material and is subject to PII." Admittedly, we cannot jump to exaggerated conclusions about this reply but, by employing a most sober understanding of this sentence, it points to a tacit acknowledgement and acceptance that Snakeshaft is indeed a signed up fully fledged police informer. Bit by bit, drip by drop, the facts are coming out and it won't be long before the dam bursts and the full extent of the set-up is there for all to see.

As any long-term prisoner will tell you, it is very difficult for prisoners to hide anything in prison, more especially from other prisoners. Whether it be a physical ailment like a chesty cough, a peculiar mannerism like a nervous tic, a psychological disorder like paranoia or an emotional trait like anger or rage. Whatever the human trait or condition, you will be sure someone will spot it in the kaleidoscopic vista of prison life. The same goes for the almost continual interaction between prison staff and prisoners. There are set patterns of behaviour and procedure that are adhered to with an almost monastic observance and application. Almost any deviation or departure from these ironclad patterns of behaviour are picked up by the prisoners with all the sensitivity of a snail's antennae. Very little deviation or divergence from the norm can escape the detection of the ever alert and vigilant prisoner. For example, when I initially was placed into the HSU, Wendall had broadcast his specious version of events about the case and had denounced me as a grass. In effect, the HSU was his forum and those who did not know me listened to his embittered hard luck story. Once I had reached the HSU, however, and had spoken to a friend who knew me on the outside the tide began to turn.

The tide began to turn as not only was I coming from a supreme position of strength, honour and truth, but also Wendall's arguments could be examined, verified and denounced as lies. It was a classic case of the dissemination of poor quality propaganda and disinformation to undermine and slander an adversary that had uncovered the nauseating extent of his treachery. The problem for Wendall was that I was in a position to destroy his arguments by providing a copy of the 'prepared defence statement'. This proved Wendall was lying to save his own skin. It was a clear case of objective facts versus subjective misrepresentation and lies.

As the facts, the true facts began to emerge, the HSU screws ordered several prisoners on my spur to move over onto Wendall's spur. On each occasion they were asked to move, they refused claiming that they did not wish to be housed on the same spur as Wendall as it was feared he was a professional police informer. The screws asked one prisoner to put his objections in writing, otherwise he would be placed on Governor's report for refusing an order. He did and was allowed to remain on my spur. The upshot of this observation was that Wendall was losing the propagandist campaign to smear my name. He was losing the battle of facts versus lies and I knew, given time, the psychological pressure would get to him. The crunch came when the screws in the HSU asked prisoners to put in writing why they would not move onto Wendall's spur. I knew then that there would be a radical development in the *status quo*.

Several days later, on 22nd February 2002, Wendall was swiftly transferred to Smitemoor Prison in Cambridgeshire under the pretence from his brief that he was a serving prisoner whose parole licence had been revoked. In the same vein, Billy Todd on my spur had just been sentenced to life imprisonment and was awaiting trial for his dramatic over-the-wall escape from Wintester Prison. He was informed that he could not be transferred to a dispersal prison until after his case had been resolved. Obviously the prison authorities had made an exception in Wendall's case. It was almost meaningless observations and events like these that helped to colour the broader canvas of the set-up. The far-reaching tentacles of power and influence of the CPS went so far as to help Wendall circumnavigate or overcome the many obstacles and difficulties that lay ahead. In my view, this flies in the face of normal prison policy, as the screws love nothing better than to see two hardcore villains at each other's throats, tearing lumps of flesh out of each other. The prison authorities do intervene, but only after the drama has ended. I have known the Home Department, Governor grades and senior screws, whether wittingly or unwittingly, put two arch enemies not only in the same prison, but even on the same landing in cells facing each other, in order to incite trouble and bloodshed. Although rare, this practice does go on in British prisons.

The ultimate difference in this case was, however, as the unalloyed facts came out about the case, the balance of power and reason was tilting towards the truth and it was becoming too uncomfortable for Wendall. I knew that my position could only get stronger while he could only get weaker, until his tenuous position and arguments became completely untenable. The psychological pressure of bottling up such a corrosive secret that was in circulation on the landings of British prisons would be too much for him. The perceived whispering and gossip, whether imaginary or real in his mind would become a nightmarish worry or burden for him. In essence, Wendall had become the master and engineer of his very own head fuck. Now where are the brains in that?

CHAPTER 30:

MORE DISCLOSURE MATERIAL

Amongst a new bundle of paperwork supplied by the CPS in late February 2002 was a further statement written by Snakeshaft dated 27th November 2001. This additional statement focuses upon phone evidence. Basically Snakeshaft claimed that apart from his home phone number he had two mobile phones, but he could not recall the contact number of them. Also Snakeshaft claimed that his accomplice, Wendall, had two contact numbers, one landline and one mobile. He could not remember these either. Moreover, Snakeshaft added that he "did not keep any written record of telephone numbers at my address." He did not store any telephone numbers on his mobile phone and remarkably he had to rely on memory to retrieve these numbers. Alas, Snakeshaft's memory is not that good, as he could not recall any of the relevant contact numbers at the time of writing the statement.

From a criminal's point of view, this resolute show of convenient amnesia would be admirable if Snakeshaft were a *bona fide* suspect in criminal investigation. But not this time as Snakeshaft was a star prosecution witness, whose overriding loyalty and allegiance was to his senior police handler. How convenient that he could not remember these details. How convenient that this additional statement materialized after I sent my six page letter regarding phone evidence to the Judge, CPS, *et al*. The golden question to ask is, was this statement written in response to my detailed letter of 12th February and backdated to look like it had been composed before receipt of my letter. It certainly looked like it was, amateurs!

Amongst the recent batch of unused material provided to the defence by the CPS there was also a printed copy of a CAD message that revealed some interesting clues to the broader picture of the set-up. For instance, at 12:23 hours, some ten minutes before I am chaperoned to Snakeshaft's house by Wendall, a Police Sergeant Tuna is instructed by Chief Superintendent Linley at Havering Police Station to phone the Incident Room at New Dockland Yard through a 999 call to notify 'Gold London' that there is an armed operation being conducted in Bornchurch.

During the call PS Tuna proclaims that he does not know the significance of 'Gold London'. After providing the Incident Room with the appropriate designated Trojan ARV call signs, PS Tuna is then given an armed operation number, 588.

A remarkable feature of the emergency 999 call from a police station is that PS Tuna claims that this mission has been slung on him and he has been trying to contact "Chief Constables in Essex and all sorts." Several relevant questions arise out of this 999 call: One, what does "Gold London" refer to? Two, why was the call routed via a 999 call from a Police Station? Three, why was the 999 call done so late in the operation? Four, why was PS Tuna trying to contact Chief Constables in Essex when it was part of the Crown's case that they did not know my identity? Five, what has Essex Police got to do with a predominantly Metropole Police operation? And lastly, after putting this emergency call through to New Dockland Yard, CSI Linley instructs PS Tuna to be his 'urgent loggist' throughout the armed operation in order to log all communication between himself and the gung-ho 'governor of the armed operation', DI Helliman in Trojan One.

Ostensibly, I believe the term 'Gold London' was possibly a codename for a joint covert police operation the subject and focus of which was Terence Diamond. The genesis of the joint inter-force operation probably evolved in response to the so-called 'Bermondsey Job' that the police believe I committed. I also believe the reason why the Borough Commander instructed PS Tuna to notify 'Gold London' at such a late stage in the 'spontaneous firearms operation' was because, given sufficient time, the set-up could have been compromised by a higher police authority. DI Helliman and his henchmen may have been ordered to stand down from the operation so as not to jeopardize a wider and more comprehensive strategy. Thus, by notifying 'Gold London' at the last minute and knowing the 'target' was in possession of a lethal Uzi submachine gun and 376 live rounds of ammunition, DI Helliman was seeking to usurp the glory of the arrest and also acquire an ironclad conviction.

In my opinion, in order to cover himself in the tragic event that the psyched-up armed police shot and killed me, CSI Linley instructed the loggist to monitor and record all communication between himself and DI Helliman. The last thing the Borough Commander would have wanted was to face possible prosecution for the premeditated death of a suspect who had been set-up. He wanted to cover his arse no matter what! The loggist was his trump card that put the responsibility for the operation back on DI Helliman's shoulders. CSI Linley was no mug. He should have a bright and illustrious career in front of him and he was not about to compromise it through the over-zealous actions of the senior police controller and handler.

CHAPTER 31:

MARCH 2002

In early March 2002 the defence took possession of eighteen pages of telephone billings in the crude form of raw data. This data was in relation to my home address landline number. When I flicked through the pages I noticed that the data had been jumbled about purposely so as not to convey any chronological sequence. After painstakingly trawling through the data, more specifically on the relevant dates of 4th and 6th of June 2001, I noticed that my wife had allegedly phoned a Cambridge landline number on the day after my arrest. The call had lasted for a mere seven seconds and it was to a girlfriend's house of a male friend of ours. This appeared extremely odd, as my wife Stacey and I both knew that my male friend did not live at that address anymore, as they were temporarily separated. In my view, it meant that the police had retrieved the Cambridge number from my wallet on arrest and inserted it in the raw data to look like I was not on a mission to drop the 'valuable printing presses' to Cambridge for Wendall and Snakeshaft, but that I had another agenda. This was particularly damaging to my defence and it meant that the depraved detectives wanted to see me convicted so badly that they were prepared to insert incriminating phone calls on my home phone records. It was a clever ploy, but a perilous one because if we ever obtained the indisputable, original, itemized billing it would reveal the amateurish tampering of evidence.

Due to the close density of so many top security prisoners being housed in the HSU it was not unusual to know which prisoners were currently on trial and which ones were not. Over the last month, from mid-February to mid-March 2002, my friend Kevin Brown and others had been on trial at a provincial Crown Court for serious charges of conspiracy to rob security vans in the Kent and Sussex areas. As usual, each day when Kevin returned from court we would meet up at our cell windows to catch up on the progress of the trial. On paper the prosecution's case against him and his girlfriend, Angelique, was very suspect. Kevin had one very dubious identification of him taking part in a robbery and a welter of insipid circumstantial evidence that placed him some twenty miles from the vicinity of a robbery at the time.

The prosecution's case against Kevin took a tumble, however, when the defence team found out that the chief eyewitness against Kevin had served six-years for serious sexual offences. The nonce gave his evidence and claimed that he was 'not sure' that Kevin was the man he had fleetingly seen in a rear view mirror on the day of the robbery. The case was slipping through the prosecutor's hands and he knew it. Dramatically, the trial then collapsed. Apparently a female juror, who was the reputed wife of a Judge and QC, had written a lengthy letter to the trial Judge. She proclaimed that one of the female jurors had a crush on one of the defendants and that she and other female jurors were pressurizing her to find the defendants not guilty. Remarkably this occurred at the conclusion of the prosecution's case. As a result of this, the Judge ordered a mistrial and a new trial was ordered to commence in May 2002.

What is undeniably terrifying about the collapse of this trial is the ease with which the Judge stopped the trial because the jury was learning towards the accused. The salient question is, would the Judge have ordered a retrial had a juror complained that he or she was being pressurized into finding the defendants guilty? Or would it have been appropriate to dismiss the juror and continue with the trial? I find it very disturbing that even when the trial is going in the defendant's favour the Judge, prosecution and police have the legitimate ability, under one pretext or another, to stop the trial and start it again because they are not happy with its overall direction. It gives me great cause for concern as, in a patently police-constructed case like mine, where there are senior detectives fighting to stave off a major inquiry, suspensions, sackings and possible criminal charges, they will do anything to secure a conviction. I believe it is not entirely unknown for police gangsters to nobble juries in order to stop a trial, declare pseudo-intelligence to the Judge that a jury may have been nobbled or put up some other Machiavellian artifice to stop a losing trial. I wonder what incredulous strokes they are going to concoct in my trial when things don't appear to be going their way?

CHAPTER 32:

PUBLIC IMMUNITY INTEREST or PII

As the moment of truth arrives, coming closer and closer, day-by-day, week-by-week, I realized that we had some immense legal challenges ahead. None more important and testing than persuading the trial Judge to rule that it was essential to the defendant's case, in order to prove his innocence and avoid a potential miscarriage of justice, for the defence to be told whether or not Wendall, Snakeshaft, or both of them and others were police informants.

Basically, under the judicial or legal concept of PII, the Judge could rule, at the behest of the prosecution, that it was not in the public interest to disclose material that would reveal the source of the information to arrest me. Naturally this would put the accused at a massive disadvantage. More especially, in the way that I have been lured, steered and chaperoned to Snakeshaft's address by Wendall and then had the 'blue bag' containing the Uzi planted in my vehicle by Snakeshaft. Without beating about the bush, this issue goes to the epicentre of the defence case to have it officially confirmed whether or not these two people are police informers.

In order to prepare for this epic legal battle I have had my head submerged in reams of legal documents and texts supplied by my solicitor over the last two days, sifting through the pros and cons of PII disclosure procedures and rulings. The most relevant PII argument for disclosure of the identity of police informers appears to be R v Keane (1994) 1 WLR 746 that states, "If the disputed material may prove the defendant's innocence or avoid a miscarriage of justice, then the balance comes resoundingly down in favour of disclosing it." Conversely, however, the prosecution can argue, as in R v Hennessey (1978) 68 Cr App R 419, "It is well established that witnesses may not be asked, and if asked, should not be permitted to disclose, the names of informers and to ensure that the supply of information about criminal activities does not dry up."

In another landmark ruling, R v Agar (1990) 2 All ER 442, that has very close similarities to my case, the defendant alleged that the police had arranged with an informer to ask the defendant to go to the informer's house, where drugs, allegedly found on him, had been planted by the police. It was held that the defence should have been allowed to cross-examine police witnesses; to elicit the fact that the informer had told the police the defendant was coming to his house, in order to establish a defence that he had been set-up by the police and informer acting together.

Obviously there are numerous other relevant rulings that focus upon this sticky area of disclosure, more particularly in R v Haghighat-Khou (1995) Crim L.R. 337 that states, "The defendant was charged with possessing opium with intent to supply, but he claimed that he did not know what was in a carrier bag found in his car. He said that he was minding it for a man who had since gone to Iran and whom he now suspected of setting him up." The Court of Appeal held that the trial Judge had been correct to allow defence counsel to ask questions of the police suggesting a set-up or that the absent man was an informant, but had also been right to refuse questions designed to elicit the source of information. There was no need for the prosecution to disclose material relating to the source of this information because it had not prejudiced the appellant in putting forward his defence." (Source Biblos p.141)

On the face of it, there appeared to be many similarities between the facts of R v Agar and R v Haghighat-Khou and my case, because not only was I steered and chaperoned to the venue (Snakeshaft's house) but also I was later stopped by armed police in my car where they seized a 'blue bag' with the firearm inside it. The more I turned this issue over and over in my mind, it seemed highly improbable that the trial Judge would deny the defence access to this truth-revealing material. The Judge, however, down to sheer obstinacy and bias might proclaim that we could put forward a viable defence of set-up without knowing the identity of the informers.

What made this case unique, in my view, was that Snakeshaft was more than a police informer volunteering snippets of gen and gossip, but he had become the principal prosecution witness who had actively participated in this police constructed crime. He participated so much that the new squad taking over the case hours after my arrest had to arrest and charge him for firearms offences. It was the depth of Wendall and Snakeshaft's involvement in this case that, in legal terms, pointed unequivocally to a potential miscarriage of justice if the defence were not allowed access to this material. We knew the prosecution would love to focus solely upon the 'absolute offence' of possession of a firearm and body-swerve the provenance of the operation to arrest me. But that was where the temple of truth lay, the core of the set-up with Wendall, Snakeshaft and DI Helliman. Would the trial Judge order disclosure? Was he capable of refusing our request given the existence of compelling legal arguments for disclosure? We would have to wait and see. I was not optimistic but I had hope!

According to English law, if a defendant submitted a defence statement under Section 5 of the CPIA 1996, which outlines the bare bones of the accused case, he or she is permitted to submit another one in accordance with Section 8 of the same Act. The main purpose of this is to liberate further prosecution material, over and above a secondary disclosure that is being sought by the defence.

The significance of this additional defence statement is that if the prosecution refuses to comply with the defence request in the statement and seeks official sanctuary behind the administrative bulwarks of PII, the defence can then ask the Judge to intervene. If the Judge then rules in favour of disclosure, i.e. the identity of the informers, the prosecution would have two options, either enforced disclosure or discontinuance with the case.

Now if that awkward dilemma were to arise for the prosecution, what route would they take? We must remember the original 'prepared defence statement', that I made when I was initially arrested, had already, because the set-up squad were taken off the case, resulted in the arrest of one potential police informer (Snakeshaft) who had, at the behest of his handlers, been persuaded to turn QE. The preponderant reason for this was, as my solicitor explained to me, if there was no concrete evidence that I knew what was in that 'blue bag', i.e. no eye-witness account, no fingerprints or DNA evidence, who is to say that I was not telling the truth? There would, in effect, be no case to answer. In legal parlance, it would be wholly unsafe to leave it to the jury to decide, as the offence would not have been proved beyond reasonable doubt. I believe that is why the senior police handler had to compel Snakeshaft to lie and say that I handled the weapon at his address and to insert the ludicrous expression, "This will do a good job as the Bermondsey job."

The crux of the issue was the senior police handler had already convinced Snakeshaft to turn QE, which, by extension, means the prosecution are most likely to concede his role as a state-paid police informer. But what of Wendall? If ordered by the Judge to reveal his role as a police informer or concede the case, what would the prosecution do? Evidently, my solicitor confirmed that it is not up to the prosecution to publicly expose a police informer, unless the prosecution perceive the informer to have transgressed the contractual rules and regulations of police informing, i.e. broken the law, which Wendall and Snakeshaft have done in this pernicious set-up. I discussed this possible sequence of events with several fellow prisoners at Cellmarsh Prison and although most of them cannot foresee Wendall turning QE and getting in the witness box with his accomplice Snakeshaft, one perceptive prisoner has enthused what alternative has Wendall got?

Let us not delude ourselves; I said that Wendall set me up. Snakeshaft claimed that Wendall ordered the Uzi for Diamond. The prosecution claim that Wendall is at the core of the case and are pursuing the *Two Strikes* mandate. Last but not least, the trial Judge might well order the disclosure of the identity of the informants. The upshot for Wendall looked grim indeed. Firstly, Wendall could persuade the prosecution, if they felt fit, to drop the *Two Strikes* against him, he could then plead guilty to the three lesser counts and submit a 'text' to the Judge for a light or nominal sentence. Secondly, Wendall could plead guilty, turn QE and submit a 'text' to the Judge for a light or nominal sentence. Thirdly, perhaps, the prosecution would have none of it, for whatever reason, and would use Wendall as a veritable scapegoat. It was his plan to set me up so were they going to withdraw his official protection and anonymity in order to exonerate the depraved and dishonest detectives of any malpractice in providing the weapon for the set-up in the first place?

Ironically, whatever way we look at it, Wendall and his elusive sidekick Snakeshaft had rather poetically set-up themselves. Their intended 'target' Diamond would be going home while they would have to face the consequences of their actions. What they had done was not only a vile offence against common decency and morality, it was a vicious offence against humanity—a bit like shooting Santa Claus on Christmas Eve. We awaited further developments ...

CHAPTER 33:

NEW PHONE EVIDENCE

Over the long and boring Easter weekend of 2002 I was hoping I would receive some disclosure from the CPS as I liked nothing better than pitting my wits against 'the three men of sin'. Strangely I felt as if I was due some mail from my solicitor and was quite disappointed when the screw who was delivering the mail walked past my cell door. Normally my intuition and instincts were right about these things. A bit like the strange feeling I had outside Snakeshaft's house on the day of my arrest when I felt like I was being observed. My strong sense of disappointment soon evaporated, however, as the screw back-tracked along the landing and pushed a large brown envelope through the sizeable gap around the cell door. As I opened the letter on Easter Sunday I noticed, to my surprise, it was the long awaited telephone log of Wendall's mobile phone records that he had used on the day of the set up. Once again it was in the crude form of raw data, but that did not bother me, as it was just what I needed over a long and tedious weekend, six fat pages of telephone data to examine, explore and evaluate.

Over the course of the next ten hours, I mentally scanned all the new phone numbers in the log, cross-referenced them with other telephone data and then constructed a laborious chronological telephone chart of Wendall's and my mobile phone records. I was looking for patterns of calls, odd numbers called, the extraordinary length of calls, the frequency of calls made, anything that would prove my primordial instinct that I was dealing with a rat. It took hours and hours, but I knew that lurking deep amongst the phone data was evidence that I had been set-up. It was there for sure, but if only I had the brainpower and intelligence to extract it.

Again, like an amateur sleuth, I began with the process of elimination. The log recorded calls from 16th May to 6th June 2001 that included the all-important day of my arrest, 5th June 2001. I noticed that between the time Wendall left my address on Canvey Island at 5 pm on Monday 4th June and 1 pm, the time of my arrest, the following day, Wendall had only phoned his accomplice Snakeshaft once and that was for two seconds. I knew that this was nonsense and the telephone data had to have been edited, because when I met Wendall at midday outside Upminster train station on the 5th June, he proclaimed that he had spoken to Snakeshaft and he was on his way with the printing presses.

More specifically, to solve the perplexing enigma of the mechanics of the set-up, I had to do something I had learnt during GCSE history lessons at Flankland Prison many years ago. I had to empathize with the subject. I had to make out that I was a Jew in a café in Nazi Germany and imagine how it felt to be penalized and persecuted by the totalitarian tormentors. Similarly, I had to put myself in Wendall's shoes and, ashamed as I am, think and feel like a state-registered informant involved in serious organized crime. Quite simply, involved in every event there is a beginning and an ending, i.e. the 4th, 5th and 6th June in this case.

To plan and organize this set-up there had to be a flurry of communication by phone on the 4th June, more especially prior to Wendall calling me at 14:15 hours to announce that he wanted to come and see me with a view to collecting and delivering the print presses. Obviously, he had been told by his venal paymasters that the lethal Uzi was ready for him and to put the collection and set-up in motion. The troublesome fact that I was unavailable due to other commitments temporarily upsets Wendall and his handler's plans. Arguably, however, using a process of logical deduction, Wendall must have contacted someone or been contacted by someone prior to his call to me at 14:15 hours on the 4th June. Someone had to tell him the Uzi was ready and to put the set-up in motion.

A close examination of the mobile phone records revealed that Wendall received a text message at 12:10 hours on the 4th June. Remarkably this was Wendall's first call of the day as, usually, going by the chronological sequence of Wendall's calls, he was on the phone as early as 8-9 am to his accomplice Snakeshaft. Next Wendall embarked upon a flurry of seven calls between 13:10 and 13:22 hours. All these phone numbers were new numbers that were not replicated anywhere else in the phone records. The most suspicious digits among these seven calls was an 0800 number. More interestingly, the last four digits of the

0800 number matched that of a landline directly underneath it. With the splendid assistance of a fellow prisoner in the HSU at Cellmarsh Prison we got someone to go to a public phone box in a remote part of West London and ring the 0800 number. It claimed to be a removal firm. When the person phoned the corresponding landline number the operator proclaimed that it was a 'messenger service' and the caller required a pin number to use the service. What was a quasi-legitimate removal service doing requiring its customers to have a pin number? Moreover, the male operator was very arrogant and assertive wishing to know the name of the caller and how the person had come into possession of the number. The male operator even accused the caller of finding the number on someone else's mobile phone and appeared worried.

I asked someone else to phone another number in the block of seven calls where Wendall was on the line for nearly three minutes. The operator answered to the name of 'Shifters' and the caller promptly hung up. When we contacted Directory Enquiries to ask about all three suspicious numbers the operator declared that they were all unlisted numbers. Bingo! This was the best news I had had since my arrest. Wendall was contacting his senior police controller or handler using a pager system. The handler could then ring him back on a safe and secure line. That way the informant wouldn't need to carry the number around with him all the time and possibly lose it.

Wendall, the legendary prison helicopter escaper, armed robber and professional prisoner, had made a Faustian pact with the devil. More than that, he had plotted and planned the ruthless set-up of an old friend who had held out the generous hand of friendship and love when he was released from prison. I had invited this man to my home. He had held my newborn baby in his arms. I had hugged and cuddled him, given him money, a respectable vehicle and clothes from my wardrobe and all along he was plotting and planning my devastating downfall. To what bottomless depths of roaring evil could this man go? If this person detested, hated and resented me so much, why did he not attack me, stab me, or shoot me like a proper villain? No, the scumbag decided in his own Mephisophelean way to let the armed police send me to my grave, or imprison me for life; but the grand plan of distorted and deformed vengeance and iniquity went disastrously wrong.

I have always believed that somewhere in the myriad secret police files of New Dockland Yard there is a folder bulging with 'contact sheets' where Wendall and Snakeshaft had been passing specious and incriminating information to their senior police handler about others and me. In fact, absurd as it seems, I even had a vivid dream about this several months ago. I dreamt that there were official contact sheets over five inches thick dealing with Wendall and Snakeshaft's covert activities and also envisioned that when I eventually took possession of them they would make me physically sick.

For the last ten months my life has been a veritable nightmare where I have been insidiously arrested and charged with a serious criminal offence, represented by a duplicitous female lawyer, stonewalled by the CPS, ignored by a so-called close friend, sent anonymous hate mail, dismissed as guilty until proven innocent by Magistrates and High Court Judges, cynically made a top security prisoner in prison, denigrated as a 'grass' by the person who set me up, encouraged to plead guilty by the self same person, and had to sit by and watch as my close and loving family were trawled through the same unforgiving hell. Amidst all the psychological and emotional torture and torment of fighting to clear my name, my direct family and I always expressed a boundless faith that despite being left floundering in a sea of doubt and disbelief, the bright and beaming sunshine of truth and factuality would come out. And today after a long, black and starless winter the first rays of redeeming sunlight have eased the tortuous grief and pain of Wendall's intrinsic nastiness. As the great civil rights activist, Martin Luther King, proclaimed, "Truth crushed to earth will rise again!"

On a personal level, although this was a massive breakthrough for us, as we now had empirical evidence that Wendall was the one who set me up, on a legal level we still had to prove it in a court of law. It could be that the Crown would decide to concede the point that I had been set up and persuade both Wendall and Snakeshaft to give evidence against me in a last ditch attempt to salvage the case. Who knew? But the legal position had become quite absurd where two police informers have been recruited to plant an Uzi submachine gun inside a perceived major villain's car. By a curious quirk of events, they were arrested by their senior police advisors in an effort to camouflage the fact that they were wrong'uns, when in law and reality, they had done nothing wrong as they were acting on behalf of their police paymasters. Whatever the case, even I was interested as to how the case would be conducted by the bungling detectives and the legal wizards and witches at the CPS.

CHAPTER 34:

APRIL 2002

A month before the start of the trial and the case was still evolving like some terrible monster in metamorphosis. Some days I heard good news and some days bad news. Some days I felt like punching the air and calling a taxi and some days I felt like the monumental might of the State with its endemically biased legal system was going to crush me like an ant underneath an elephant's foot. I could, perhaps, have handled the dark moments better if I had been legally and morally guilty, but these dark periods were further exacerbated by the fact that DI Helliman and his two wilful accomplices would have loved to see me languishing for a decade or more in one of Her Majesty's Prisons. The thought of this was enough for me to dig deep into my spirit and fight to be with my loving family once again.

During the previous couple of weeks there had been a long string of developments that had left my wife Stacey and I feeling like we were against the whole world. The long awaited and potentially winnable Custody Time Limits hearing at the High Court had been delayed and delayed to such an extent that I felt very cynical about those conducting it. Because of the deep-seated shenanigans that had gone on in this case, sometimes I felt, whether rightly or wrongly, that my solicitor was taking instructions from someone else, as the inordinate delay in getting this to court smacked increasingly of a desire to postpone it until the onset of the trial. There was some suggestion that the police were desperate to keep me in custody in case I could locate the black guy who allegedly supplied the Uzi to Snakeshaft. It appeared that they did not want me out of prison at any cost, even if it meant subverting the integrity of my solicitor. The question I was asking myself was whether my solicitor was a good guy or an impostor working in tandem with the police and louche lawyers, whose tentacles of crookedness and corruption reached into the higher echelons of the judiciary. Sometimes I felt as if there had been a 'red flag' attached to my case because of the political consequences should we expose the extent of malpractice and corruption that had gone on. If we did expose the real nature and objectives of this case, the political and legal ramifications of it could be catastrophic for the Metropole Police Force. Not only could it possibly result in an internal or independent inquiry into the handling of the case, but how many other cases had DI Helliman been involved in where there had been an unhealthy miasma of malfeasance and wrongdoing.

The point I am making is my well-respected junior barrister had tried to wriggle out of representing me for this case. The perceived reason being, his clerk informed us, is that he is booked in quadruple on the day of my trial where one case is a potential profitable murder brief. I spoke to my solicitor and because we had guarantees that the junior barrister would defend me, and also under the 'cab rank rule' of taking cases he was duty bound to fulfil this obligation.

In a similar vein, because the CPS want a Queen's Counsel to conduct its case, it transpired we were also allowed to have a senior barrister to conduct our case. My solicitor had sought the assistance of David Blackhouse QC, a reputedly distinguished advocate on the upward slope of success and stardom. Evidently he accepted the case, read the case papers and had to pull out because he had represented Wendall many years previously for another offence and had a massive fall out with him. The upshot was if David Blackhouse QC represented me and ripped into Wendall during cross-examination, Wendall could claim that he was only doing it because of their previous differences and disagreements. Although on the surface this appeared like a perfectly valid reason to pull out of a case, it did little to alleviate my burgeoning paranoia and waning confidence in the legal world.

At this stage in the case, the defence strategy was to compile and construct a new defence statement under Section 8 of the CPIA and submit this to the court before a PII Mention Hearing in order to extract more information and material regarding the provenance, participants and particulars of the set-up. The defence wished to initiate this PII application for disclosure before the trial so that it gave us enough time to examine and explore any potential new leads or avenues in the case. The PII hearing had yet to be arranged, like the judicial review regarding the Time Custody Hearing, it had been delayed and delayed, which once again undermined my faith in the legal aid realm of law and justice.

Please God, a set-up of this magnitude never happens to anyone that reads this book, but if it should, make sure the victim has plenty of money to pay for their own defence. Although the legal aid system acts as a vital safety net for those unfortunates who cannot pay for their own defence, the legal aid system puts the power of the defence case firmly in the hands of solicitors and barristers who frequently put their interests first and not those of the defendant. Some may view this as under-the-belt criticism of the legal aid system, but there was a very strong possibility, due to a legal error, that I had been held illegally in prison custody since 29th January 2002. As at 16th April 2002 and I was still waiting for my solicitor to take the matter to the High Court. I was certain that if I had been paying for the judicial review hearing myself—I was quoted £7000—it would have been heard within a week of the legal blunder. Surely that was why legal aid was invented to counterbalance the omnipotent legal muscle of the State versus the weak and indigent individual.

I often wonder what would have happened in this godforsaken case if I had not been so alert and sentient to the outrageous machinations of the police, CPS and the judicial system. As an example, my long running legal battle over access to the telephone records of Wendall, Snakeshaft and myself continued. The CPS produced a snazzy 'Telephone Analysis Booklet' that purported to have been compiled by a trained intelligence analyst posted to the Serious and Organized Crime Group at New Dockland Yard. Part of the training entailed professional tuition from SO11 Criminal Intelligence Branch and other special outside agencies. In other words, the person who compiled and constructed the 'Telephone Analysis Booklet' was involved in matters that might concern the security of the State. Need I say more?

On close examination the professionally prepared glossy booklet, that looked very official and convincing, was bereft of any phone records and billing with regard to Snakeshaft's home landline number. This phone evidence was crucial to the defence case as we claimed Snakeshaft may have phoned his police controller directly after I left his premises with Wendall on the day of my arrest, thus informing the waiting surveillance team exactly where my vehicle was parked. Secondly, the landline phone number of Wendall's home had been edited on the crucial dates of the case from 2nd-7th June 2001. Why would the police wish to edit the phone records between three potential villains who were allegedly involved in the procurement, supply and possession of a lethal Uzi firearm? It pointed to one overriding scenario, to prevent the truth from being exposed about the police-crook set-up! Thirdly, and most worryingly, in order for the defence to examine and assess the probative value of the Telephone Analysis Booklet we would require access to the primary source material that the intelligence analyst used to compile the booklet. Quite plainly, the defence argued, that until we were able to view and scrutinize the original telephone billings, the Telephone Analysis Booklet was and remained a secondary source material document and should not be passed off in open court as valid and lawful evidence.

At that time, the defence argument was it had only received telephone records in the crude form of raw data and not the itemized phone billing that you or I would receive directly from the phone companies. We argued that. because of the bizarre circumstances of my arrest, i.e. the set-up, the probity and integrity of the investigation into the case would become a central feature in the forthcoming trial. Therefore it was essential that we be able to compare and contrast the primary and secondary source material to establish its authenticity.

In order to make myself heard I, once again, took the unusual step of writing to the trial Judge, CPS, the case officer and my own solicitor highlighting the above issues and considerations. I knew, given the right questions by counsel, we could prove there were some serious irregularities in the telephone booklet where phone numbers had been inserted and deleted to suit the prosecution case. The fact that the intelligence analyst proclaimed in an accompanying statement that, "I can confirm that no original telephone data has been altered in any way," is open to serious scepticism. We hoped that the trial Judge would listen to our argument and rule in our favour.

I had spent many long nights slaving away over the secondary source telephone material in order to uncover the pattern of communication between Wendall, Snakeshaft and their police handlers. Several patterns emerged, more especially when they were contacting other known drug dealers and criminals. As a result of these findings I made a list of sixty-three possible contact numbers that we got a private investigator to check. We already knew that Wendall contacted his handler an hour before he came to my house to ask me to collect the printing presses. But how were we going to prove it?!

Not surprisingly, my wife and I were not the only ones feeling the psychological stress and strain of involvement with the police, prosecutors and the prison authorities. A fragile Turkish prisoner called Mayrak, in the cell next to mine, tried to commit suicide last night by tying a plastic prison property bag over his head to suffocate himself. I had been saying for ages that the High Secure Unit at Cellmarsh Prison was nothing more than a glorified punishment block where security and containment was preferred over and above that of productive association and recreation. The prisoners, many of them similar to me who were not only unconvicted but also innocent, were locked up in their cells for excessively long periods of the day when we could all have been unlocked to freely associate with each other.

When I approached the Prison Governor in charge of the HSU he proclaimed that it was the HSU policy to treat all the prisoners in the Unit the same whether they be unconvicted or convicted. This was exactly my point. The HSU wished to penalize the unconvicted prisoner by making them suffer the severely restricted regime that had been foisted upon the convicted prisoners. The austere regime at the HSU was further compounded by a traditional culture of negativity and refusal that had been adopted by the staff. For example, one day there was an electrical fault with the unlocking system and we were not allowed outside our cells for association. Because the regime in the HSU is conducted with military-like precision, any deviation from the proscribed times of unlock and meal times was met with a strong sense of bewilderment and confusion by the prisoners. Like Pavlovian dogs deprived of their reward, the resulting salivation transmutes into frustration and anger. When the prisoners asked for their loss of valuable association time to be reimbursed in one way or another, the Governor promised to look into it and to reply to us all in writing. Several days later, when the prisoners inquired about the progress of the promised reimbursement, there was open animosity and hostility by the staff on the Unit towards us, just because we had the audacity to ask for what we had been rightfully promised.

From experience, this anti-convict culture of hostility and dismissiveness can be seen throughout the prison system, more particularly where long-term prisoners are given the individual labels of category A top security prisoners, etc. This is because the rank-and-file screws resent the fact that they have to 'baby-sit' or 'pussy-foot around' with perceived dangerous and extrovert criminals. Put bluntly, the social interaction between the screws and prisoners is always under constant strain because the notion of professional detachment, combined with the insidious indoctrination of labelling prisoners, will always provide fertile ground for conflict and disagreement. Add these prison-induced ingredients to the abnormal confines of a High Secure Unit and what have you got? A Cellmarsh-ite form of Nazism in the 21st century, where the persecution and penalization of prisoners is refined to the *nth* degree of basic, standard and enhanced regimes; and they are put into practice even before the prisoner has been tried and convicted.

A classic example of the pervasive culture of denial and dismissiveness may be seen when I made a formal application for an exercise mat to conduct physical exercise upon in the exercise yard. The reply was, "No unfortunately you may not have a mat due to health and safety issues. All sports activities must be supervised by a PEI or sports and games officer." Not satisfied with this curt official rejection, I submitted a fresh application that stated:

Sir,

With all due respect, in acknowledgement to the reply to a previous request for an 'exercise mat' for the 'exercise yard' there appears to be some confusion about this issue. I fully understand that all 'sports activities' must be supervised by prison staff, but by definition exercise is not a 'sporting activity'. According to the Collins Dictionary, 'exercise' means 'to take exercise, or perform exercises; exert one's muscles, in order to keep fit'. See page 534. A sporting activity often involves exercise where physical capabilities are tested in the form of a competitive game. Seeing as the prison exercise area is called an 'exercise yard' and is used for taking 'exercise' as opposed to a sports area or yard, it is a perfectly legitimate request to ask for an 'exercise mat'.

Similarly, the point is taken about the Health and Safety issues. Is it the case that the 'exercise yard' has been examined by the local Health and Safety Executive and deemed unfit for exercise, or individual exercise, such as yoga, etc. with an exercise mat? If this is the case, please may I have a copy of the HSE's observations and ruling on this matter in support of the HSU rules and regulations?

Please, please, do not misunderstand this application. This is not an exercise in stubbornness or a facetious request. As an unconvicted prisoner I am cooped up in a concrete cubicle for excessively long periods of the day. In the short time that I am allowed out of the cell for exercise I feel I should be allowed to do just that and the prison authorities are duty bound to provide facilities for that purpose. Therefore, I respectfully ask that you reconsider the request and provide the prisoners with an exercise mat.

Two weeks later the reply to this request was:

Whilst I understand your comments with regard to the dictionary definition of exercise as opposed to sporting activity, the Prison Service regards exercise as walking in the outside air which requires supervision by discipline staff. Any other form of exercise would require P.E. staff.

The Health and Safety officer has cleared the yard mainly for walking in outside air and all other forms of exercise within the prison must be supervised by P.E. staff. Whilst I understand your frustrations, I would dearly like to be able to provide a full regime for all prisoners including access to the gym for those who wish it. Currently I am unable to do so due to staff shortages in the prison as a whole. I have made the Governor aware of the situation and as soon as it can be resolved it will. Therefore I am still unable to meet your request for an exercise mat, Sorry.

Signed the Principal Prison Officer of the High Secure Unit.

As you can see, although the reply is seemingly sympathetic to my request the answer is still "No!" But what is very interesting here is that the Prison Service has imposed its own semantic definition upon the term 'exercise' for its own purposes. In the light of this, I was going to apply for the latest edition of the Cellmarsh English Dictionary as it appears to be applying its own meaning to words that are in current usage. All in all, according to the gospel of Cellmarsh, the affirmative term 'Yes' is equated with change and weakness as opposed to the negative term 'No' which is synonymous with conformity and strength. The battle for minor concessions still continues at Cellmarsh, but the prisoners have more chance of hitting a sparrow perched on top of Canary Wharf

Tower with a catapult than acquiring them.

While in the Cellmarsh Prison a fellow prisoner arrived at the HSU as an unofficial punishment transfer. This confirmed our feelings in the HSU that it was indeed being used as a punishment unit. The prisoner, John Felley, serving 15 years for armed robbery, had been ghosted out of Smitemoor dispersal prison under the ludicrous claim that he had maps in his possession of Long Larkin Prison. In fact, the maps were legitimate defence material being used in a civil claim against the Prison Service for injuries received when he fell over on a slippery floor.

During a conversation outside the cell window one evening, John told me that he was at Full Shutton Prison in the spring of 2001, before Wendall was notified that he had got parole. Apparently Wendall had boasted to Felley and other prisoners that he felt he would be granted early release on parole despite having nearly five years left of his sentence to serve and still being a High Risk category A prisoner. Such confidence on early release is at variance with Wendall's position unless he already knew that he was to be granted parole.

It has always been a strong belief or assumption of mine that Wendall's Faustian pact with the police for early release was a result of his accomplice Snakeshaft's regular prison visits, where he told Wendall that he had access to a 'top cozzer' and could arrange some help for Wendall when he became eligible for parole. Until shortly before Wendall's release on parole, it was always Home Department policy that prisoners being classified as a security threat, under the umbrella of category A security status, could not be considered for early release. This archaic prison policy was revised shortly before Wendall's early release on licence when a small handful of high profile villains serving very long prison sentences were released on parole. Felley proclaimed Wendall had received parole as a High Risk category A prisoner but, absurdly, due to his high security status, he could not be told the date of his release. Wendall was then downgraded to standard category A before being released.

If this is true, and Wendall was awarded early release on parole licence as some sort of incentive to work as a signed up, state paid police informer then the Early Release Board have got a lot to answer for having let potentially remorseless villains out of jail knowing that they would be mixing with and setting up other perceived criminals and villains. Once again the idealistic vision of a potentially reformed and remorseful prisoner being released from a prison sentence early is incompatible with someone who has been recruited to mix in criminal circles in order to incite, encourage and participate in serious organized crime. This makes a laughing stock of the Early Release Board along with the police who are putting the public at an unnecessary risk.

Evidently when Wendall was arrested for the second time on 2nd November 2001, the police found two sets of legal papers to do with the Uzi case at his address despite, up to that time, Wendall not being charged with the offence. As part of the disclosure procedure the defence received copies of these legal papers. In amongst them was a police custody record of Snakeshaft when he was taken from Wentonville Prison on the 20th July 2001. We had been asking the CPS to provide us with a copy of this document on numerous occasions but with no response. Basically the custody record told us that Snakeshaft was transferred from prison to police custody by police officers from SO11 under the guise of a seven day production order. Oddly, despite being taken from Wentonville Prison at 10 am on Friday 20th July 2001, he did not reach Bornchurch Police Station until 7:30 am on Monday 23rd July. The desk sergeant noted that no previous custody details arrived with the prisoner.

What is indeed relevant about this episode is that the defence received the mobile phone record of one of four phones seized at Wendall's address on the 2nd November 2001. Amongst the itemized billing, we noted that Wendall had phoned Snakeshaft's home address twice throughout the complete record of this mobile phone and the calls were made at 16:57 for 9 units and 17:14 for 54 units on the 20th July 2001. The question is, why did Wendall phone Snakeshaft's address on only these two occasions? Did he know that Snakeshaft was out of prison custody? And if Snakeshaft was escorted out of prison by SO11 police officers in a secret operation, how did Wendall know that he was home? One explanation is that his police handler must have told Wendall this sensitive information!

CHAPTER 35:

WHERE DID THE UZI COME FROM?

In Snakeshaft's Q.E. statement he claimed that he met a black fellow with distinctive turned up teeth, called Rob the Porpoise, at a well-known East London gymnasium and struck up a deal to supply the Uzi submachine gun for Wendall. From a defence perspective, this was a very valuable aspect of the case that appears to have been left unexplored by the police. I say unexplored, but that is not entirely true, as the police did send two local uniformed police officers to the gym some nine months after the offence was committed. They spoke to the acting manager of the gym and asked him if he knew anyone called Rob the Porpoise, Elvis and a guy called Noddy, the three principal players in the supply of the Uzi saga.

The half-hearted almost cursory nature of the inquiry was obviously a mere formal exercise and nothing more. No doubt this was done so that the prosecutor could jump up at the trial and pompously proclaim that all avenues of the investigation were explored and exhausted. The salient problem for me was whether Rob the Porpoise was a real character and if so was he a *bona fide* criminal, a police informer or even a long-term SO10 infiltrator working for the police? To find out I spoke to someone at the gym who confirmed that he was indeed a real character and had been visiting the gym for about five years. Obviously I told my friend to 'mark his card' that Snakeshaft had stuck his name up in a police statement as the supplier of the weapon. A remarkable event occurred, however, when my friend met with him at the gym. While he was speaking to him, several people entered the gym and said there were a lot of police around the streets near the gym. In my view, this meant one of two things, either Rob the Porpoise was an active career criminal and was being 'bottled' by a police surveillance team or he was a police operative working undercover and he needed very close back up in case he was going to be threatened or attacked by close friends of mine. Directly after leaving the gym, he phoned the gym and asked the owners if they could remove his personal details from the gym's computer. The answer was, seeing as he had only recently left the premises, if he wanted to discuss the matter further he should return to the gym. He did not return.

Due to the fact that I was the victim in this case, I became, quite understandably, increasingly cynical and suspicious of everyone and everything. Evidently, the Porpoise was born and bred in Bethnal Green, had left to live in Manchester as a child and had returned as an adult to the London area. Oddly this mirrored with a classic cover story of police infiltrators that had 'come their lot' in well-documented novels and magazine articles recently. Nonetheless, let me make it quite clear, this was not to taint the black guy's reputation as he may well be a proper upstanding villain with a staunch pedigree, but I had got a sneaky suspicion that something was not right about the guy in this case. No man – especially a white man – is going to get an Uzi submachine gun, shoulder stock, loaded magazine, silencer and nearly 400 rounds of ammunition on bail from a black guy that he hardly knows. Transactions like these just do not happen in the modern criminal arena. I believe that this was a cover story for the fact that corrupt police may have supplied the weapon from a secret armoury to Wendall and Snakeshaft, which explains the half-hearted measures that were taken to find and arrest the Porpoise!

The problem was exacerbated for me because if I revealed 'the Porpoise's real identity in court and he was a good upstanding villain, it would be entirely justified for people to denigrate me as a wrong'un in the so-called criminal underworld. Due to the very serious nature of the charges that I was facing, however, which included a life sentence if found guilty, I sent a message to the Porpoise and asked him to come and give evidence for me in order to discredit the evidence of Snakeshaft. He declined. Now, did he decline because all he could see was grief from the police or did he decline because it could possibly compromise his police-orientated position?

The Porpoise dilemma became even more bizarre when we learned that I had been imploring my solicitor to visit the gymnasium to acquire some more information about him from my friend who works there.

Countless times I asked my solicitor to visit the gym and collect this information but my requests were delayed and ignored. It reached the stage where I had to write to my solicitor and furnish him with explicit instructions to visit the gym and acquire the personal details and photograph of the Porpoise. For some reason, my solicitor had been very uneasy about doing this and he asked if I could get someone to deliver the material to him? But my friend at the gym was adamant that it had to be done legitimately with the solicitor visiting the gym.

My plan was to take possession of the photograph of the Porpoise and show all the black prisoners in Cellmarsh Prison and ask them if they knew of him and whether or not he was indeed a genuine guy. If the Porpoise was a proper villain then someone in the jail would know him and vouch for him. Cellmarsh Prison was, in effect, the ideal place to hold such an exercise and I was optimistic about its results, providing I had the photograph.

When my solicitor did eventually visit the gym he came back to me empty handed and had somehow circumnavigated and ignored my explicit instructions. The feedback was that the Porpoise would not let my solicitor interview him, nor was he prepared to give evidence for me but he was prepared to answer a list of questions that was prepared by me. My solicitor appeared happy with this compromise, but I was not! Not only had my solicitor wilfully ignored my specific instructions, but also he had done things his way! This coupled with all the other events surrounding this matter, such as his reluctance to visit the gym and the idea that he wanted a middle man to collect and deliver the material, made me believe, whether rightly or wrongly, that he was maybe taking instructions about my case from someone else?

These burgeoning misgivings about the probity and sincerity of my solicitor had been festering away for some time. The very first instance of this occurred when he first took over the case from the duplicitous female solicitor. It all centred around the phone evidence. From day one I had urged, implored and encouraged my solicitors to secure the telephone records of all the individuals in this case. The female lawyer even went so far as to leave this central request off an important 'defence case statement' produced at a crucial Pleas and Direction Hearing in September 2001. As for my second solicitor, as soon as he took over the case I gave him a list of the phone records that we required, which later, through his inaction, became a central feature of a Custody Time Limits hearing. As a result of the inaction it eventually allowed the Judge to extend my stay in prison. I knew the intrinsic value and importance of this evidence and had constantly brought the issue up at legal conferences with little effect. Hence as I have already stated, I decided to write to the CPS myself and ask for the mobile phone records.

These anxieties and concerns over the phone issue were further compounded when speaking to my solicitor on the prison payphone one day. He declared, "Do you think by writing to the CPS and asking for these mobile phone records that you will be giving Wendall more ammunition to call you a grass?" This was an absurd thing to say, because here was my solicitor who believed that I had been set up and yet he was now arguing against the idea of acquiring crucial evidence that could prove my innocence. Moreover, Wendall was already sending letters around the prison system claiming that I was a grass when the truth was it was *his* accomplice Snakeshaft who had implicated *his* role in the sad saga. Lastly, all the mobile phone numbers that I was asking for were there bold as brass in the *unused material* that was supplied by the CPS! Therefore I was not divulging any new information or material, the police already had it but did not want to act on it.

After the call, I told a friend in the HSU about it and he blurted, "That isn't right, your brief should not be talking to you like that?" Indeed, it was an outrageous thing to say, more especially as he knew the way I felt about the police informers. It is all well and good to let your solicitor run your case for you, but in a sordid and putrescent case like this you get no points for sitting on your arse and letting the bastards walk all over you. Innocent prisoners do not act like mice, they have to stand up and fight for their lives until their dying breath and beyond.

Then another strange event occurred. My solicitor had prepared for me two chunky folders of defence material that I had been giving to him since my arrest. On receipt of them, I decided to flick through them and reread what I had written when I found an eighteen-page phone record of my home address. I thought this was strange as it had been served on my solicitors two weeks earlier and my solicitor had not given it to me then. When I studied and analysed it, I found the police had inserted two phone calls on the record. The first was someone who had apparently phoned my mobile number using my home landline number. This was absurd as my wife and children never used the indoor phone to contact my mobile – they always used their mobile phones. The solitary call on

27th May 2001 had lasted for only fourteen seconds but it was enough for the elite telephone analyst to use in his 'telephone associations chart' in the 'Telephone Analysis Booklet'.

More incriminatingly, on the day after my arrest 6th June 2001 there was a call made at 11 am to a Cambridge landline number that we covered earlier. The inference being that I was not delivering the valuable printing presses to a friend of Wendall and Snakeshaft near Cambridge but I was taking an Uzi submachine gun to my friend there. My wife Stacey assured me that she had not phoned the Cambridge number as she had no reason to and also she knew that our friend in Cambridge had split up with his girlfriend. The theory is that the Cambridge landline number was found written in my black wallet with other numbers on arrest and it was extracted from there and inserted on the home phone record.

To try to discredit this evidence we asked for our own itemized BT phone record and, lo and behold, both of the above calls were on the billing. But how could they be? They had to be physically inserted in there. It meant, as far-fetched as it seems, that someone had been tampering with the phone record and that is why the calls were for such a short duration, as it would have had a discernible effect on the actual phone bill. God, if this was the case it meant that the fuckers wanted me really badly, so badly that they were willing to subvert authentic phone records and get my solicitor to slip them into me through a bulging defence material folder hoping that I would not find them. I know that this sounds like something out of a Robert Ludlum spy novel but it is true.

CHAPTER 36:

CUSTODY TIME LIMITS REVISITED

The next drama relating to my second solicitor focused upon the inexorable farce of the proposed Custody Time Limits Judicial Review Hearing that was to be heard at the High Court. We claimed there was a fundamental legal error when the Judge extended the Custody Time Limits on the 28th January 2002 by nine days so the CPS could provide further evidence that they had acted with 'due diligence and expedition' in the preparation of the prosecution case. Therefore, we claimed the ruling by the Judge was unlawful and that I was being held in Cellmarsh Prison illegally since that date.

My solicitor spotted the legal anomaly and sought professional advice from the legal wizards at The Temple in central London. The feedback was favourable and it appeared that we had a valid argument and case. The solicitor proclaimed that we should be up at the High Court within a week or two of the Judge's blunder. Firstly, however, we had to secure the transcript of the Judge's ruling. That took longer than normal because, allegedly, the Judge at Thamesmead Crown Court had ordered the official court stenographers to print up the wrong transcript. Then there was an absurd succession of excuses, delays and postponements due to briefing of counsel to conduct the hearing, the construction of the arguments and problems with the High Court itself.

This went on for nearly three months and my patience was wearing thin due to the constant stream of delays and problems. Deep suspicion and cynicism began to calcify into justified paranoia about the intentions and motives of my solicitor because, if I was right and we won the Custody Time Limits Hearing, the High Court would have to treat me as if I had been acquitted and that would have been an inconsolable blow to the police and CPS.

After constant pressure from my direct family and me the solicitor was finally tied down to a fixed date for the hearing. He claimed that it was to be heard on the 11th April **2002**. Then, on 10th April, my solicitor visited to inform me that counsel earmarked to conduct the hearing had not read the paperwork and needed more time to prepare his arguments. By now my wife Stacey who has the incurable Crohn's disease – after years of remission – had suffered a relapse and had to return to powerful steroidal medication that meant that she had to stop breast feeding our new born baby.

Our suspicions that something was amiss were confirmed, however, when Stacey had taken enough of this hideous brinkmanship and phoned the listings office at the High Court and asked the clerk if there was a judicial review hearing booked in the name of Terry Diamond on the 11th April **2002**? The listings clerk claimed that there was no such hearing booked in my name and nor was one ever cancelled. It meant that my solicitor had been wilfully misleading my family and me and, for some reason, trying to eke out the hearing until the forthcoming trial date. If this was the case, then it meant that my solicitor had either been taking instructions from someone else or he was plain and simply incompetent or lazy. It did not help my burgeoning paranoia and cynicism to learn that the boss of my solicitor had been in constant contact throughout my case with Wendall's louche solicitor, an ex-SO8 policeman who had worked under the guise of a solicitor's clerk? Everyone that was anyone in the legal profession knew that this pseudo-brief was neck-deep in police corruption and malpractice. There was an infamous occasion where it was alleged that this person had circumvented the tight security at a police station where he drove a large consignment of drugs out of the police compound. A laudable feat providing that it was done in the interest of a suspect and not his uniformed friends.

As a direct result of these problems, that I put to my solicitor over the prison payphone, I decided to part company with him as he simply could not be trusted. Naturally this was easier said than done so the plan was to write to the High Court and ask them to confirm or deny whether there was a Judicial Review Hearing fixed for me on the 11th April 2002. This whole putrescent affair was indicative of the deeply ingrained machinations that were going on behind the scenes of the sad case. The long tentacles of dishonesty, depravity and corruption appeared to be coming out of every corner of the case.

I am not naïve enough to believe that it has not always been so in cases such as these, but it is terrifying to know that all the cogs of corruption and deception were turning in order to railroad this case into a conviction despite the fact that they all knew, the whole fucking lot of them, that I had been wilfully and ruthlessly set-up.

I had often felt that I was up against everyone in this case, that is, the police, prosecution, lawyers, Judges, co-defendants, their lawyers and their families and absurd as it seems, it was as if I was the bad guy for exposing the mechanics of the set-up. This egregious case had caused so many sleepless nights and legal problems for all involved that it became very uncomfortable for the 'legalized gangsters' who manufactured the case against me and now they were pulling every conceivable stroke in the book to undermine or disprove my innocence.

In many ways this only made me stronger as I seem to thrive on adversity and conflict. As the old adage exclaims, "At times of crisis comes forth opportunity" which has provided the genesis of this book. I am a great believer that there are so many more twists and turns to come in this case that one day it will make a very intriguing dramatic drama or film.

On a personal note, at this stage of the proceedings, some three weeks before the start of the trial, I had been trying to study and analyse the depth of duplicity, deceit and animosity towards me over this case and try to understand why I found myself in this nightmarish position. As I have often said, my faith in humanity has been radically undermined but, despite being seemingly surrounded by Machiavellian scumbags who wish to see me suffer painfully and the relentless travails and ignominy of a very long indeterminate prison sentence, I have to keep repeating to myself that there are good and decent people out there, like my loving wife and family who represent the more conducive bright paths of human warmth and loveliness. To give this heinous case a religious slant, it had transformed into a veritable Good versus Evil, light versus darkness clash. I just prayed for the sake of Goodness that it would win the day, for if it did not, the evildoers would get stronger and stronger and humanity would become the ultimate loser.

With barely three weeks to the start of the trial, I felt as if the defence case was showing signs of weakness and collapse. My solicitor had told me that the prosecution was to have an *ex parte* (private) PII hearing with the trial Judge on the 22nd April to decide what sensitive material might or might not be disclosed to the defence. Directly after the hearing, if there was no new material forthcoming, we would be allowed our own hearing with the Judge to argue why the defence should be allowed such material.

My excellent Junior Counsel, James Goodwyn, who I had hand picked myself, alluded to the PII hearings as like a game of battleships where the defence pinpoint exactly where they think the interesting information is on the grid and the prosecution have to confirm or deny that it is a direct hit. But in the modern legal arena, because of the exponential growth and development of state-registered police informers due to unreported crime in the drug world, trial Judges are very reluctant to order the revelation of the identity of a police informer as so many cases are falling at great public expense. And the way the CPS are getting around disclosure or discontinuance of cases is that they have become the gangsters of language and deception where, if the defence does not ask the right type of question, the CPS will not provide an answer, or the answer will be purposely ambiguous or vague. For example, we wanted to know if there were any participatory police informers in this case and it was perfectly legitimate, absurd as it seems, for the CPS to deny this, knowing that Wendall and Snakeshaft were indeed police informers but they may not have been participating in any official operation on the day of my arrest. I know this sounds ludicrous, but please believe me, these are the type of mind games the gangsters of language and deception are playing in every CPS office up and down the country.

My solicitor also claimed that the long awaited Judicial Review Hearing was to be heard on 25th April 2002. Whether justified of unjustified, such is the level of distrust towards my solicitor that I had written to a new solicitor, David Burner of Feenan & Co, and asked him if he would be willing to take over my case at this late stage in the proceedings. I had also written to the High Court and asked them to confirm or deny that there was a Judicial Review hearing booked for the 11th April. In adition, I wrote to the clerk of the court at Thamesmead Crown Court and asked them to produce me at any PII hearing for the defence should there be one. In short, I desperately wanted to be there and hear Counsel ask the right questions.

This marrow-deep distrust and cynicism directed towards my solicitor, in my view, was not without foundation as my solicitor now claimed that in order to initiate a Judicial Review Hearing at the High Court, the merits of the case had to be reviewed and validated by a single Judge before it could go before an open court. If this were the case, then surely the applicant would receive a court reference number for the preliminary hearing? And also, if it is indeed the situation, why weren't we told about the preliminary hearing prior to the earlier Judicial Review date on the 11th April and where was the court reference number?

The predominant question is, why had my solicitor been misleading my family and me? When the Custody Time Limits Hearing did eventually get off the ground, I was told in writing that the grounds for the Judicial Review were lodged at the Queen's Bench Division of the High Court on the 23rd April and we were given a court reference number of RO/1898/2002. Mrs Justice Ferndale reviewed the grounds the very next day and the hearing took place on the 30th April 2002. Taken altogether, it is patently clear that there was never any Judicial Review High Court hearing booked for me on the 11th April 2002 and it gives unrestrained credence and justification for the way that I felt about the handling of this case by my legal advisor. The disagreements that I had with my solicitor did, however, have the desired effect as he finally got the judicial review off the ground.

On 26th April 2002 I had a legal visit from my solicitor and things appeared to be hotting up in all areas. Firstly and most importantly, the prosecution PII hearings concluded that day and the trial Judge at Thamesmead Crown Court ruled that the CPS must disclose some material they sought to bury to the defence. We did not know what the material was at that time, but we were hopeful that it would confirm our long held belief that this case was rotten to the core and it was time to expose and smell its putrid contents.

Secondly, my solicitor compiled a six-page letter that outlined the reasons for his strange behaviour of late. He claimed that he was unable to give me the letter, as he wanted to let his boss read it first. I said that it would be unreasonable for me to read and assimilate its contents there and then on the legal visit as we did not have the time. I suggested that we shelve our differences about recent developments in the case until I had heard from the listings clerk at the High Court regarding the controversial Judicial Review Hearing on the 11th April. I did add that I felt my solicitor would not willingly, of his own volition, mislead or lie to me about events and issues in this case, but I stressed that if it was going on, he was doing it under duress or threat from a third party. We agreed to drop the matter until I had received the six-page letter and had heard from the High Court.

On a more progressive note, I was able to obtain and read both the grounds for the Judicial Review Hearing and the new defence statement under Section 8 of the CPIA Act. In all fairness, my solicitor had done well in the preparation of these documents and I felt that we had a compelling argument with regard to the Judicial Review. As for the new defence statement, it was a very comprehensive document that accused the police of using Wendall and Snakeshaft to set me up and, more specifically, once the set-up had been exposed, it accused them of conducting their investigation in an unscrupulous manner to the extent that proper police codes of practice and procedure were wilfully ignored or bypassed.

With regard to the continuing access to the original phone records saga, the case officer now claimed that he was awaiting the original telephone billings from the phone companies. If this was the case, how did the telephone analyst manage to compile and construct the 'Telephone Analysis Booklet' without the original billings? To conclude the legal visit, I provided my solicitor with a checklist of important things to do prior to the start of the trial. These included the taking of several witness statements from family, friends and those that had offered to help me discredit the evidence of Snakeshaft.

For some strange reason, the case officer decided that rather than provide the defence with the original itemized billing from the phone companies, he got a senior BT operative to write a statement saying all the phone records that BT supplied were genuine. In anyone's language, a statement accompanying raw telephone data is not original billing. Moreover the telephone analyst based at New Dockland Yard claimed that the defence could not have access to the computer disk with all the raw data on it. To save time and public expense we wanted this for comparison purposes, but it seemed the material on the disk was too sensitive to reveal to the defence. Or would it prove my point that there had been some serious tampering with this evidence?

Lastly, three requests by the defence for the original billing of Snakeshaft home address proved unsuccessful. My solicitor claimed the CPS were in breach of the trial Judge's ruling, passed on the 6th February, that all the phone records should be given to the defence by the 7th April

2002. It was then the 29th April and we were still getting bumpf telephone records and not the original itemized billing.

It is amazing how a trial Judge can give a direct order to the CPS in open court but then the CPS can override it through a secret PII hearing with the Judge or completely ignore it, knowing the trial Judge would not penalize the CPS by chucking the case out of court. The trial Judge may act like an omnipotent referee in his court, but it carries little judicial weight and effect when all the skulduggery is going on in the changing rooms away from the pitch!

At long last, on the 30th April, the Judicial Review regarding the Custody Time Limits hearing went ahead at the High Court. Mr Sayers represented the prosecution and Mr Roger Tindal the defence. I was not present at court so I had to rely on the observations made by my wife Stacey. She said that because our counsel was not fully aware of the background to the case and our solicitor was late getting there, this gave an unfair advantage to the prosecutor who presented the facts of the case to suit the Crown. Not surprisingly, the two High Court Judges ruled against us claiming the Judge was perfectly entitled to extend the time limits so that he could listen to further evidence that supported the supposition that the Crown had acted with 'due diligence and exposition'.

In my view this was nonsense. The law book states one thing and the Judges interpret it in a way that suits them. We had the prosecution worried, however, as during the Judge's deliberations he sidled over to our counsel and said that if we did win the Judicial Review he wanted me to surrender my passport, submit to a curfew and sign on at a local police station three times a day. The mere fact that the prosecution felt that we could win the Judicial Review was evidence enough that he must have felt we had a powerful argument and case. Personally, given the facts of the case I didn't see how we could have lost. On the other hand, I was not about to kid myself that the High Court was going to free a man who was arrested with an Uzi submachine gun found in his car. I had more chance of finding a winning lottery ticket on the landings of Cellmarsh Prison.

CHAPTER 37:

MAY 2002

On the morning of 2nd May 2002 the screws in the High Secure Unit moved a prisoner in the cell below me onto my spur. Ray Betson had been convicted and sentenced to eighteen years imprisonment for the Millennium Dome diamond robbery, where a number of unarmed robbers were caught red handed trying to steal the Millennium diamond from the Money Zone in the complex. There was nothing unusual about prisoners being moved from cell to cell or spur-to-spur in the HSU as the screws like to keep the prisoners moving around so they could not settle. In the afternoon, however, the 12 prisoners on our spur were coming off the exercise yard when we heard that Wendall had returned from Smitemoor Prison and was placed in the cell directly below mine.

Whether this was done on purpose so that Wendall could talk to me out of the cell window or it was a pure coincidence I do not know. All I do know, it was imperative that I had no communication with him as it could ultimately damage my defence case. I approached the screws about the situation and they agreed that I could switch cells with another prisoner on the other side to my spur so that he could not talk to me.

The next day I had a social visit from my wife Stacey and our baby Sonny. She said that a strange incident had occurred the previous day. She said an elderly gypsy woman and a young girl about five years old had called at our house in Canvey Island, Essex. The elderly gypsy women said "You are going to have some good luck this week, and you will hear some better news by the end of May." The gypsy woman then gave Stacey a small beautiful seashell and a small granite stone for luck. My wife gave the woman a £5 note and as the woman and child walked away along the driveway she turned around and added, "Oh, one last thing, don't trust your neighbours!" I do not know if I should give the incident any significance at all, only that the elderly gypsy woman and young girl have never been seen ever since.

Recent developments in the Mark Knight and Arthur Weal drug case, where it is alleged Snakeshaft coerced them to look after a bag of MDMA powder and the National Crime Squad later raid their premises and arrested them in possession of the drugs, is also suffering from the grim machinations of the CPS. At a preliminary hearing at Knaresbrook Crown Court, the presiding Judge ruled that the defence could call the suspected police informer Snakeshaft and his handler DI Helliman in order to prove that they had been set-up. The CPS opposed this position claiming, for security reasons, that Knaresbrook Crown Court was not safe enough for a protected witness of Snakeshaft's status. The Judge then transferred the case to the top security Thamesmead Crown Court. At this court the Judge examined the merits of the case and ordered that Knaresbrook Crown Court was perfectly able to accommodate the evidence of a protected witness and he sent it back to Knaresbrook Crown Court. The trial was adjourned until after the Uzi trial on the 10th July 2002.

The MDMA case was a perfectly straightforward case of possession of a bag of drugs. Were the defendants guilty or had they been forced to look after the drugs for the scheming Snakeshaft and his senior police controllers? The trial should have been a straightforward affair and been dealt with under the fast track legal system, but the CPS did not want this case heard before the Uzi case, because if the defence was able to discredit Snakeshaft's evidence it would go some way to help me in my case. Therefore, once again, the gangsters of language and deceit at the CPS managed to adjourn the MDMA case until after my trial.

On the 3rd May 2002, I received a bulky parcel of legal papers from my solicitor. Inside were 632 pages of Snakeshaft's debrief process when he decided to be a witness for the Crown. Basically, all criminal police witnesses who turn super grass have to go through the debrief process where they admit all their crimes in order to be taken as a witness of truth by the court when they give their evidence to a jury.

During this process Snakeshaft was given the fictitious name of Billy Brown and he was interviewed on tape by two SO11 police officers, DC Lawson and DC Hines. After a quick read of the papers, it was revealed that the debrief process began in Wentonville Prison where, soon after Snakeshaft's arrest, he volunteered to become a witness for the Crown and 'come his lot' about all his past criminal exploits. This began as early as the 4th July 2001 and was written down long hand in a debrief notebook called 'Book 112'. This meant that the police were fully aware of Wendall's role in the Uzi case prior to him walking into Wilford Police Station on the 24th July 2001 and yet he was still given police bail for another four months before they decided to arrest for a second time and formally charge him. If they knew of his role in the case at that time, why did they not arrest him then? The only explanation can be they did not want to for some reason.

From the debrief statements we learned that Snakeshaft had admitted perjury. The facts were that, in June 2000, Snakeshaft and three others were arrested in two vehicles on the M11 motorway. Inside the van driven by Snakeshaft was 100 kilos of cannabis resin. All four people were charged and appeared at Knaresbrook Crown Court. At the trial Snakeshaft alleged that his solicitor, the dubious former SO8 solicitor's clerk, now Wendall's brief, provided him with a concocted defence. His defence was he did not know that there were drugs inside the van; he believed them to be cigarettes and booze from the Channel ports. He said that a known police informer called Dave Stilson had planted the drugs inside the van so that he was arrested with them in his possession. Snakeshaft added that he was told to tell the jury this by his solicitor. The jury acquitted all the defendants. After the acquittal the other defendants smelt a rat and it is alleged the debt for the drug was put on Snakeshaft. The owners of the cannabis employed a local henchman to take over the debt of £150,000 and that is why he became involved with me because he wanted me to intervene on his behalf and call off the wolves. Complete and utter nonsense.

In the debrief Snakeshaft also claimed he went to the Eastside Gym in Canning Town where he sat and drank tea and talked to all sorts of criminals and crooks. It was here, because of his credibility, that he gleaned information about other villains. He implicated me in four murders and the Bermondsey job. The Bermondsey job alluded to a daring robbery in the Docklands area of South East London where "a gang of armed robbers … executed a precision-planned ambush of an armoured security van." It was alleged that the robbers "used two heavy duty vehicles to ram the security truck" on a public road and "hydraulic gear was used to prise open the escape hatch of the truck." It was believed the "band of highly organized criminals" escaped with a "substantial" amount of cash. The robbery itself was later shown on the Crimewatch television programme where there was mention of a large reward for the capture and conviction of the robbers. The Flying Squad officer in charge of the investigation was DS Herbert, the detective who walked into my police cell, on the day of my arrest for the Uzi set-up, and made out that he didn't know my identity.

In the debrief interview papers Snakeshaft appeared rather hesitant and unsure about the role of the black guy, the Porpoise, in supplying the Uzi firearm. To conclude after reading the whole document I believed Snakeshaft was nothing more than a policeman's puppet and when it came to him giving evidence his memory would be so flawed that the jury would be able to see through him and judge him accordingly. What is interesting, however, we had still not been told at this stage whether or not Wendall and Snakeshaft were active police informers. In spite of all the information in the debrief process and Wendall's Houdini act in not getting arrested, we still needed more disclosure!

On the morning of Saturday 4th May 2002, my solicitor was supposed to go to his office and meet a defence witness of mine who had some valuable information for us concerning Snakeshaft going around East London claiming that he knew a 'top cozzer' and could supply information about the location of listening devices in suspected drug importers' houses. My solicitor claimed he could not make it because he was locked inside his girlfriend's flat. The witness informed me that he did contact my brief at two other times but nothing materialized.

The following Monday, 6th May, my solicitor was due to visit me at Cellmarsh Prison for a legal visit but it was abandoned because he failed to produce his official pass – a confirmation letter – at the prison gate. This was not the first time that my brief had missed or cancelled a legal visit, but being so close to the trial and occurring directly after my deep concerns about his integrity, it did not help my confidence.

On the 7th May 2002 I appeared at Thamesmead Crown Court for a Mention Hearing in front of His Honour Judge Atkinson QC, Jonathon Maskell for the Crown, Cyril Upstep QC for Wendall and David Gallant QC for me. Upstep was reputedly a very senior prosecution counsel, perhaps one of the best at the time, and he had just successfully prosecuted the Millennium Dome robbers and sent them to prison for a total of 74 years. Here though, Upstep was rather unusually working for the defence, or was he employed to use his acumen and influence to save Wendall? We would have to wait and see?

Remarkably, however, my solicitor was informed that we were allowed to extend the legal aid order to employ the services of a Queen's Counsel solely because the Crown were seeking the services of a senior counsel. But this was not the case. The prosecutor was not a QC. The only logical reason why the legal aid order was extended could only be for Wendall's benefit, that was why he was able to get one of the best prosecutors in the land defending him. Wendall was allowed a QC because he and his senior handlers were worried a jury could find him guilty on the *Two Strikes* mandate and he could be sent to prison for life. Once again, it revealed the levels of power and influence the State will go to in order to protect a valued and valuable police informant. I have never ever known a case where the defendants on legal aid were allowed the services of senior counsel while the prosecution preferred to conduct their case with a mere barrister. Naturally, I was not complaining, but once again, the rules and regulations governing our deeply flawed judicial system were being moulded and manipulated to suit the machinations of the CPS.

At the above hearing, however, there was an application to oppose count one, possession of a firearm with intent to endanger life. The defence arguments focussed upon whether the ammunition, magazine, stock, silencer, etc. were part of the transaction and therefore represented specific intent. Mr Upstep QC argued that seeing as Wendall was the alleged middleman how could it be taken that he was involved in any intent? The mere fact that someone passes a gun from one person to another does not constitute 'intent'. The Judge overruled the defence arguments and let the intent count remain on the indictment.

During the hearing the Judge did proclaim that he had been reading PII documents all week, some 1500 pages of it and he had ordered the Crown to disclose some of it. He openly expressed the view that it should give all those involved some thinking to do. The Judge appeared to be gloating upon this issue. We were told that 'Book 112', the Snakeshaft debrief book was to be disclosed. The trial was to start on the 13th May and the Judge was going to swear in the jury and then listen to PII arguments from the defence. During the hearing Mr Gallant QC made it plain he wanted disclosure of lots of other material beyond that already mentioned.

After the hearing my legal team said they would remain at the court and visit me in the cells to discuss tactics and strategy regarding the defence case. David Gallant Q.C. was trying, in his most subtle way, to steer me away from a cut-throat trial with Wendall as, from experience he said, cut-throat trials were very rarely successful. By the term 'cut-throat' I mean I was strenuously saying that Wendall and Snakeshaft were working as a team for the police and they were organizing crimes and letting the police arrest their victims once they had walked away from the scene, as seen in the Mickey Macitto drug case that occurred less than four weeks before my set-up. Evidence for this could be traced to the earlier mobile phone records of Wendall and Snakeshaft, who had stopped using their mobile phones and discarded them less than one hour after the Macitto arrest, and yet they could not have known about the arrest because they were not there at the scene. It all pointed to prior knowledge about the arrest and the destruction of evidence to cover their tracks in case others became suspicious.

Alternatively, Wendall was saying that he was not a police informer and that *I had asked for the weapon and he was merely the middleman in the operation.* But why was Wendall saying this at all? I was asked to collect 'valuable printing presses' not an Uzi submachine gun. Why was he saying that I asked for a gun? He did not need my permission to tell the truth. He was obviously still working with the police and CPS and in order to make the case stronger against me he was going to claim in open court through his eloquent QC prosecutor of a counsel that I had asked for a weapon! A cutthroat trial obviously suited the Crown as half their work was done for them. Both Wendall and Snakeshaft were claiming that I had asked for and handled the weapon.

Mr Gallant QC was concerned about the absolute offence of possession, but I had been through this before with my former and present solicitors and, no matter what, I would be fighting the case even if the Judge had it in mind to direct the jury to find me guilty of possession. He also asked me to think about the possibility of getting a life sentence and would I be prepared to accept a five stretch *in lieu* of a trial. Personally I don't know if this was a conversation disguised as a deal, or if he had been asked by the prosecution to put it to me. I did not need to ask him as there was no way that I was going to plead guilty to a crime where I had been blatantly set-up. I said it is all or nothing; let's get the cut-throat trial on, because there was more than my innocence at stake in this sordid case. Wendall had been going around with his toxic tongue saying that I was a 'grass' and therefore it had also become a matter of pride and principle that I exposed these two arrant scumbags.

Later in the afternoon, both junior and senior counsel went off to see the prosecution and came back with two pages of disclosure material. The prosecution was ordered by the court to disclose the following sensitive material.

Firstly, on 19th January 2001, Daniel Snakeshaft was registered as an informant. On that date, police records noted, Snakeshaft was motivated by the possible financial rewards that his role might provide. Secondly, on 11th April, Daniel Snakeshaft received payment of £1500 for information given to police. Thirdly, on 30th May 2001, Daniel Snakeshaft was cancelled as an informant. Fourthly, on 15th June 2001, Daniel Snakeshaft was de-registered as an informant. And lastly, payment in the sum of £4000 was outstanding for information, which Daniel Snakeshaft gave to police during the period he was registered as an informant.

This document had a footnote at the bottom of the page that stated, "This material has been redacted pursuant to the order of His Honour Judge Atkinson QC. This format has been adopted wherever the order has been made." Not surprisingly the disclosure material also stated, "Daniel Snakeshaft also works in conjunction with [...32...]", a numerical identification code for someone the police and prosecution wish to remain anonymous.

To summarize this document, apparently Snakeshaft was a *registered* informant before the set-up, then his informant status was *cancelled* during the set-up and he was *de-registered* after the set-up. Yet Operation Salieri was also going on during, or over-lapping the set-up. The more I studied this document the more it looked like the powers behind the set-up were trying to force square pegs into round holes and that there was a massive damage limitation exercise going on behind the scenes. For instance, how can a person be a police informant on a Friday, have it cancelled over the Saturday and Sunday and be de-registered on the Monday. In my view, Snakeshaft was either an active police informer during my arrest or he was not. The mere fact that he was not de-registered until after my arrest points to the fact that he was an active and possibly a participatory informer at the time of the set-up.

The defence team's advice for me to keep an open mind about Wendall's role in the set-up and not go down the cut-throat road was too vague and misleading. In my view, the CPS had to surrender Snakeshaft in order to save Wendall and to continue the case against me.

I knew that if I had a face-to-face trial with Wendall a jury would believe me, because it was obvious that Wendall had covert assistance from the police in this operation.

At this stage, I was determined to continue with the cut-throat case as not only was it the truth, but if I did not go down this path it would allow Wendall to wriggle out of being exposed as the type of person he had become. He needed to be exposed big time and the only way to do it was to go for his jugular!

Another issue discussed during the conference with counsel was whether or not we should call the dubious former SO8 solicitor's clerk, who allegedly supplied Snakeshaft with the false defence in the van load of cannabis case in June 2000. The reason for calling the solicitor's clerk was that he would be able to deny the accusation and discredit Snakeshaft as a prosecution witness. Mr Gallant QC was against this for personal reasons, but I said that if he were not able to destroy Snakeshaft's evidence in the witness box I would be instructing him to call him.

Counsel did confirm, however, that the prosecution had verbally admitted that Snakeshaft was not merely a listening informer, but he had been a 'participatory informer' in the past. That is the reason why the Crown had to claim that Snakeshaft was de-commissioned during the set-up. Otherwise why was Snakeshaft arrested? If he was an active and participatory informer in the eyes of the law he did nothing wrong and he was only following official instructions. Slowly, bit-by-bit, the reasons for the complex cover up were emerging. The police were using Snakeshaft as a puppet, as they had done in the past sixteen years, and now they pushed the issue for Snakeshaft to bolt for cover and turn QE because not only was I too strong for Wendall and Snakeshaft but the mastermind behind the set-up was concerned about his role in the affair. It was his job to sort out this putrid affair but it would take the best legal brains in the world to unravel this one and still push for a conviction against the intended victim Diamond.

In essence, the set-up had gone boss-eyed big time and I should have been released from Bornchurch Police Station after I had stated in the 'prepared defence statement' and in interview that I had been set-up. But the over-zealous detectives were so blinkered in their ambition to get a conviction, they continued with the perverse prosecution and selfishly broke and bent almost every police rule and regulation in the book to satisfy their insatiable desire to see me perish.

Also at this conference we were given additional unused material from the prosecution, the most prominent being from a fingerprint expert stating that there were no identifiable fingerprints on the Uzi firearm. This was amazing considering that Snakeshaft claimed that I had put together all the component parts of the firearm and dismantled it without wearing gloves. More than that, Snakeshaft openly stated that he expected my fingerprints to be all over the weapon.

All in all, it was a good day for the defence. At last the prosecution had conceded that Snakeshaft was a state registered, state paid police informer and also agreed that my fingerprints were not on the firearm. As I was pondering on these significant events, my mind drifted back to the incident the previous week when the elderly gypsy woman and young child had came to my address on Canvey Island and predicted the onset of good news. Could it be true? Could our lives be preordained? Could fellow human beings predict and know the future? I don't know, but all I do know, it pays to keep an open mind about such strange and inexplicable issues.

Later the next day I was told that Wendall's wife, Carol, had become abusive in the public gallery towards my wife, Stacey. She had called Stacey a 'slag' and had threatened to push her under a bus. Much later I did speak to my wife on the prison payphone from Cellmarsh Prison and said I was sorry she had been subjected to this manly and uncouth behaviour. My loyal wife had been a paragon of virtue and devotion throughout a very long prison sentence in the past and she did not deserve this type of disgusting treatment. Earlier during the case, my wife would see Mrs Wendall outside the prison gates at Cellmarsh and she would not say a word, not even acknowledge her presence, which was very unusual for someone of her brazen, in-your-face character. Her unusual reticence spoke volumes. In our view it was a sign of guilt as she was in her husband's vehicle on the day of my arrest! She knew exactly what was going down that day. Who knows, perhaps she was a fully signed up operative of the state too – nothing would surprise me in this case.

The 8th May – during the previous twenty-four hours I had given counsel's warnings about a cut-throat trial a great deal of thought but I had decided to stick to the original plans and rip into Wendall during the trial. The salient reason being, I did not see why I should evade the truth to aid Wendall's defence when he was the prime mover in this pernicious set-up. He had wilfully and sinisterly plotted to set me up and now he should face the facts. If I did alter my defence—to suit counsel—one iota and fall, I would have no one else to blame but myself. Therefore, I resolved to continue with the cut-throat trial and put my faith in the jury to see through the fog of deceit and deception and attain the truth.

I was concerned but not shocked at my senior counsel's subtle and probing attempts to redirect my defence case. His insipid arguments that I should be worried over the 'absolute offence' palaver, the tentative suggestion that I could put my hands up for a five stretch and avoid a cut-throat trial were all indicative of the psychological pressure that I was under to select another road and avoid exposing Wendall as an informer and possibly make the case fall completely. I decided yet again to stick to my guns on this issue and expose the truth!!!

On the 9th May I returned to Thamesmead Crown Court for a legal conference with senior counsel, my solicitor and a solicitor's clerk. Mr Gallant QC spent all day trying to deter me from having a cutthroat trial with Wendall. He claimed that he did not want me to face Wendall's notorious prosecution counsel Mr Upstep QC as if I did opt for a cut-throat trial we would both perish.

I detested the fact that I might have to swallow the cut-throat defence and let Wendall's informant status slip the net. I understood that Wendall might be pleading guilty to the three lesser charges and was obviously fighting the *Two Strikes* automatic life sentence count claiming that I asked for a gun and he merely supplied it. Evidently, soundings suggest, Wendall will not be giving evidence. We all knew that with one look at him a jury would be able to see that he was the type of person who would be capable of such a treacherous act. I had some grave thinking to do over the weekend and, alas, I might have to succumb to the QC's advice.

I did understand counsel's arguments, for example, let's dissect and destroy Snakeshaft in the witness box, criticize the police handling of the case and then leave it to the jury as how could they convict anyone on the word of a self-confessed liar and perjurer who would say anything to save his own skin, as he had done in the past, on oath to a jury.

We received some more disclosure materials from the prosecution. These were the operation Salieri observation logs and 'contact sheets' between Snakeshaft and his many controllers and handlers. One in particular was where Snakeshaft phoned his handler on the day after my arrest – ironically during and then after my police interview – and claimed he was fearful that I might have tumbled him as an informant and he was also concerned that I might expose him in court and blow his cover. By coincidence, the mobile phone number that Snakeshaft contacted to speak to his handler is identical to the one that he phoned directly after I contacted him on the day of my arrest. This was absurd for a police informer whose informing status had, according to disclosure material, been 'cancelled'!

As I had said earlier, about six months before this nightmare ordeal the elderly psychic woman in Canning Town had warned me that someone with a tattoo on their arm saying 'Mum and Dad' would betray me. Concerned about this, the next time I saw my close friends and associates I asked them if they had any tattoos on their arms, especially containing the words 'Mum and Dad'. None of them did. When I was arrested, however, at the Magistrate's Court I did see that Snakeshaft had a large tattoo on his arm. I later found out that it was a tattoo of the West Ham United Football Club 'Hammers' symbol.

Then we were given some 'intelligence reports' about Snakeshaft and some of his associates and to my amazement, high up on the other arm, Snakeshaft had the words 'Mum and Dad' tattooed on his shoulder. I was gob smacked! How could anyone predict such things? I sat there on my bed in my cell and stared at this intelligence sheet for what seemed like hours and hours. How can we mere mortals begin to explain the inexplicable? All I know is that I was absolutely astonished.

Also shortly before my arrest, in March 2001, two associates of Snakeshaft were arrested with a 9 mm handgun and a shotgun. The way they were arrested was a mystery, but in the contact sheets of Snakeshaft there was mention of it. It now looked as though Snakeshaft was the informant in this case too. Perhaps that was why the police still owed Snakeshaft £4000 in unpaid reward monies. While the principal person for this offence was in prison custody for these serious firearm offences, Snakeshaft was visiting him on a regular basis. Later this person appeared at Knaresbrook Crown Court and despite having previous convictions for firearms offences he was sentenced to *eight months* imprisonment. In criminal parlance this would be interpreted as a major result. Good luck to him, but even my counsel looked at me in askance?

To summarize the profile of Snakeshaft in this case so far, we learned that he was a registered police informant who is motivated by reward money. He was a self-confessed liar and a perjurer on oath. He was involved in guns and giving information about guns to the police. He owed £150,000 to serious drug importers but he didn't tell his wife about the debt. He borrowed £30,000 from his wife to pay off the debt and didn't tell her about threats directed at him and his wife and children. He was worried that his cover as an informant might have been compromised. He sought sanctuary in the Police Witness Protection Scheme and then decided to turn QE against the man he helped to set-up with Wendall.

Two days before the commencement of the trial, in traditional scheming style, the CPS finally disclosed the phone records of Snakeshaft's home landline phone number. The late disclosure of this vital material is all geared so that the defence have very little time to examine and analyse the phone record. There was one phone call on the day after my arrest that had been deleted. Why tamper with phone records at all if this was a *bona fide* police operation?

CHAPTER 38:

THE TRIAL

After nearly a year in prison custody the trial finally got under way on the 13th May 2002. Presiding over the trial was His Honour Judge Atkinson QC with Mr Jonathon Maskell (leading counsel) and Mr Ian Sayers (junior counsel) representingd the Crown. Mr David Gallant QC and Mr James Goodwyn (junior counsel) acted for me and Mr Cyril Upstep QC and Mr Richard Cox (junior counsel) were representing Wendall.

Before the start of the trial I had decided not to get embroiled in any slanging matches with Wendall as the trial was the time to get to the truth and expose this scumbag. I was escorted to the entrance of the court first and Wendall followed a short while later. Both of us were double handcuffed, which is normal procedure for top security prisoners and also surrounded by about eight screws. By 'double handcuffed', I mean my two wrists were cuffed together with a separate set of handcuffs attaching one of my wrists to a screw's wrist.

On reaching the top of the steep internal stairs we began to glare at each other. Personally I felt like smashing him to pieces and pummelling him into the ground, but I wanted to listen to every syllable that was said during the trial. Wendall noticed that I was carrying the 'Telephone Analysis Booklet' and called me a 'grass', because I had written off to the CPS and asked for the mobile phone records of Wendall and Snakeshaft, the latter now confirmed as being a police informer. Upon hearing this I went ballistic and tried to attack the rat, but being double handcuffed and surrounded by a wall of screws I was unsuccessful. I did manage, however, to gob in his face and replied, "You've got some front to call me a grass and you have been having it with a registered police informer, you rat!" I am not proud of spitting in anybody's face, in fact, I find it utterly repulsive, but when someone says such disgraceful and untrue things about you and you are unable to attack them, save with your mouth, I feel sadly it is justified. He deserved it anyway. He had been recruited by the police to set me up and to get me shot and killed in a pre-planned police-crook operation and now it was my time to listen as the truth unfolded. Obviously, the police and CPS had created a smokescreen to camouflage the set-up, but juries are not as stupid as people or the police believe and I had faith that we would get to the bottom of the nightmare ordeal.

What is interesting, however, my solicitor had previously warned me that by asking for the mobile phone records – which the police were eager to suppress – it would provide Wendall with ammunition to call me a 'grass'. It's strange how it came to pass, eh! Perhaps my solicitor is psychic too? The screws dragged me away from him and took me into the dock and they left him in the corridor until the Judge entered the court.

The day started with legal arguments regarding various documents and articles that were retrieved from inside my vehicle on arrest. The prosecution wanted to cite them as evidence but the Judge ruled that the items did not help the prosecution case in any way to prove possession of a firearm. The Judge also ruled as inadmissible a further statement by Snakeshaft who claimed Wendall was asking him about security vans and their contents. The statement itself was all nonsense. Wendall would not have gone to Snakeshaft to ask about the contents of security vans as it would have been a bit like asking a professional footballer to explain the complexities of netball. The statement had obviously been written to make it look like Snakeshaft was implicating Wendall in serious crimes, but if that was so, why didn't Snakeshaft place Wendall in the upstairs back bedroom where it was alleged I had assembled and dismantled the Uzi firearm? It was all nonsense as the only time Snakeshaft could have done Wendall any real harm he claimed Wendall waited downstairs in the front room of his house. The 'three men of sin' thought that they had it all worked out, but to me it was just another pathetic scam that damned their arch plan to destroy me.

As the jury were sworn in I was looking for any possible or potential police sympathizers. In the front row there was a smartly dressed black guy about 28 years old, an elderly male of wise disposition, a 25-35 year-old ethnic woman and a young white fellow in his twenties who later became the foreman. In the middle row there were two men and two women. One of the men was a tubby fellow who you would probably meet in your local pub and share a pint with, the other was about 25-30 years old and looked educated. As for the women, one was a white haired pensioner who looked as if she had worked all her life and still lived on a rundown council estate and the other was middle aged and had long dark hair with wisps of grey in it. In the back row there was a middle aged male wearing jeans and a casual top and a smart middle aged Mediterranean fellow who came to court with a briefcase and looked as if he was in the car trade. Also, there was a young attractive female about 28-30 years old who the screws accompanying me were salivating over. And lastly there was another wise male juror, about 45-50 years old, who had obviously seen enough of life to know the difference between the truth and lies.

Taken altogether, although I felt there was a possibility of getting a rogue jury to deliberate over the facts of this case, I always felt that any jury, in any court in the land, would be able to see through the sordid machinations of this case. I just wanted to get the trial started and get some answers as to how the police were going to justify and legitimise their conduct, even though the set-up and the informers had been exposed.

The previous day during a legal conference with counsel and my lawyer, I had explicitly stated that I wanted counsel to ask the Judge in open court whether or not Wendall or anybody else mentioned in the case were police informants. The senior counsel said that he had asked the prosecution and they had said that there were no more informants in the case. I was not happy with this as I specifically stipulated that I wanted it voiced in open court.

After the jury were sworn in they were told to return two days later so that counsel could continue with legal arguments. I was hoping that counsel was going to discuss disclosure issues, including my request, but they did not. I was getting increasingly frustrated as here I was making a specific request and it was not being carried out. As far as I was concerned, prosecution counsel claiming there were no more police informers in the case, in a general conversation with defence counsel, was not good enough. Because should there be a miscarriage of justice in this case and I was convicted, I wanted it on record in open court that I had asked whether or not Wendall was a registered police informant and the prosecution counsel had answered the question.

Full credit to my junior counsel, Mr James Goodwyn, who said it was obvious that I felt so strongly about the issue that it would be sensible to clear it up so that we could move on with the defence case. I knew from Wendall's behaviour, both before and after my arrest, that he was a police informer and that he was trying to set me up to do an armed robbery, asking for drugs and firearms. I knew that he had contacted his police handler by pager using a pin number system hours before he came to my house and asked me to collect the 'valuable printing presses'. I would not, therefore, let the subject or request go until counsel had done what I had asked of him.

The general plan for the defence case was not to focus solely upon 'The Set-Up Theory' because if the prosecution could successfully camouflage or disprove that Wendall was an informant our case would be over. The idea was to keep 'all our balls in the air' so to speak, and if one area developed we would seize it. Although I was not entirely happy with this approach, because I wanted to steam into the prosecution from the beginning, I had to concede the tentative approach did have its advantages as the prosecution expected us to come tearing into them. We decided that our case would be run upon the fact that I was definitely misled or duped by Wendall and Snakeshaft or both and that I might have even been set-up too. The overriding notion being that if we could establish that I had been misled into delivering the 'printing presses' by the dodgy duo, the case would result in a just acquittal.

Rumours were circulating in the case that Wendall was still running a cut-throat defence. He was claiming that I asked him for an Uzi firearm. My junior counsel viewed this as extremely odd, because Wendall could quite easily hijack my defence and ride on my back and thus avoid a cut-throat trial. My theory for this strange behaviour is quite straightforward. Wendall could not run any other defence because the police, CPS and the prosecution counsel all knew of Wendall's active role in this affair and he was, in effect, guilty of possessing a firearm to set me up. Wendall could not really claim that he knew nothing about the Uzi, hence this line of defence. Whatever, Wendall's conduct in the case, as always, was not making sense to anybody save me who still saw him as an inept police informant who would eventually have to put his hands up and receive a nominal prison sentence or alternatively concede that he was a police informer and go QE like his arch accomplice Snakeshaft.

On the disclosure front, we had received several new documents. They were an unedited version of the debrief notes, now that prosecution had conceded Snakeshaft was an informer; a section of new debrief notes pages 633-722; telephone subscriber checks carried out by SO11; a document from a police liaison officer at Wormhood Shrubs Prison stating that Wendall had visited Snakeshaft; another intelligence communiqué stating that Mrs Wendall had called round to see Mrs Snakeshaft at her home with a male friend, but she did not want to press charges, i.e. perverting the course of justice; a police statement claiming Snakeshaft was suspected of being involved in the importation of drugs; and, lastly, a statement from a fingerprint expert claiming there were no identifiable fingerprints on the money seized during my arrest.

To recap on events, whether rightly or wrongly, but who could blame me, I was very suspicious and cynical about my senior counsel's reluctance to confront the issue over whether or not Wendall was an informant in open court. Mr Gallant QC states that he will do this when the trial recommences in two days time. I also wished to clarify the approach to the case as, although I can understand the notion of tip-toe-ing our way through the minefield, I didn't want to lose a golden opportunity where we could force the prosecution in to the position of disclosure of other informers or discontinuance. One consolation, I was pleased that I had got junior counsel, James Goodwyn, on board to challenge the anomalies and inconsistencies in the so-called 'Gallant Theory' of deception, duping and a possible set-up! I am not saying that my leading counsel did not have my interest at heart. He most certainly had, but I found it increasingly difficult to get my head around the 'softly, softly' approach, when I knew that we could have the case won even before it started providing we asked the right questions and demanded a clear and unambiguous answer from the prosecution.

DAY TWO OF THE TRIAL: Rest Day

Back at the High Secure Unit in Cellmarsh Prison I contacted my solicitor on the prison payphone and reiterated my anxieties, concerns and fears about the way we were going with the case. I asked my solicitor to contact leading counsel and instruct him to ask the relevant question in open court tomorrow.

DAY THREE OF THE TRIAL

The day's legal proceedings were due to start at 10:15 am but, for some reason, the court was told Wendall was refusing to come up from the cells. Was the pressure getting to him? Something was bugging him big time. The Judge adjourned the case so that Wendall could be present. When the trial continued at 11:10 am Wendall was present.

Mr Gallant QC got the proceedings off to a dramatic start by stating that there was still a lot of disclosure material being sought by the defence. More specifically a question Mr Diamond wanted answered in open court – whether or not there were any participatory informants in this case, namely Wendall, Snakeshaft, the Porpoise, Elvis or any others. Mr Gallant claimed that we had asked the prosecution to provide us with an answer in writing but so far the Crown were unprepared to answer one way or another.

At this stage Wendall jumped up in the dock and shouted out to the court that he was not a police informer. He stated that he also wanted the Crown to answer the question in open court too! Wendall then kicked the dock and left the court swearing and 'blinding'. As this was all happening the screw sitting next to me looked at me in amazement and said, "That was a bit melodramatic wasn't it?" As if to say, was it an act, because it did not look genuine.

The Judge then stated that he would not make an order for the prosecution to answer the question and added that he hoped Mr Wendall would come back. At this stage I was fuming as I knew, through reading the lawyer's bible *Archbold's*, that in order to prevent a miscarriage of justice or establish the innocence of a defendant the Judge is duty bound to have the question answered by the Crown. Due to Wendall's melodramatic outburst for his family and friends in the public gallery, the Judge adjourned the trial for five minutes.

When the court reconvened Wendall had still not returned to the dock, Mr Gallant continued with the same line of questioning as before as we wanted a definitive answer. He claimed the court had seen the original defence case statement that had been served nine months earlier and it clearly stated that we would like to know if Mr Wendall was an informant in this case. The Judge replied, "This is the ruling that I am going to make. The answer is *no for the moment*. Matters of police intelligence are not to be disclosed."

Mr Gallant then added that if we could conclude this matter the rest of the case could be eased as the underlying defence case of Diamond is that he was duped into carrying what was in his car for someone else. We have provided the Crown with a more recent and detailed defence case statement and it should be in the interest of the Crown to answer this question. At this stage the prosecutor jumped up and replied, "I am not prepared to answer that. I am not going to disclose at this stage."

The Judge then added, "I am not going to direct the Crown to disclose that information."

Sensing that we had both the prosecutor and the Judge on the back foot, Mr Gallant continued, "I simply ask this since it all goes into ways Mr Diamond might have been set-up. In my submission the Crown should answer the question."

The Judge then stated, "I've given the ruling three times, I am not going to give the ruling a fourth time."

As I was sitting in the dock absorbing all this professional evasion of the truth I was getting increasingly annoyed and frustrated. Why wouldn't they simply answer the question? If the answer was "no" and Wendall was not a police informant surely it would have been in their interest to say so and conclude this issue once and for all.

At 11:53 am Wendall decided to return to the court. The jury were then asked to take their places in the court and the prosecution began to open its case. Before he opened the case, the prosecution counsel handed to each jury member a small bundle of documents in a folder. He then took the jury through each of the pages in the folder.

In the first section was the indictment, in the second section was exhibit PH/2 which was a copy of my 'prepared defence statement' which the prosecutor read out in open court. This was the document that Wendall and his wife had been saying I was a grass for making. Yet when it was read out it explicitly states, "I cannot supply the details of the people involved. I realize that these are dangerous villains and I fear for my life and that of my wife and children … I know that it would be helpful if I named the people involved, but it would be the end of my life and that of my family."

The reason for denigrating my good name was obvious. The 'prepared defence statement' blew the set-up wide open and meant that the new police (Flying) squad that took over the case had to investigate the mechanics of the set-up and therefore arrest Snakeshaft because he was seen placing the blue bag in my vehicle. I was pleased that the 'prepared defence statement' was read out in open court for all Wendall's family and associates to hear as it made the grassing accusation appear exactly what it was, a police inspired propaganda exercise to discredit my impeccable reputation.

There was more drama to come, however, when the prosecutor asked the jury to examine section three in their folder, which contained exhibit DN/1. This was a copy of Wendall's 'personal jottings' found in his wardrobe during his second arrest on 2nd November 2001. The prosecutor once again read the handwritten document out in open court. It stated:

I keep hearing rumours that there is
a question mark against my name and
that Terry is putting it there. Is that
true. Does Terry believe I grassed him.
Terry wasn't to pick tool up that day
Someone else. Terry to collect tool later
That day. That plan was changed by Terry
And Terry said he would pick tool up himself
So Terry couldn't be set up or grassed on
for collection there.

When Terry was arrested they didn't know
Of Terry's name until the next day. If
Either myself or Snaksey had grassed him
They would have known Terrys name
Straight away.

If you read my interview with police you
Will see they mentioned that they showed
Me a photograph of Snaksey and me on
May 10th while under observation. This
Date is some four weeks before Terry's arrest.
I suggest that Snaksey was under observation
And that they knew of him inquiring after
A tool or they saw him buy that tool.

If Terry is thinking why I haven't been charged
Yet with the evidence available then ask his
Solicitor why. For me to be charged with
Possession then I have got to be in possession
Of the tool which I never was at anytime.
Also I was never in company with either
Terry or Snaksey when they were in
Possession of the tool.

When I heard the prosecutor read these 'jottings' out I was gob smacked. I had known about a letter or *something* found in Wendall's wardrobe. I had even asked my solicitor to write off to the CPS and ask for it, but nothing materialized. Perhaps the screw sitting next to me summed up the situation regarding the 'letter' when he said to me later, on the way back to the court cells, "Why would a proper villain write or leave a letter like that in his bedroom?"

The other question was, why had the defence not been shown a copy of this 'letter'? How comes the first we knew of its contents was during the opening speech to the jury? Its concealment by the scheming CPS was obviously to protect Wendall while he was in prison as, if I had had a copy of this 'letter' while in Cellmarsh Prison, most prisoners with any sense would be able to see Wendall was working with the police and CPS to strengthen their case against me. In essence, I had not only been set-up with an Uzi submachine gun being planted in my car, but once the set-up had been exposed I was being set-up a second time by Snakeshaft going Queen's Evidence and Wendall writing and leaving this pathetic, but highly damaging, 'letter' in his wardrobe for the police to conveniently find when they eventually decided to arrest him.

The main purpose of the 'wardrobe letter', or 'personal jottings' as the Crown referred to them, was to establish that I had prior knowledge of what was in the 'blue bag' and that I was party to a transaction to collect a lethal firearm. What with Snakeshaft claiming I had actually handled the weapon and now Wendall claiming in writing that I was party to a transaction to collect a 'tool' the case looked more ominous for me. The slags were trying to rump me every way, even to the extent where they were willing to compromise Wendall's reputation as a 'sound villain' by letting him leave an incriminating letter in his wardrobe.

In my opinion, on closer examination of the 'personal jottings', we can see that the 'letter' was obviously written by a policeman, most probably the senior police handler or controller in the case. For instance, the style of writing and language used in the document was not that of Wendall's at all. Wendall would not have used the phrase, "*I suggest* that Snaksey was *under observation* ..." or "... that they [the police] knew of him *inquiring* after a tool ..." Wendall would have said that Snakeshaft was "*asking for a tool*".

More significantly, the 'doughnuts' who composed this letter state that it was Snakeshaft who was under observation. How did Wendall know that it was specifically Snakeshaft who was under police observation and not the pair of them, or even Wendall himself who was the more prominent villain and had only recently been released from a long prison sentence? The 'letter' was full of preposterous errors, such as, "*When Terry was arrested they did not know of Terry's name until the next day. If either myself or Snaksey had grassed him they would have known Terry's name straight away.*" Of course the original set-up squad knew my name, that is why the defence were not allowed access to the ARV briefing and debriefing notes prior to and after my arrest as they would have shown the involvement of participatory informers and the identity of Diamond as the proposed target.

The 'letter' was a very unconvincing tactic by Wendall and the depraved detectives to get me convicted. Because the jury would surely ask why a so-called top London villain left a letter of such incrimination in his wardrobe for the police to find? It was no coincidence that the word 'Terry' was used *thirteen times* throughout the document and surely this document points to Wendall's knowledge and guilt of the alleged transaction? So how was Wendall going to fight the case with this self-confessional document being shown to the jury? Or is it his intention to fight the case in an effort to bring me down, because I have exposed the man for what he is? Who knows, but one thing is for sure, the smell of disgust and treachery around Wendall is getting stronger and stronger to the extent where a gasmask will soon be required.

After experiencing this bombshell of a 'letter', the prosecution took the jury through the other sections of the folder and showed them some photographs numbering one to ten. These were of my black BMW, the 'blue bag' in the passenger seat footwell, the weapon and all its accessories laid out like a trophy back at the police station and the map, mobile phone and a piece of paper showing Snakeshaft's mobile number at the material time.

OPENING SPEECH FOR THE CROWN

The case in a nutshell—At about midday on the 5th June 2001 the two defendants, Diamond and Wendall, went to the home address of a man called Daniel Snakeshaft. When, a little later, the three men emerged Snakeshaft was carrying a 'blue bag'. It contained an Uzi submachine gun and a large quantity of ammunition.

Diamond and Wendall went off in one direction, chatting together as they walked. They arrived at Diamond's BMW which had been left not far from Snakeshaft's home address. They opened the boot and stood there talking to each other. Snakeshaft then turned up. The 'blue bag', containing the submachine gun and ammunition was put into the passenger side of the BMW. Diamond got into the driver's seat and drove off. Snakeshaft and Wendall got into Wendall's car and drove off. Wendall dropped Snakeshaft near his home address.

Not long afterwards Diamond was arrested by armed police officers in the BMW. The 'blue bag' was in the front passenger footwell. The submachine gun and ammunition were inside along with a wooden shoulder stock, silencer and magazine that also contained rounds of ammunition. Before being arrested by DC Cole, Diamond was asked if he had a gun in the car. He said, "No way." Of the bag, he said that he had, "just picked it up for someone … don't know [what's in it], never looked … I don't know nothing about a gun."

Diamond was arrested and taken to Bornchurch Police Station and later questioned in the presence of his solicitor. Snakeshaft was arrested in the evening of the next day. Wendall was not arrested until over a month later in July 2001. He too was interviewed in the presence of his solicitor and elected to make no comment to all the questions that were asked of him.

THE EVIDENCE

Snakeshaft first met Wendall some years ago, not long after leaving school. They became friendly. Snakeshaft came to know Wendall's family. They kept in regular, reasonably close contact over the years. In April 2001 Snakeshaft gave Wendall a sum of money to tide him over. So did others. Diamond gave him a silver Vauxhall Vectra motorcar. Wendall asked Snakeshaft to get an Uzi submachine gun. Snakeshaft was heavily in debt at the time and he did what he was asked to do. At a local gym called 'The Eastside Gym' he found someone who had access to such a weapon. He spoke to him and reported back to Wendall. For reasons of his own Wendall wanted to keep his distance from this transaction. A price and date for collection were set. The price was £2500. The date for collection was 4th June 2001. Wendall had told Snakeshaft that the gun was for Terry Diamond. Snakeshaft did not know Diamond anywhere near as well as he knew Wendall.

On the day of the pick-up, 4th June, Snakeshaft drove to a prearranged meeting place. The vendor said, however, that the Uzi was not ready, but it would be the following day. The two men met the next day, on the morning of the 5ᵗʰ June. Another man actually handed over the merchandise. Snakeshaft returned to his home address in Bornchurch, Essex. On the way home both Diamond and Wendall telephoned him, no doubt anxious to find out about the progress and success of the deal. Snakeshaft told them he had the gun and that they should met him at his home. The two defendants arrived at Snakeshaft's home. Diamond went upstairs with Snakeshaft and examined the weapon and put it back in the bag. The two men then went back downstairs. Diamond and Wendall left Snakeshaft's home together.

At the specific request of Diamond, Snakeshaft was told to bring the bag to his, Diamond's, car that was parked nearby. Snakeshaft did as he was told. Once he had placed the bag into Diamond's BMW he was paid £2500 and Wendall was in 'spitting' distance of this part of the enterprise. Snakeshaft then joined Wendall in Wendall's car and Wendall dropped him off near his home. In due course Snakeshaft then paid the vendor for the Uzi.

Later in the day Wendall telephoned Snakeshaft to say that he had been unable to contact Diamond. That was hardly surprising as unbeknownst to Wendall and Snakeshaft, Diamond had been arrested. Snakeshaft failed to raise Diamond on the telephone. The next day Wendall contacted Snakeshaft and was irate when he found out what had happened to Diamond, namely that he had been arrested. He blamed Snakeshaft for this and made a passing threat. The next day Snakeshaft was himself arrested.

ARREST AND INTERVIEW: DIAMOND

At the police station Diamond was searched. On him was found nearly £750 in cash. When the 'blue bag', found in the passenger seat footwell was searched it revealed the following contents: a yellow towel, a black bum-bag containing 376 bullets, a black Uzi submachine gun, a wooden shoulder stock, a black silencer and a magazine containing 29 bullets. Diamond's black BMW was driven to the same police station and when it was searched the following items were found in it: a mobile telephone in the driver's doorwell, a piece of paper with a telephone number written on it, found in the centre consul—this was the telephone number used by Snakeshaft at the material time —and a street map of

Cambridge and St Neots.

Diamond was interviewed the next day in the presence of his solicitor. He elected to make no comment to all the questions that were asked of him. Through his solicitor he produced a 'prepared written statement' which was a denial of involvement with and knowledge of a gun, ammunition or any of the accessories found in the 'blue bag' taken from his BMW. The 'prepared statement' contained an innocent explanation for Diamond having been at Snakeshaft's address on the 5th June.

When he was re-interviewed the next day, once again in the presence of his solicitor, he again elected to make no comment to many of the questions asked of him, save to emphasize the fact that he:

"… would love to elaborate on matters. I really would love to, but my life, my family's life are (sic) in danger if I mention more than what I have said at the moment … I cannot elaborate on it. If I tell you names, anything like that, more than what I've said, then my life, my family's life, my kids, my children, will never be the same again, I might as well hang myself. I couldn't live with it. I'm in a dilemma at the moment. I've got… I can… I've got the two evils, I've got you, face the music with what has happened yesterday… or I've got the situation with my family. Now what would you do?… I know what I'd do, say nothing, tell the basic facts what happened and then later, if it comes to it and I have to elaborate, I'll elaborate, but I can't elaborate too far because, like I said, my family's in danger."

Diamond insisted that the prepared…

"statement is not a concoction, a fiction, this is the truth, it's the absolute truth. I had no knowledge of that gun in that car. Not at all… well, I was surprised when your officers said there's a gun in there, I was shocked and I… I just can't believe it, even now, you've heard me speak to my wife on the phone, you've heard me say, I'm dumbfounded. I did not know it was there, I swear on it, I swear on my children's life I did not know that gun was in my car. I would not have touched it if I'd known that and I'm annoyed with the people involved, because they've put me in a situation, but I can't start naming names

… these people [are] proper people, like *proper villains*… I can't name them, I would be bang in trouble."

At 5 p.m. on 6ᵗʰ June he was charged. In reply he said:
"I swear I have never seen that gun before in my life and I had no knowledge of it in my car."

ARREST AND INTERVIEW: WENDALL

On 24ᵗʰ July Wendall was seen at Wilford Police Station. He was accompanied by his solicitor. He was arrested and interviewed that same day. He elected to make no comment to all the questions that were asked of him but, through his legal representative, he produced a prepared and brief written statement in the following terms:
"I wish to make the following statement. I have never possessed any Uzi firearm. I have no knowledge of any Uzi firearm."

At that time no further action was taken in relation to him. In October 2001 Snakeshaft pleaded guilty to his part in these events. He expressed his willingness to give evidence for the prosecution against both Diamond and Wendall. As a result you will be hearing his account of how he became involved in these offences with the two defendants.

On 2ⁿᵈ November 2001 Wendall was re-arrested at his home address in Upminster and in due course taken to the police station. He was again interviewed in the presence of his legal representative and he again elected to make no comment to all the questions that were asked of him. He was charged the same day. He made no reply.

SEARCH OF HOME ADDRESSES

As Diamond made clear in the prepared written statement he produced to the police through his lawyer, when he was interviewed, he was coy about his home address. When his home address was searched nothing of evidential significance was found.

A search of Wendall's home address when he was initially arrested on 24ᵗʰ July 2001 revealed nothing of evidential significance. A search of his home address when he was re-arrested on 2ⁿᵈ November 2001 revealed the following:

In the bedroom in which Wendall dressed whilst the police were at the premises – on the top shelf of the wardrobe – a Sainsbury's carrier bag containing papers; a quantity of cash – £675 (this was left in the bedroom); – by the side of a large wardrobe in the main bedroom – a set of papers in the case of Diamond and Snakeshaft; and four mobile phones.

FORENSIC AND OTHER EXPERT EVIDENCE

During the examination of the firearm and ammunition the Uzi submachine gun was tested to see if it could be fired. It "worked faultlessly". The ammunition from the magazine was also tested. The magazine fitted the gun. The ammunition was found to be live. The other 376 rounds of ammunition were also tested, 375 of them being suitable for use in the gun. When the expert test-fired a sample of fifty of these cartridges 28 of them misfired, 22 of them fired and were therefore live ammunition. Both the silencer and wooden shoulder stock fitted the weapon. The gun also possessed both single and fully automatic capabilities. When fired in automatic mode it was capable of discharging between 600-650 rounds per minute.

With regard to the telephone evidence. The mobile phones found in possession of Diamond, Wendall and Snakeshaft were interrogated and the billings obtained and analysed. Essentially there were six points of particular interest to note:

1. Between 4th and 6th June 2001 the three men contacted each other.
2. On the morning of 5th June Diamond and Wendall contacted each other.
3. On the morning of 5th June, after Snakeshaft had collected the Uzi on their behalf, both Wendall and Diamond contacted him. Wendall first at 11:36 a.m. and Diamond subsequently half an hour later, just after midday, at 12:05 p.m.
4. The call Diamond made to Snakeshaft at 12:05 p.m. was the only one made by Diamond using that particular telephone.
5. Throughout 5th and 6th June contact was maintained between Wendall and Snakeshaft.
6. For some reason neither Wendall nor Snakeshaft were named as the subscriber for the mobile telephones most frequently used by them. The named subscriber of Wendall's mobile phone was a person called Quyum. The named subscriber of

Snakeshaft's mobile was Anjum Fut. These named subscribers were shown to share the same address in Birmingham. Quyum and Anjum Fut were one and the same person.

With regard to fingerprint evidence, we learnt that there were no identifiable fingerprints found on the gun, the shoulder stock, the silencer or the black magazine. Wendall's fingerprints, however, did appear on the 'personal jottings' (DN/1) found at his premises when he was arrested in November. They were also found in Diamond's car and on the papers in the case of Snakeshaft and Diamond found at his premises when he was arrested in November.

DANIEL WILLIAM SNAKESHAFT

He has pleaded guilty to his part in these events at an earlier Court hearing and in due course will be sentenced. He will be called to give evidence against these two defendants. He will give evidence about:

1. How he came to know them both.
2. How he came to be asked to make enquiries on their behalf in relation to the purchase of the gun.
3. How the deal progressed.
4. How the events of 5th June unfolded.

Once he had expressed his willingness to give evidence against the two defendants he was interviewed on tape by officers independent of this investigation during a prescribed procedure. As a necessary part of that procedure he told officers not only about his part in the offence he committed with Diamond and Wendall, but also about other criminal offences he had been involved in over the years. Of his own volition he told the officers he had been involved in drug offences and that on one occasion, when he had been tried with a number of other men at a Crown Court in London for a drugs offence, he had lied on oath when he gave his evidence. He explained he had done this at the explicit suggestion of the solicitor's clerk who was defending him. He also explained to the officers interviewing him that the solicitor's clerk had suggested a defence to him which was that he, Snakeshaft, should find out the name of an informant and put the blame for his involvement in the case at the door of the informant. Snakeshaft explained how he followed the advice given by the solicitor's clerk and found out the name of such a person. When the time came for him to give evidence before the jury, during the trial, he continued in the vein suggested to him by his legal representative. The foundation upon which that evidence was based was a lie. He, along with the other defendants, was acquitted. Snakeshaft perjured himself. He was separately charged with that offence, pleading guilty to it he now awaits sentence.

It may be that the defence will highlight this aspect of his character, coupled with the obvious comment that he has lied successfully on oath before and therefore he's doing it again now in this trial. Naturally you wish to consider that point if it is made. One thing you may think important to bear in mind in that context is this – he volunteered it. He need not have done so. If he had not mentioned it during the interviews no one would have been the wiser. No one would have known. He would not have laid himself open to adverse comment and attack upon the point. By telling the truth about his past he may well have done so.

During the time Snakeshaft is giving evidence it may be that you will find out a great deal about his background, character and motivation. His evidence will be very significant in the case and will obviously need to be examined, assessed and weighed in exactly the same way as any of the other evidence in the case.

However, it will not be the only compartment of evidence in the case. Alongside the evidence that he gives you will wish to consider:

1. The relationship between the two defendants, Diamond and Wendall.
2. The reasons for their being present at Snakeshaft's home address at the time that this Uzi, its accessories and live ammunition were all present at the address.
3. The reasons for Snakeshaft, not Diamond, putting the bag containing the Uzi, etc, in Diamond's BMW.
4. The reason for Wendall being present at the address and outside Diamond's BMW.
5. What the defendants said to the police, the documentary evidence. (Particularly in the case of Wendall; the 'personal jottings' and the papers in the case of Diamond and Snakeshaft— no doubt acquired from some source or another

after the arrest of those two on 5th and 6th June, upon his own release from the police station after his arrest in July.)

6. The forensic evidence.
7. The telephone evidence.

THE CASE
COUNT 1: Possession of a firearm with intent to endanger life

This is not an ordinary weapon and is, quite obviously, lethal. It is designed to terrify, kill and/or maim instantly or at will, depending upon the person who is pulling the trigger. It did not fall into the hands of these two defendants by mistake or accident. They ordered it. It was provided, costing a substantial sum of money to acquire. It comes with the wherewithal to unleash death, terror and destruction. It is specifically designed for one of those, or any of those, particular purposes. It came with a silencer.

Those who sold it have not been found. There is, quite understandably, a high degree of circumspection, suspicion and anonymity held amongst, and maintained by, those who possess and sell this type of weapon and those who wish to buy and use it. This type of weapon is not acquired so that it could be put on a mantelpiece to be admired as a trophy. It is bought for a purpose – armed robbery, contract killing or other strong-arm activities. These two defendants, Diamond and Wendall, had known each other for a long time by 5th June last year [2001]. At the time of these events they no doubt trusted each other. Secrecy, confidentiality and trust are three of the necessary hallmarks or ingredients of a plan and agreement to acquire a weapon such as this.

In addition, it may be that whatever may have been the purpose they had in mind for this weapon, its accessories and its live ammunition, at the very least their joint intention was "to endanger life." Why else go to the trouble of obtaining such a lethal and working piece of weaponry?

They knew full well what they were going to look at and pick up from Snakeshaft's address that day. They knew full well what he came out of the house carrying in the bag. Diamond was prepared to, and probably designated to, carry it away. He shouldered the risk of arrest while Wendall left without a physical trace of the deal on him. Snakeshaft was the 'gopher'. You may come to the conclusion that Diamond and

Wendall were the 'end recipients' and, by inference at the very least, the intended 'end users'.

Diamond's protestations of innocence on arrest, in interview and being charged were, the Crown suggests, the best attempts he could make to distance himself from the weapon and its accessories, having been caught 'red-handed' not far from the spot where he first took knowing possession of them.

If, having heard all the evidence, you are satisfied, so that you are sure, Wendall knew the 'blue bag' contained a firearm it is no defence to Count 1 for him to say, "I did not physically touch it." Similarly his own analysis of the law is wide of the mark when he wrote in his 'personal jottings':

"… if Terry [Diamond] is thinking why I haven't been charged yet with the evidence available then ask his solicitor why. For me to be charged with possession then I have got to be in possession of the tool which I never was at any time. Also I was never in company with Terry or Snaksey when they were in possession of the tool."

In the circumstances of this case if Wendall knew, as the Crown say he did, then he is capable of being a joint party to the possession of that firearm just as much as Diamond, who physically touched the metal, is.

COUNT 2: Purchasing or acquiring a prohibited weapon

This count is largely self-explanatory.

COUNT 3: Possessing a firearm when prohibited (Diamond)

This is self-explanatory.

COUNT 4: Possessing a firearm when prohibited (Wendall)

This is self-explanatory.

THE JUDGE'S RULING ON WENDALL'S POLICE INFORMANT STATUS

At the end of the Crown's opening speech the jury were released until after lunch at 2 pm. Once the jury had left the courtroom the Judge said that he had reconsidered the earlier ruling regarding whether or not Wendall was a police informant. The Judge said that usually there was a total prohibition on disclosure of police intelligence, but in this case, however, as it was in respect of a co-defendant it was different. The

Judge continued saying, if Mr Diamond believes Wendall was involved in his arrest, then Wendall's defence case would be at a disadvantage. Therefore, if it were the position that Wendall was not an informant, there is a powerful argument that the defence should be told, otherwise Wendall would be disadvantaged by the suggestion. It is my ruling on the issue that the court should be told if Wendall is *not* a police informer and I emphasize, the court should only be told if Wendall is *not* a police informer. If the Crown know something else it will have to reconsider its position. The court was then adjourned until after lunch.

When the court reconvened at 2:10 pm Mr Cyril Upstep, QC for Wendall, asked if the court could delay the evidence-in-chief of Snakeshaft while he took instructions from his client Wendall. Similarly, Mr Jonathon Maskell for the prosecution wanted to delay the evidence of Snakeshaft but the Judge was having none of it and he ruled counsel could have as much time as they wanted after the evidence-in-chief from Snakeshaft. The main prosecution witness for the Crown, Daniel William Snakeshaft, was then brought into the court at 2:26 pm.

THE EVIDENCE-IN-CHIEF OF SNAKESHAFT

The following account of Snakeshaft's evidence was taken from contemporaneous notes that were compiled by a solicitor's clerk in the courtroom.

Snakeshaft:

Yes I am in custody at the moment. I have been in custody since 6th June last year. I am 38 years old and I am married. I got married in 1985. I have two children, two boys aged ten and fourteen years old. I have known Mr Wendall since I left school. I left school when I was sixteen years old. Wendall is approximately 14-16 years older than me. Over the years I got to know his family and have kept in reasonable contact with him. I do not know Terry Diamond as well as I know John Wendall. I have only met Terry Diamond once before at a football match. I only know one Terry Diamond.

I am willing to answer questions regarding my involvement with the Uzi offence. I was arrested in the evening of 6th June last year. I pleaded guilty at Knaresbrook Crown Court in October last year to three counts, they were selling and transferring of a firearm; possession of a firearm when being a prohibited person and; lastly, having a firearm and ammunition in a public place contrary to the Firearms Act of 1968. I pleaded guilty to all three counts on the indictment.

In April last year I met up with John Wendall. I gave Wendall £3000 and Terry Diamond gave him a Vauxhall Vectra car. Mr Wendall asked me to purchase an Uzi for him. Around May time he asked me if I could get hold of an Uzi. I asked around where I thought I might be able to get one. I asked people at a local gymnasium in Canning Town, East London, called 'The Eastside Gym'. Mr Wendall also went there sometimes.

I spoke to a man by the name of Rob in the gym. I do not know his surname, I only know him as Rob. He is black, about 6 foot 2 inches with tight curly hair. I have seen Rob at the gym before and I know him as a regular there. On one occasion I heard him talking to another man about guns and I asked him if he could get hold of things like that and he said that he could. He said that he could get hold of an Uzi and that it would cost £2500. I then went back and told Wendall and he asked me to get it. I went back to Rob and told him to get it.

On the evening of the 4th June last year I went to The Britannia Hotel in the docklands area of East London to meet Rob. He said that it was not ready and it would be ready the next day. I told Wendall that I could not get it that night and it would have to be the next day. Mr Wendall told me that the gun was for Terry Diamond. The next day I did collect the Uzi. I drove to Hackney Marshes and followed Rob to a flat in Islington. Rob was driving a white Peugeot. He was driving alone. He drove down a street where there were some maisonettes. He told me to get out of the car and to follow him into the flats. He told me that he was going to meet his business partner called Elvis.

When we got to the flat, Elvis opened the front door and invited us inside. I would describe Elvis as about 5 foot 10 inches and he is half-caste with black tight short hair like Rob's. Once I was invited into a room, he pointed to a bag and said that, "It is in there." I took the Uzi gun in the bag and went to my car. I placed the bag containing the Uzi in the boot of my car and drove to my house in Bornchurch, Essex.

While in my car I received two telephone calls, one from Mr Diamond and one from Mr Wendall. The bag with the gun inside was greenish and it had a logo on its side. It had a drawstring –I would describe it as a duffle type bag. I told Diamond and Wendall that I had collected what they asked for. I said to one of them, I am not sure which one, that I had got it on board and for them to meet me around my house at about midday.

When I got home I took the bag upstairs to the back bedroom. I did not look in the bag. I saw my job as purchasing what they had asked for. I took the bag into one of my boy's bedrooms. My boys were at school and my wife was at work. Both Mr Diamond and Mr Wendall then turned up at my address. When they came into my house, Mr Diamond came upstairs with me and Mr Wendall waited downstairs. There was no conversation between us as far as I recall, except I must have asked him to come upstairs. Mr Wendall waited in my front room. Both Wendall and Diamond were in my hallway when I said to Diamond to come upstairs and look at it.

The telephone call I received from them must have been anywhere between 11-11:30 am. Mr Diamond looked into the bag and started putting it together and looked to see that everything was there with it. He looked at a clip thing like a magazine. There was a shoulder thing made out of wood. Something like a silencer. I did not know what was going to be there. There were bullets in the bag as well. Diamond checked the bullets and assembled the gun. He then dismantled the gun and put it back in the bag.

He asked me if I would look after it for him and I said no! He asked about the capabilities of the gun. He said this would be a good job for the same thing as … It was an armed robbery that took place about two years ago. It was on Crimewatch UK. He asked me if I could keep it for a day or two. I said no! He said that his car was parked in the next road. He said give me five minutes and meet him around the corner. He said all this in my bedroom. He went downstairs and I waited in my back bedroom as I was going to wait five minutes before taking the bag around to his car. Diamond and Wendall both left my house together.

After five minutes I went back upstairs and put the holdall with the gun over my shoulder and went and saw Diamond in his black BMW. He told me to put the bag inside the front footwell, which I did. He came out and paid me £2500.

The journey from where Diamond's car was parked to my house takes a couple of minutes. Mr Diamond then drove off with the bag in his car. I walked back to my address and met Mr Wendall. I suppose Mr Wendall thought everything was okay. We drove 100 yards up the road to a park. We went into the cafeteria that was in the park where we met Mr Wendall's wife who was waiting there. We drove in Mr Wendall's car, a Vauxhall Vectra. I did not know that his wife was going to be there. We had a cuppa tea and then I went to the Eastside Gym to give Rob the money. I met Rob and gave him the money. The time now was approximately anytime between 4 pm to 6 pm.

Mr Wendall told me that he had difficulty getting hold of Diamond. I tried to get through to him as well. I did not know that Diamond had been arrested at this time. Mr Wendall said that he was concerned. I did not know what to think. In the afternoon of the next day I received a telephone call from Mr Wendall to meet him at the Albion Public House in Rainham. When I got there Mr Wendall was in a vile mood. Rainham is approximately four mile from my address. Mr Wendall was already in the car park when I got there. He said that Mr Diamond had been nicked and it seems like he was stung. Mr Wendall took my mobile phone off me and took the chip out of it and threw it away. He did that because it was the contact number from me to him and Diamond. He was aggressive towards me in the way that someone is worried that something is wrong. We were only at the pub for 5-10 minutes. I met Mr Wendall at the pub at about 3 o'clock-ish. I went home afterwards. There was no contact between Wendall and myself after we left each other. I was then arrested the next day on the 6th June.

I have been involved in other criminal activities. I was charged with three counts for this offence. I also pleaded guilty to supplying a controlled class B drug, amphetamine sulphate to a Mickey Macitto. This offence occurred in May last year. I have been interviewed by police officers while I was in custody. I expressed a willingness to supply information respecting the involvement of the two defendants. I have admitted a number of offences in relation to my form. A total of nine other offences between 1998 and 31st May last year. These are in relation to drug matters, namely cannabis and amphetamine substances. There are three offences between January 1996 and the 31st December 1997. These are regarding the handling of stolen TV sets and some stolen clothes, jeans. In addition I pleaded guilty to a charge of perjury last week and I am awaiting sentence for that offence.

The reason why I got involved in these offences was I was being bullied. I was being bullied by a man called Robert Knowles. He was bullying me over a debt that I owed. The debt was for £150,000. During this year (2001) and last year I was asked if I could deliver some beer and cigarettes. I was stopped on the M11 motorway by officers in a van because they thought there were drugs on board. This was found to be true.

I was charged and taken for trial at Knaresbrook Crown Court and I was found not guilty. The drugs (100 kilos of cannabis resin) were destroyed by the police. As a result of that I was held responsible by the others. I was the cause of the van being pulled over by the police. At the time he (Knowles) said the debt was for £100,000 but it kept going up. I paid £30,000 from the sale of my wife's father's house. My wife and her brother purchased the house from her father. Unfortunately he died last year. My wife received some of the proceeds and so did her brother. Mr Knowles was satisfied for a little while. I thought that if I do the Uzi job for them (Diamond and Wendall) who I knew were respected in the East End that they might be able to sort out the situation for me.

Snakeshaft's antecedents were then read out in open court and it was stated that all his criminal convictions stopped in 1983. At 15:40 hours Snakeshaft concluded his evidence-in-chief and was released for the day. The jury were asked to wait outside. Counsel for Wendall wanted to have the whole of the next day free to have a conference with his client. The jury were brought back in and told they would not be sitting the next day and to return on Friday. Before the court was adjourned for the day the prosecution asked for a PII hearing with the Judge, obviously to discuss the earlier sensitive issue of Wendall's informant status. This was granted.

Afterwards, in the cells beneath the court I have a conference with counsel and the solicitor's clerk, Phil Bunter. We all agree that Snakeshaft looks under immense pressure with sloping shoulders and downcast eyes. He spoke with a soft and nervous voice and was taken through his evidence very tentatively. Visually, for a man of 6 foot 2 inches and of heavy build he looked as if he had the world on his shoulders. He looked pitiful and pathetic and tried his best to avoid any eye contact with anyone else save the prosecuting counsel. For what it was worth, the screws said that it was definitely a day for me. The prosecution failed, however, to mention that Snakeshaft was a registered police informer, but evidently we may bring this up during cross-examination of the witness.

My leading counsel declared, "Snakeshaft was the worst grass he had ever seen!" The contradictions with his debrief notes and his police statements are voluminous and we hope to explore and expose them on Friday. When counsel came to the cells to speak to me he claimed the prosecution had told him there are no "participatory informers" in the case, which effectively is not an answer to my question. I have said before that the CPS are the gangsters of language and syntax and if the defence do not phrase a question in the appropriate way the CPS are at liberty to avoid or ignore the question. I had not asked if there were any "participatory informers" in the case, I had asked the specific question of whether or not Wendall was a registered police informant. We still have not got a definitive answer to that specific question and it seems ironic that the prosecution counsel has sought an immediate *ex parte* PII hearing with the Judge at the close of play that day. I am not happy with the reply at all and I can sense we have the police, CPS and senior counsel for the prosecution worried by our request. Mr Gallant QC claimed that was the only definitive answer we are able to get, but I am not going to let it go at that as when I go into the witness box I am going to get some answers.

We concluded the conference with a discussion about uniting defences and forces with Wendall. We all agreed that having two defences working together against Snakeshaft is much better than playing into the prosecution's hands by having a cutthroat trial with Wendall. I am not happy about this either, but deep down I know it makes sense and I realize that I have to think of my family and swallow a little pride as it is essential I return home to them rather than commit myself to a suicidal defence strategy.

DAY FOUR OF THE TRIAL:
Legal Conference at Thamesmead Crown Court

At midday I had a legal conference with my solicitor who, *inter alia*, asked me if I would be prepared to have a legal conference with both Wendall and his solicitor. Reluctantly I agreed to this out of necessity, as I was aware that Wendall now wanted to change his defence to that similar to mine. Apparently, Wendall has been advised that a cutthroat trial would be against his/our interests. Some members of my family, friends and lawyers have been urging me for some time to "at least talk to him", but I feel that they just don't understand this man is the living embodiment of evil. He has set me up, tried to get me ironed out by armed police and once all this failed, he has grassed me off and then gone a step further in the set up once it was going pear-shape by writing an incriminating 'wardrobe letter' and leaving it in his house for his mates in blue to find. Wendall was the last person that I wanted to talk to, it was only three days ago that I spat in his face and now the rat wants to have a comfortable *tete-à-tete* with me.

My reasoning was this, if I couldn't prove Wendall was a police informer in court I would look pretty foolish suggesting things that I could not support or establish. More pertinent, the police and prosecution would love to see Wendall and Diamond cutthroat each other while the other scumbag, Snakeshaft, walked away laughing. Inwardly, however, I still felt I was one hundred and ten per cent right in my views about Wendall being a registered informant and no one could convince me otherwise. If this was the case how were the Crown going to save him from facing the *Two Strikes* automatic count as, if the jury believe me, they could well acquit me and convict him. Somehow they have got to save him as this, "I am a proper villain charade" has gone on long enough and now we were getting to the nitty-gritty of the case. More seriously, I had been told by my solicitor and counsel that I should focus upon the goal and forget about Wendall's role in the set-up as we were both facing life sentences and had enough ammunition to destroy the Crown's case through the pathological liar Snakeshaft.

Shortly before the lunch period, very reluctantly, I agreed to a legal conference with Wendall and our solicitors. Mentally, however, although I agreed to this, I wanted it to be on my terms as I felt as if all the people in the room wanted this 'jolly get-together' more than me. As I entered the conference room Wendall and his solicitor were already there. I said to Wendall, "The only reason I am here is because at the moment Snakeshaft is our enemy and he is trying to life us off. I am prepared to speak to you only to win the case!" Wendall acknowledged this and we sat down and began to discuss the case. As we were sitting there speaking I was conscious I was sitting amongst a vipers nest of evil and treachery and the only reason they were there was to pick my brains about the case and report back to their handlers and friends in the CPS and blue. Therefore, I kept things close to my chest and told them I had powerful telephone evidence that Snakeshaft was contacting the police shortly before my arrest on the 5th June.

After the conference I was put in a cell with Wendall over the dinner period. He started talking about the case and said that he only compiled the 'wardrobe letter' because I was accusing him of setting me up and calling him a grass. I said why hadn't he gone around to see my wife then, or see my brother Eugene and tell him rather than write a letter and leave it and not deliver it. He said he did visit my wife's address and she would not open the door (nonsense) and my brother refused to see him (again utter nonsense).

Wendall asked me why I began to blame him for setting me up. I said that it was because of his blatant inaction as a so-called friend after my arrest and the anonymous hate mail that I received while I was in Cellmarsh Prison that made me believe he was behind the whole set-up. I didn't bother going into the way he wanted me to commit a robbery with him and then Snakeshaft, or the fact that he wanted me to organize a drug deal for him, or the fact that he wanted me to supply him with a gun, or the fact that I knew he had a pin number and was contacting his police handler and controllers through a messaging service literally hours before he had come to my house and asked me to collect the 'valuable printing presses'. I did not want to divulge all this, as I had to play him at his own game and conceal the truth.

After hearing my reasons for thinking he had set me up he agreed that I was "in order" for believing it, but said he felt I should have said this to him in private and not in public. This was all bollocks, as my greatest weapon was to expose 'the three men of sin' for what they were and compel them to make mistakes in the case and possibly help to reveal their treachery in open court.

As we were speaking Wendall apologized for writing the 'wardrobe letter' and added that he wouldn't go into it now, but it was a problem and we had to think of a way around it in the case. I said that I had not given it a great deal of thought – which was a lie – as it was his problem and not mine, as he was the one who wrote it. I said that I would think about it overnight and give him my thoughts about it in the morning.

As I was sitting there with him I had an overwhelming urge to smash him in the face with my fist and pummel him into the ground, but I knew that I had to play this rat at his own game and think of my family. Wendall added that he had been told that the only sentence he could receive would be a concurrent prison sentence which meant it would run in tandem with his present prison sentence of twenty-nine years. He also stated that he hadn't known Snakeshaft was a police informer up until three weeks ago. Again this was all bollocks, as Wendall had phoned Snakeshaft at his house back on the 20th July last year when SO11 officers had taken Snakeshaft out of Wentonville Prison for seven days! How could Wendall have known about this top-secret police operation? The only way was through his very own senior police handler. More damagingly, in the debrief notes of Snakeshaft the following dialogue took place:

DC Lawson: So he [Wendall] knew that Diamond had been nicked by now?

Snakeshaft: Yeah, he's got his ... he contacted his wife. He said someone will get their head blown off over this.

Was Snakeshaft about to clumsily state, "Yeah, he's got his handler to find out?" I know that this is not conclusive evidence of Wendall's police informing status, but spliced together with all the other powerful clues and behaviour and ask yourself one question, would you ever trust this man?

Because of the changing circumstances in Wendall's defence case, he was obliged to change his legal team for professional reasons.

Apparently, in the legal sphere, it is fundamentally wrong for a barrister to be briefed about a defence and then be asked to run an entirely different line of defence in court, knowing that the previous line of defence inferred that the defendant was guilty. Mr Cyril Upstep QC had been instructed that Wendall had ordered the gun from Snakeshaft and that it was for me and he was to defend Wendall in a cutthroat trial that in effect would have meant Wendall's eminent prosecuting counsel would have been prosecuting me. Therefore, Wendall had no option but to change his legal advisors. Wendall asked if we could both have my solicitor representing us. Both the solicitor and I were against this as it could create a whole flotilla of problems and difficulties later on. It was decided that Wendall would seek alternative legal representation elsewhere.

After the conference I had a private chat with my solicitor and he felt that my chances of acquittal had definitely improved with this tactic. He claimed that two defendants fighting in tandem was much better than a cutthroat *ménage trios*. I sensed that he was right but I still wanted to know of the outcome of the *ex parte* PII hearing that was held at the close of play the last time we were in court. Why would the prosecution seek a private conversation with the trial Judge shortly after we had asked the golden question in open court as to whether or not Wendall was a police informer? The secret chat wasn't to discuss cricket was it?

DAY FIVE OF THE TRIAL

On arrival at court the solicitor's clerk met up with counsel and was informed that something had come afoot that could jeopardize the whole trial. It seemed that now Wendall has come on board with us and will have to change his legal team the trial may not continue and it may be adjourned until July. At 10:10 a.m. all counsel involved in the case were called into chambers with the Judge to discuss the issue. Why this could not have been done in open court I do not know.

When David Gallant QC emerged from chambers with the Judge he stated that the Judge agreed to the withdrawal of Wendall's legal team and would allow him time to find other representation. Strangely the Judge asked my counsel if we would be willing to continue the trial against me alone. The Crown, however, wanted to try both defendants' together and were in favour of an adjournment.

Some time lter, a friend of mine who was still in contact with former Irish prisoners told me that when the Diplock courts sat in Northern

Ireland during the troubles, if there was a police informant among the defendants, the Judge would hear the trial of the main defendants first and deal with the police informant at a later hearing. I was told this was a classic legal manoeuvre within the Northern Ireland judiciary and it appeared to be happening here.

We were then all called in to court at 11:00 am and there was an application by the Crown to adjourn the case so that we could be tried together. The Judge was not in agreement with the Crown and stated the case could no longer proceed against Wendall but the case would continue against Diamond. Our only concern was exhibit DN/1, the 'personal jottings' that were conveniently found in Wendall's wardrobe and the fact that the jury had already heard about and seen them. Mr Gallant QC stated he would like them removed from the jury's folder and a short explanation given the jury to disregard the evidence and they be destroyed by shredding by the court usher.

Meanwhile, while all this Machiavellian manoeuvring was going on upstairs in the court, downstairs in the cell I was banged up with Wendall. He had asked me the day previous to work out a way that we could explain away the reason for the pathetic 'wardrobe letter'. Overnight I had been dwelling on a way to circumvent or at least dilute the impact of the 'letter' to the jury. I thought long and hard about the issue and decided that there was no point going into court and lying about the 'wardrobe letter' as it would only make things worse. All along my only friend in this case has been 'the truth'! I decided to tell the truth and that way we could turn a potentially damaging piece of evidence into a powerful point showing the extent to which the police would stoop to acquire a conviction in this case.

Basically, I said to Wendall in the cells, the only explanation for this letter was that there had been a conspiracy going on between Snakeshaft, you and the police to strengthen the case against me because Snakeshaft was worried that if I was not sentenced to life imprisonment there may be serious problems later on. Therefore it was imperative that both you and Snakeshaft, at the behest of the depraved detectives, concocted more evidence against me. As I was telling Wendall this I was enjoying every moment of it as I was basically telling him exactly what he had done. I continued; I had told them that you had visited Snakeshaft in prison in September last year and that you had sent him in some money by registered post. I said it was then that Snakeshaft told you to write the letter on behalf of the detectives and leave it in your wardrobe so that they could find it and subsequently use it as evidence that I had prior knowledge of what was in the 'blue bag'. As I was telling Wendall this he looked at me in amazement, it was as if I was there when the plan was being originally concocted.

I told him it made sense and I was sure we could convince the jury that he was forced to go along with Snakeshaft's plan, as the jury would be asking one important question. Why would a top London villain want to leave such an incriminating letter against Diamond in his wardrobe? There was only one reason and that was because he was advised to by the depraved senior detectives in the case. I added that the type of language and sentence structure used in the letter were not his writing – quoting examples – and we could prove that only a detective in the case could have written the letter, as only the police were saying it was solely Snakeshaft who was under surveillance. If Wendall had genuinely written the letter he would have surely thought that one or both of us were under surveillance. To put in the letter that only Snakeshaft was under surveillance meant that the person who did compose the letter must have had inside information about the investigation and in effect the case. At the conclusion of this exposition of Wendall's rank treachery, he pathetically said, "That is a good idea, do you think that I could have it in writing?" Can you believe this rat? He was still seeking to acquire evidence about the case so that he could give it to his police handlers and show the Judge behind closed doors as evidence that I was concocting a defence. I said that I would do it through my solicitor.

The beauty of this explanation for the 'wardrobe letter' was that I was telling Wendall directly to his face what he had done but disguising it as a devious plan to explain away the damaging letter. I could see the fucking wanker's brain working so fast to keep up with me that he was shell-shocked at the knowledge I had about the sordid case. The seventeen years that he had done in British long-term prisons had definitely addled his brains. He was not a clever man. He was a grade A failure who thought that by working with the police he could enhance his life and lifestyle. I would rather sit and rot in prison than betray my principles and morals. Because at the end of the day, when your life is near its end, all one can do is sit and reflect upon the type of person you have been throughout your life and if you have been a nasty, treacherous bastard, then by hook or by crook it will show.

A short while after this I was called into a legal conference with counsel and was told that Wendall was to be discharged from the case and the Crown were to proceed with me alone. I was very pleased about this as it gave me a free run at Snakeshaft and the case in general. But what was bugging me was why would the prosecution and Judge let Wendall slip out of the case when with Wendall in the case their chances of conviction were greatly enhanced? In my view, I believe the case was close to falling against me because of the Wendall/informer issue and it was imperative to get Wendall out of the case before the Crown would have to "put up or shut up!" Rather than discontinue the case against me, they had decided to get the rat out of the case. I always wondered how the police, CPS and prosecution counsel were going to save Wendall from facing the *Two Strikes* count and here it was, get him out of the case on the pretext that he had to change his legal representation. No wonder the Judge wanted to start the trial and listen to Snakeshaft's evidence before these matters were discussed. It made a mockery of the whole judicial system and exposed the perfidious ways that police, CPS and Judges work together to cover up malicious prosecutions through the use and abuse of state registered police informers.

Back in court, however, the Judge addressed the jury and explained that the case would no longer proceed against Wendall and that it was in no way adverse to Diamond. He added that it was not a disadvantage to Diamond. The court was then adjourned to allow time for Snakeshaft to take the witness stand.

THE CROSS-EXAMINATION OF SNAKESHAFT
Snakeshaft:

> I have known Mr Wendall for many years. We are very good friends. For a good part of that time Mr Wendall was in prison. He was in prison for seventeen years. I visited him regularly while he was in prison. I used to take his wife on prison visits on the Isle of Wight. Wendall came out of prison in April last year (2001). I collected him from prison with his wife. I gave him some money. Terry Diamond gave him a car. Other people also gave Wendall money. I do not know the names of other people who gave Wendall money other than the £3000 I gave to him.

Q. Who is Billy Milton, did he give Wendall some money?

A.   Yes, that was part of the £3000 that I gave to him.

Q.   Who else gave money included in the £3000?

A.   Billy Milton, Tony Eagles and myself.

I only met Terry Diamond once at a football match. The next time I saw Terry Diamond was at my home address when he collected the Uzi. I was in regular contact with Wendall. One of the offences that I have pleaded guilty to was relating to the supply of amphetamines. This was in respect of a Mr Mickey Macitto. The handover of the drugs was being watched by the police. Just before the handover I was with Wendall. The arrest of Macitto was on the 14th May last year. I did purchase a new mobile phone days after the Macitto arrest. I also purchased another mobile phone for Wendall. I purchased them in case we were under observation from the police. I have never told anybody else this prior to today in court. I purchased the mobiles phones from a shop in Rainham, Essex. A number of days went by after Macitto's arrest and we were not arrested. We did not begin to wonder why? I still purchased the phones in case. Mr Wendall asked me to purchase them. I do not appreciate that the police were watching my home for a number of months.

I am a regular visitor to the Eastside Gymnasium that is in Canning Town. A number of my associates also visit the gym. I would say 75% of my associates or people that I know have been in trouble with the police. The types of crime they are involved in are drugs.

Q.   What about guns?

A.   Only Wendall.

I do know a man called Tony Formby. He was in prison last year. I met him in Wentonville Prison last year. He does not visit the Eastside Gym. Formby was in prison for a gun offence, a shotgun and a handgun. I have not got any previous convictions for gun offences. Last year I went to the Magistrate's Court to see Formby who was appearing at court for gun offences. I only attended to stand bail for him. You can contact his solicitor to find out? There are some people that I know are connected with crime that are not connected to the gym. Mill Street is about four miles from the gym. That is where the Bermondsey robbery took place. It was on Crimewatch UK. I cannot remember if a large reward was offered. I knew about all these crimes without the assistance of Mr Wendall and Mr Diamond.

I was arrested driving a van with 100 kilos of cannabis resin in the back of it. The job was for a Mr Broom. Mr Broom and Mr Bright were also arrested. I had a trial at Knaresbrook Crown Court and was acquitted at that court. Mr Bright and Mr Broom were also acquitted. I thought that it was booze and cigarettes in the back of the van and not drugs. It was me that committed perjury during the trial not the others.

Q.   When was the first time that you told the police that you had committed perjury?

A.   It was in July last year.

Yes, after the arrest for this offence. During the trial I said that I was sent to collect the goods from a man called Dave Stilson. He was a police informer back in the 1980s. Yes, I invented the story and told the jury it was Dave Stilson who told me to go and collect the booze and cigarettes. I never blamed the police.

Q.   Did you say to the jury that the Brooms had asked you to collect this van or that it was Dave Stilson?

A.   I have already told you that it was Dave Stilson. Yes I said that it was Dave Stilson and not the Brooms. I was advised by my solicitor to say that name. I was prepared to go along with that defence. I was advised by my defence solicitor. In doing this I rowed out the Brooms and in doing so I made their case better. They said that they had come along with me. The Brooms never mentioned Dave Stilson's name.

Q.   Have you anything against police informers?

A.   No, I have nothing against police informers.

Q.   That is because you are a police informer, aren't you?

(As counsel put this to question to Snakeshaft he looked towards the jury for their response.)

A.   Yes, I am a police informant. Yes I was responsible for the loss of the cannabis and the debt for the cannabis was passed onto Robert Knowles. I owed the debt to Robert Knowles. I hoped that John Wendall and Terry Diamond would ask Knowles to lay off me if I helped them out.

At the time of my arrest I had been a police informer for six months. I did not ask the police to take me out of circulation to get me safe from Knowles. Nor did I ask for a new identity. I told the police about Knowles in January 2001. No, I did not tell the police about the perjured evidence that I gave at Knaresbrook Crown Court. When I became a police informer I was given two handlers. I did not tell the handlers about the perjured evidence. I did the Brooms a considerable favour giving the perjured evidence I gave as the Brooms went down there thinking it was booze and cigarettes. I have known the Brooms for seven years. They come from East London. They come from Canning Town, East London, where they have some property, a yard.

Knowles claimed that I owed him money so I asked my handlers to get me out of the debt using recourse, but they would not do it. I don't know if Knowles is a drug dealer. I don't know whether or not he is a main man. He must be a debt collector as he said that I owed him the money. I have known Knowles since school. He has an oil business, selling diesel. I cannot remember what day but I was summoned to his house.

I do know about illegal drugs but I would not say that I was an expert. In my interview with the police I told them about many slang words used in the drug trade. I told them that Dickie Davis was slang for cocaine. Bob Marley is puff. Garden furniture was grass. I only knew about lorry loads of drugs not other shipments. I also told the police about slang words used for quantities of drugs. I heard the slang words from conversations down the Eastside Gym. A dog running tomorrow means that the drugs are coming tomorrow. A dog won means the drugs got through the ports. If a dog fell it means the drugs were intercepted. Yes there was familiar slang used with people involved in drugs. I don't know if I was a major target by the police for drug offences. I have been hanging around those sort of people from the age of sixteen, so I was bound to pick up those sort of words.

A copy of a contact sheet was then handed to the witness and the Judge. Defence counsel then explains that the defence have been given some documents, which set out the information that Snakeshaft gave to his handlers regarding this case. Snakeshaft agrees that he has been a registered informant from January of last year (2001). Snakeshaft then states that he would like a chance to look through the contact sheet so that he can familiarize himself with it. The Judge then adjourns the trial until after lunch so that Snakeshaft may read the contact sheets.

After lunch the cross-examination of Snakeshaft continued. While looking at the contact sheet, Snakeshaft agrees that he did not tell the police that Knowles had threatened to kill him unless he paid the £150,000 debt on this occasion. I told the police that Knowles had met me a number of times.

Q.   Mr Knowles rang you up as he thought that he was being watched by the police?

A.   Yes!

Q.   This is the man that threatened to kill you?

A.   Yes! I told the police that he wanted to come around to my home address and I did not want to meet him. Knowles did know where I lived. I think he said on one occasion when he threatened me that he knew where I lived. He was worried that I might have said something to the police. I think that Knowles was pumping me to see if I would say anything.

Snakeshaft is then asked to look at a new contact sheet dated 4th February 2001.

Q.   You are now up to 60 calls to the police. You told the police that Knowles wanted £50,000 by Friday. Now look at the contact sheet dated 9th February 2001? It was on this occasion that you met your handlers at an address in Victoria?

A.   Yes! I told them about how I came to have the debt from Knowles. I told them about the evidence I gave at Knaresbrook Crown Court and I told them that I was advised by a solicitor to use that defence.

Counsel reads out the document in court so that the jury can get the full flavour of it, as they do not have a copy of the document.

Q.   You were saying all this information in February last year to curry favour with the police as an informant?

A.   Yes, I have received money from the police as an informant. I have received £1500.

Judge: Are you telling the police on the 9th February last year that this was a completely bogus defence?

A.   Yes, I told the police that I had a solicitor that I rated highly who had helped me with my defence at Knaresbrook Crown Court. I did not tell the police that I committed perjury, I told them that in July. Yes, I told the police that for money my solicitor would offer me something that would bolster my defence. I told the police about Knowles on the first occasion that I met them in January last year. Yes, I stated that he threatened me and that my life was in danger.

Q.   Can you look at another contact sheet on page 274? Did you tell the police on this occasion about two Purdey shotguns for sale?

A.   Yes! I heard about it in the vicinity of others.

Q.   Please turn to page 122. Did you phone the police on 23rd March last year and tell them that Mr Knowles wanted you to go to the Magistrate's Court in order to monitor the hearing on his behalf in respect of Tony Formby in relation to gun offences?

A.   I went down there to stand as a surety!

Q.   Mr Formby is Mr Knowles's friend? Mr Formby is your brother-in-law in effect?

A.   Yes!

Q.   So Mr Knowles who had threatened to kill you for £150,000 wanted you to go and check Mr Formby was okay at court.

A.   Knowles said I'll blow you away and kill my family.

Q.   Formby was purchasing guns for Knowles?

A.   I grew up with Formby. Before he was arrested he lived out in Portugal for six years. I did not know the guns were for Mr Knowles until I saw Mr Formby in prison.

        Yes, I contacted my handler the same day that I went to the court. I went to the court in the morning and I left in the morning.

Q.   Do you know what a 9 millimetre gun is? The shotgun and 9 millimetre were for Knowles?

A.   I got that information from Formby when I visited him in Wentonville Prison.

Q.   Knowles is in dispute with Robert Henderson and Billy Milton?

221

A.   Yes, it says that in the contact sheet. Yes, there is a war going on between Knowles and Milton.

Judge: These are the things that you told your handlers?

A.   Yes!

Judge: You don't know how they were written down by the police?

A.   No! I was told that there was a war going on between Knowles and Milton.

Q.   In March last year you were on the side of Robert Knowles who you believed had killed people in the past.

A.   Yes!

Q.   And Billy Milton and the others were at war?

A.   The Uzi was not intended for Billy Milton or Robert Knowles.

Q.   Do you think that you have any difficulty mentioning people's names in the court?

A.   No, I don't think so? Milton lives in Noak Hill, Essex. He used to live in Canning Town. Henderson lives in Barking and Knowles lived in Romford.

Q.   Please turn to page, report number 206, dated 26th March 2001.

A.   Yes, Knowles runs a diesel company, it's called Discount Fuel I think. I was asked to take down his telephone number by the handlers. Yes, I went to Knowles's yard on the 23rd March last year after I went to the court. I went to tell him that Formby could not get bail. Yes, I was going to stand surety for Formby. I was told to stand surety by Knowles. I did not want to say no to Knowles. Yes, I went on contacting the police through April and May last year. I stated in the debrief that I was scared as I kept meeting two police officers everyday.

Q.   How many times have you contacted the police between 21st May and June last year?

A.   Didn't see the police.

Q.   Why didn't you tell the police that you were being asked to supply an Uzi submachine gun? You did not want the police to know that you were being asked to supply a submachine gun did you?

A.   That's not correct!

Q.   Did you tell the police about the supply of amphetamines to Mickey Macitto?

A.   No! I was getting scared of the different number of handlers I was seeing.

Q. Mr Diamond drove off from the vicinity of your address at 12:40 pm and was stopped by armed police some 15 minutes later. There is a call at 12:27 and one at 13:29 from your mobile phone. You went to a cafeteria in the park with Wendall and his wife Carol. If Mr Diamond drove off at 12:40 pm how long did you spend with Mr Wendall with the cups of tea?

A. No more than 30 minutes. I went to the Eastside Gym after approximately 5-10 minutes and then I drove home.

Q. After 12:27 p.m. the next call recorded here was a call to Mr Wendall's voicemail? Then a call from you at 13:29 to this number 07944-232985, whose number is that?

A. I cannot recall!

Q. Was it Rob?

A. Tell you the truth I can't recall? I don't know who that number belongs too.

Q. The next call is from you to Mr Diamond at 13:30. If your business with Mr Diamond was ended there, finished, why have you called Mr Diamond? What possible reason would you have to call Mr Diamond?

A. Mr Wendall told me to phone him?

Q. By what pigeon? There are no calls from Wendall to you? The last call you made before Wendall and Diamond arrived at your home is at 12:27 pm. At 12:40 we all agree that Mr Diamond drove off. At 13:10 Mr Wendall calls his own voicemail. There are no calls from Mr Wendall to Mr Diamond or Mr Wendall to you. The next call is from you to Mr Diamond at 13:30.

A. It must have been that I touched the phone in my pocket and it rang him.

Q. Is that the best you can say? There is not a single call from Wendall to Diamond. That is not until page 18, at 6 pm when Mr Wendall called Mrs Diamond?

A. I was asked by Mr Wendall to get hold of Mr Diamond. I am telling the truth.

Q. Let me suggest what the truth is? You were trying to contact Mr Diamond because he was delivering a parcel for you! You were getting worried because he was supposed to be delivering the parcel.

A.   Mr Wendall asked me to telephone Mr Diamond.

Judge: What did Wendall ask you to say to Mr Diamond?

A.   He asked me to tell Mr Diamond to ring him, as he was concerned.

Judge: That's it?

A.   Yes!

Q.   When did you ring Wendall and tell him that you could not get through?

A.   At 14:10 hours.

Q.   After ten calls of trying to contact Diamond, what did Wendall say?

A.   Keep trying!

Q.   There are very few calls from Mr Wendall to Mr Diamond. Why wouldn't Wendall just phone Mr Diamond? You have no answer for that have you?

A.   All I know is that Mr Wendall asked me to telephone Mr Diamond.

Q.   Did you phone Rob?

A.   Yes, I must have done.

Q.   Which number is his on the phone record?

A.   I don't know? I paid him at the gym!

Q.   How do we know that you paid him?

A.   Because I am telling the truth.

Q.   How do we know? What proof do we have that you paid him?

A.   Only my word. I think Rob obtained the gun within a week of me asking him for it.

Q.   When you decided to become a prosecution witness did you have lengthy interviews?

A.   Yes!

Q.   What was the first version that you told the police when you turned prosecution witness?

A.   I can't remember!

Q.   Do you want me to tell you?

A.   Yes!

Q.   You told the police that Rob already had an Uzi submachine gun and that he had it for two and half years and that he was not using it?

A.   Yes, I told them that!

Q. Is that true?

A. Yes.

Q. Where he had it he couldn't get it?

A. It was at someone else's house, Elvis's! I told him to get it from Elvis's address in Islington.

Q. Are you sure that you are telling us the truth?

A. Yes! Yes he told me how much he wanted for it.

Q. When you first gave an explanation to the police, did you say to the police that you paid for the Uzi there and then when you picked it up at Elvis's?

A. No, I never said that, I said I paid for it at the Eastside Gym! I probably told Wendall how much it was on the Saturday or Sunday because I got it on the Monday. Rob expected me to pay for the gun after it had been seen.

Q. Did he let you have the gun on trust?

A. Yes!

Q. He just happened to have an Uzi?

A. Yes!

Q. When you were giving evidence on Wednesday, you were asked if you looked in the bag? What is the truth of it?

A. I looked at it when I went upstairs to check it with Mr Diamond. I never looked at the submachine gun in the bag at Elvis's. I did not have a peak at it on my way to the car or in the car.

Q. Did Mr Diamond wear any gloves when he looked at it?

A. No!

Q. Were you wearing any gloves?

A. Yes, I wore gardening gloves in case I was asked to touch it. I picked up the gloves in my kitchen underneath the sink.

Q. Did you do all this before Mr Diamond arrived?

A. Yes!

Q. Was it only after your arrest that you knew that the police were observing your house?

A. Yes!

Q. How long were Diamond and Wendall in your house?

A. It felt like ten minutes, but if you say that the police had observed them in my house for three minutes I would go along with that. I would also agree that they had left my house for one minute before I followed them with the bag.

Q.   You told the police during interview that you looked in the bag at Elvis's didn't you?

A.   I must have done so, if you say so!

Q.   Can you look at page 276 of the debrief transcript? Is that what you told the police in October of last year?

A.   Yes!

Q.   Did you wrap that gun up in a towel?

A.   No! It was wrapped in a towel because that is how I collected it.

Q.   All you saw was a towel in Elvis's?

A.   Yes! I did not wrap the gun in a towel. All I saw was a towel wrapped around something.

The passage was read to the witness again where he stated that he saw part of the gun in the bag at Elvis's flat. Snakeshaft stated the towel was in the bag with the gun and the rest of the stuff.

The Judge stated that it was a convenient time for a break and he adjourned the case over the weekend until Monday.

The above transcript of evidence was taken from the notes made by the solicitor's clerk. When I consulted my notes made on the day of the trial I summarized the evidence in this fashion.

As a police informer, Snakeshaft had been phoning the police about guns in the past and had mentioned the names Knowles, Milton, Formby, Carrant and Henderson in the contact sheets as being involved in a gang war. Despite the fact that Knowles was going to kill Snakeshaft, he was prepared to stand bail for someone (Formby) who was supplying guns to Knowles.

Snakeshaft had made 28 contact sheets in the first two weeks as a police informer and a total of 244 contact sheets in the six months that the police claimed he was a registered informer.

Snakeshaft claimed he did not notify the police about the amphetamine or the Uzi case, but admitted contacting the police about other firearms offences in the past.

We learned, in spite of the fact that Snakeshaft's informant status had been cancelled, that he was still contacting his handlers the day after Diamond's arrest. As seen in contact sheet 244, dated 6th June 2001 which proclaimed:

Snakeshaft rang his controller on his mobile phone at 4 pm (this was at the same time I was being interviewed on tape at Bornchurch Police Station).

Snakeshaft stated that a man called Terry Diamond met a friend of Snakeshaft's at his home address. Snakeshaft declined to give the identity of the third man. Snakeshaft stated that they had a conversation which he was not party to.

After Diamond had left the home of Snakeshaft, he was arrested by police. He was found to be in possession of a firearm. Snakeshaft stated that he was worried that Diamond may think that he is a police informant as he had been to his home prior to arrest.

Snakeshaft was worried that he may be named as an informant in any future court case and he also stated that his informant status maybe revealed. Snakeshaft asked that I check to find out how Diamond had been arrested, for example, via surveillance, routine stop, etc. to give him peace of mind.

I stated that it would not be for me to acquire such information and that to give it to Snakeshaft would be inappropriate. I asked what good would it do him to know the details of Diamond's arrest if Diamond was already suspicious of him. Snakeshaft repeated that it would give him peace of mind as he feared for his safety and that of his family. In view of Snakeshaft making such comments I suggested the services of witness protection which he declined.

I told Snakeshaft that I would make some enquiries and for him to call me back at (indecipherable). In order that I could consult with the informant register/ DPS.

At 4:45 pm (by now my police taped interview had concluded) *Snakeshaft once again called to find out anything further. I stated that I had no more news. I told Snakeshaft to ring again tomorrow at noon in order that a strategy could be discussed with the DPS as to the way forward. Snakeshaft was also worried that he may be arrested because of his association with Diamond yesterday.*

As we can see from this contact sheet, it was presented to look as if Snakeshaft was not the informant in the Uzi case, yet he was still contacting his controller in spite of being cancelled as an informant and he refused to name the third person at his house. My strong theory, based on what evidence has already been mentioned in this book, is that Wendall was the real informant in this case and he was the one who was going to collect the reward monies for Macitto's and my arrest. Wendall was working in conjunction with Snakeshaft but it was Wendall's idea to set me up in the beginning.

Also in Snakeshaft's evidence he was concerned about meeting too many police handlers, but he was not exactly coy about contacting them on his mobile phone.

Snakeshaft admitted committing perjury, i.e. lying to a jury in the Broom's cannabis case in order to get them out of it. He did them a favour and in return they passed on a £150,000 debt via Knowles to extract it from him.

Snakeshaft admitted it was a 'done deal' when I drove away from his house, but then he phoned me a total of 81 times. Why?

Snakeshaft stated that he never looked in the blue bag at Elvis's maisonette. Then in the debriefing notes it clearly states that he looked in the bag and saw the weapon. Snakeshaft then agrees that he saw 'it' dismantled in the bag at Elvis's flat and then by the time he got it home it had a yellow towel wrapped around it. He admitted getting the gardening gloves from his kitchen. Therefore the inference is that he needed the gloves to wrap the Uzi up in the towel so that I could not see it. That is why Snakeshaft personally took it to my car and planted it there.

Snakeshaft admitted phoning an anonymous person soon after I drove away from his house. Counsel suggested to him that was the real destination of the gun and was the reason he tried to contact me 81 times – because he was worried that I might look inside the bag and see what was really in there.

Snakeshaft was willing to place the blame for the cannabis arrest upon an innocent man, Dave Stilson, to achieve his own selfish ends and then admitted it was a lie!

We learnt that the technical term or phraseology for a registered police informer is 'CHIS', C=Covert, H=Human, I=Intelligence, S=Source.

Snakeshaft agreed that the first person he asked for an Uzi, Rob the Porpoise, happened to have one sitting in his cupboard for two and half years. And then he let Snakeshaft have it on trust.

All in all, today was an excellent day for the defence. Wendall was conveniently jettisoned out of the trial and Snakeshaft's evidence was ripped to shreds. It proved that not only was Snakeshaft a self-confessed liar, but he was also lying during his evidence. Some of the jury, especially one young and one old fellow, had started to look over at me.

My junior counsel, James Goodwyn, came up with a valid point, namely that Snakeshaft never accepted responsibility for any of his actions or behaviour himself. It is always some else's fault. For instance:

If it wasn't for Knowles I wouldn't have got involved with Diamond.
Wendall asked me to get the gun.
Diamond ordered me to bring it around to his car.
Wendall took the chip out of my mobile phone and destroyed it.
and
It was the solicitor's fault for giving him a bogus defence that resulted in the acquittal for the cannabis case.

James Goodwyn suggested that Snakeshaft would get more sympathy from the jury if he were a little more remorseful or penitent about his criminal behaviour. But as things stood, he was in a hole and he didn't know when to stop digging.

DAY SIX OF THE TRIAL

The cross-examination of Snakeshaft continued. The witness was asked to look at Book 112, the document relating to 20th July 2001. This document was compiled as an introduction before Snakeshaft's actual debriefing process.

Q.   Did you tell the police that Rob did not have the 38s?
A.   I was asked for a number of things. But I only asked Rob for the Uzi.
Q.   Did you ask Rob if he could supply two 38s between the time of Wendall's release and the time of your arrest?
A.   Yes, but I am not sure when.
Q.   Was Robert Knowles threatening to kill you?
A.   Yes.
Q.   Did you see Wendall on a daily basis during this time?
A.   Yes.
Q.   Did you ask Wendall to talk to Mr Knowles prior to your arrest?

229

A.   No. I was going to ask him after, but I got arrested on the 6th June!

Q.   Did Diamond only ask for the Uzi?

A.   Yes.

Q.   Did Mr Diamond ask for the 38s?

A.   No, I told you he had asked me for a lot of things. On that day all he wanted was an Uzi. What I said there on page 82 is correct.

Q.   Please turn to page 87. You said to the police once the Uzi was got for Diamond that day, Wendall asked for two 38s. Please turn to page 94. There is a question regarding the 38s. Initially you said that Wendall wanted an Uzi and two 38s.

A.   When I got the Uzi I was asked for the two 38s afterwards. It was Wendall that asked me, not Diamond. I must have got it wrong!

Q.   Did you ask Rob for the two 38s before you gave him the money for the Uzi?

A.   Yes!

Q.   Please turn to page 120. Here it says Terry Diamond asked you for the two 38s. You just explained to the jury that this could not possibly be true. Why are you making up false allegations about Mr Diamond?

A.   I don't know.

Q.   Did you tell the police that?

A.   Yes.

Q.   Did you tell the police that Mr Diamond never asked for two 38s, he just drove off in his car after you gave him the Uzi.

A.   Yes. I told the police that Diamond asked for two 38s and that I was petrified and was going to telephone a police officer I know because it was getting out of hand. He is not the sort of fellow that you say no to.

Q.   Did you tell them that?

A.   Yes, I got asked for so many things at the time I thought that Terry Diamond asked me for the 38s! I would have telephoned the police straight away but I thought it would have come back to me.

Q.   So let's get this right, it was Wendall that asked you for the 38s and not the defendant Mr Diamond?

A.   Yes. I told Rob about the 38s after Terry Diamond took the machine gun away. I did ask Rob on the day.

Q. Did you tell the police that you didn't ask Rob for the 38s?

A. That is correct.

Q. So that is another lie then?

A. No, that is not a lie it is a mistake. On the day of the event I asked Rob for two 38s.

Q. No, it is not a mistake Mr Snakeshaft, you actually retract the passage and start correcting the mistake. Now you are saying the mistake you make is a mistake. That is a lie isn't it?

A. No. I don't know how that can be true. Wendall asked me about the 38s at the same time he asked for the Uzi. I was asked for a number of things, but on that day I was only asked for an Uzi.

Q. Mr Snakeshaft, you won't answer my question. Please turn to the bottom of page 127. You say Terry Diamond never asked me for the Uzi.

Judge: What is the explanation for telling the police on a number of occasions that you didn't ask Rob for two 38s? To the jury you are saying you did ask Rob for the 38s and to the police you are saying that you didn't ask for the 38s from Rob? Which is it, because both do not go hand in hand?

A. I was confused.

Judge: Are you saying that you were confused when you were asked the question by the police?

A. I was asked for so many things that I might have made a mistake.

Q. Why did you tell the police that Mr Diamond asked you for the 38s?

A. I told you this morning he didn't ask me.

Q. So you lied to the police then, because it is in your debrief notes?

A. I was asked about many things.

Q. Shall I move on?

The Judge adjourned the hearing for a 15-minute break.

Q. What time did you pick up the gun from Stoke Newington?

A. About 10 am.

Q. What time did you get to your home that day?

A. I don't know.

Q.   Well you can check from the police records and it was at about 12:30 pm.? Where did you go, as it doesn't take you two and half hours to get from Stoke Newington to Bornchurch does it?

A.   Have you seen the traffic these days?

Q.   I suggest that the police started their observations on your house at 11:20 am and you arrived at your address at 12:33 pm. Do you have a lock-up garage other than at your home address?

A.   No.

Q.   Do you own or rent a lock-up garage in London SE 10?

A.   No.

Q.   How long did it take you to get from Islington to the A13?

A.   Don't know?

Q.   How long did it take you to go from Bornchurch to collect the gun in the morning?

A.   I would not have been at home, I would have left from Stratford where I work. I got to work at 6 am as I was on the 6 am shift.

Q.   Let's move on to the money – the £2500 paid for the gun? You told the jury last week that you left your home and placed the blue bag containing the Uzi in the passenger side of Diamond's car and he got out of the car for a second or so and paid you the money.

A.   He got out of the car with difficulty because of his bad leg and gave me the money.

Q.   What was the money in?

A.   It was in a little bag.

Q.   Did you check it?

A.   No, I put the money in my pocket.

Q.   Did the police officers see any of this?

A.   I don't know what the police officers saw.

Q.   Can you remember what you just described?

A.   Yes.

Q.   Please turn to the debriefing transcript on page 548-549. You state, "He just passed me the money in the car!" That is what you told the police. Is that wrong?

A.   Yes, that is wrong because he got out of the car.

Q.   Did you say, "He handed me the money in the car when the door was open"?

A.   Yes.

Q.   Well how can you get it so wrong?

A.   I don't know.

Q.   So what you told the police on page 548-549, none of that happened?

A.   As I opened the door and put the bag inside, Mr Diamond got out of the car and gave me the money.

Q.   How can you get it so wrong about what happened that day?

A.   I didn't get it wrong, it's what happened.

Q.   Then why didn't the police officers watching see that? I suggest the only money that was exchanged that day was the £500 you gave to Mr Diamond to deliver the parcel.

A.   No that's not what happened.

Q.   I suggest that all Mr Diamond was doing was delivering a set of printing presses and you gave him the £500 for it. The only reason Mr Diamond did the delivery was because you told him that it was not drugs, which you are known for, and he was going to Cambridge for you.

A.   No, he was not supposed to go to Cambridge. That never happened.

Q.   Were you once arrested in Royston, which is just south of Cambridge?

A.   Yes, I thought that I was delivering tobacco and booze and I was arrested with the Brooms.

Q.   I suggest that is why you sent Mr Diamond to Cambridge near Royston, which is where the delivery was supposed to take place.

A.   That is not correct.

Q.   That is why when Mr Diamond was stopped and arrested, the police found a map in his car. I suggest that you gave it to him.

A.   That is not correct.

Q.   Please turn to page 9 in Book 112. Please read the top of the page. You told the police you had got Rob's phone number?

A.   Yes.

Q.   You said that when Terry Diamond got nicked you threw the chip out of the mobile phone away. Why did you tell the police that you threw the chip away?

A.   I got that wrong!

Q.   How?

A.   I don't know.

Q.   How can you make a mistake?

A.   I don't know. I haven't got an answer for that.

Q.   If it was a mistake why not correct it and say, 'Sorry, Officer, it was Mr Wendall who threw the chip away?'

A.   Mr Wendall chucked the chip away.

Q.   Did you tell the police that you knew Kenny Hoye?

A.   No.

Q.   Please turn to page 352. You said that you knew a man who was knocking off Goddard's old woman.

Counsel has misread the above passage and asked the court to withdraw that question and apologized for it. He then looked over to Snakeshaft and exclaimed, "See, we can all make mistakes!"

Q.   Did you tell the police that you were a trusted member of the criminal community?

A.   Yes, because I kept my mouth shut on two occasions when I was arrested.

Q.   Please turn to page 585 in the debriefing transcripts. Did you tell the police that you had two mobile phones, one was for work as a caretaker and the other one was purely for criminality?

A.   Yes.

Q.   What type of criminality were you involved in May last year?

A.   Drugs.

Q.   You bought a mobile phone to deal in drugs?

A.   Not to deal in drugs, but to find out things. As you know I had turned police informer.

Q.   When I asked you last week, you said the reason was because your handlers had been changed and you did not want the police to call you.

A.   I bought a number of phones and mobile chips.

Q.   Yes, you bought mobile phones to commit drug offences.

A.   I didn't know whether I was coming or going. I bought the phone due to a change of handlers and to commit drug offences and pass on the information.

Q.   Please turn to page 342. You told the police that you would not commit armed robbery for Mr Wendall. You say also that you could find him contacts to sell drugs for him, the drugs that Macitto got nicked for. We are talking about 1 kilo of amphetamine. Did you have any knowledge that the police had an operation on you for six months?

A.   No.

Q.   Were you running drugs about for the first six months of last year?

A.   Yes, I have admitted those offences.

Q.   So you bought mobile telephones to commit crimes with?

A.   Yes, I have admitted all those crimes.

Q.   Including a source of an Uzi submachine gun with a little under 400 rounds of ammunition. That is why you are respected because you are a fixer, aren't you?

A.   No.

Q.   Where you not worried that the police were watching you?

A.   No.

Q.   If I were being watched I would not go and get an Uzi submachine gun. I would want to use someone else, like Mr Diamond?

A.   No.

The court was adjourned for the dinner break.

After lunch the court resumed and Mr David Gallant QC said he had no further questions for Snakeshaft.

PROSECUTION RE-EXAMINATION OF SNAKESHAFT

Following a request from the defence the Crown handed copies of pages 276 and 277 of the debrief notes to the jury to place in their folder. These documents referred to Snakeshaft saying that the blue bag was opened in his presence at Elvis's flat and he saw the machine gun and it was dismantled. Then somehow between looking at the weapon in Elvis's flat and getting the gun to his home address there was a yellow towel wrapped around it and Snakeshaft himself admitted that he had worn 'gardening gloves' in case he had to touch the gun. The inference is why would Snakeshaft want to wrap the gun in a towel? It's obvious he did not want me to see what was in the bag when he planted it in my vehicle! The prosecution also introduced a street plan of the area near Snakeshaft's home address.

Q.	Is 205 Barren Drive your home address?
A.	Yes.
Q.	Can you remember where the BMW was parked in St Nicholas Road?
A.	Yes. I am not sure where Wendall's Vauxhall Vectra was parked.
Q.	Would Wendall have visited the Eastside Gym?
A.	Yes.
Q.	Did Wendall meet Rob at the gym?
A.	No.
Q.	Why is that?
A.	Because he did not want to be known.
Q.	Known from people involved in criminal activity?
A.	Yes, because he was released from a 35-year prison sentence last year.
Q.	Is he the sort of person you say no to?
A.	You would not say no to him. If he asked me to do something or get him something I would get it.
Q.	Are there ranks in the criminal world?
A.	Yes.
Q.	What is a collector?
A.	A collector means someone collecting something or collecting money. Knowles was a debt collector. He has a reputation as a dangerous man.
Q.	Do you remember being asked by Mr Gallant about Mr Knowles asking you to go to the Magistrate's Court to stand surety for Mr Formby? How did Mr Knowles ask you? Did he ask you politely or in a threatening way?
A.	He asked me in a threatening way.
Q.	How would you class yourself in the criminal world?
A.	I am a runabout, gopher or patsy. I would not have the clout to order Terry Diamond about. Mr Wendall held Mr Diamond in very high regard – on par with himself.
Q.	Did you tell Rob that Mr Wendall and Mr Diamond were not people to be messed about with?
A.	Yes. I never actually mentioned their names, I just said that these were people that you don't mess about with.
Q.	Did you have any need to look in the bag at Elvis' flat?
A.	No.

Q.   Referring to Book 112 and the debriefing process. Is it right there are some 600 odd pages of typed script re: Book 112?

A.   Yes, the meetings before the debrief process were reduced into 'Book 112'. I was debriefed everyday by DC Lawson and DC Hines except weekends.

Q.   Are there names that have been referred to that have been listed as numbers so the defence cannot refer to them?

A.   Yes.

Q.   Is it true, the debriefing took over four weeks and the interviews resulted in over 50 tapes.

A.   Yes.

Q.   What sort of tasks were you given as a patsy?

A.   I was told to sit down with people and to listen to what was going on in the vicinity?

Q.   How many police handlers did you have?

A.   At first I was only seeing two, then the rules were broken and I was seeing about six. I was worried because two of them were nicked for corruption at Wilford Police Station and it unnerved me.

Judge: Your reason for getting the gun for Wendall and Diamond was to get Knowles off your back?

A.   Yes.

Q.   Did you speak to Wendall about it?

A.   No.

End of re-examination of Snakeshaft. Witness excused.
The jury was asked to wait outside for the moment.

Judge: Mr Snakeshaft was authorized as an informant on the 19th January 2001?

Crown: Yes.

Judge: And he was cancelled on the 30th May and de-registered on the 15th June 2001? You may need to put that in evidence.

Crown: It will be coming in as an agreed admission.

Judge: It also needs explaining the difference between being cancelled and de-registered informer.

The jury were called back into court.

After looking at the notes I compiled in the holding cells below the court, I summarized the day's evidence as follows:

Knowles was involved in two disputes and had a need for firepower. He had a dispute with Robert Henderson and Billy Milton over cigarettes and another dispute over 800 kilos of cannabis going missing with Jimmy Carrant. The issue was raised by counsel that there was a gang war going on and the Uzi was sourced for gang warfare and not Mr Diamond!

Mr Gallant QC explored the complicated issue of the 38s. More specifically, who asked for them? Snakeshaft claimed he asked Rob the Porpoise for them at conflicting times and in the original debriefing notes that I asked him for them and he was petrified of me. Later in evidence, Snakeshaft told the jury that I never asked for them. The inference is that not only does Snakeshaft lie about the 38s, but also he embellished the lie with the added caveat that he was petrified of me when he was asked for them? Snakeshaft admitted that he got it wrong!

An important point was how it was alleged that I gave £2500 to Snakeshaft for the gun at the car? In the debriefing notes Snakeshaft claimed that I gave him the money inside the car when he placed the blue bag in my vehicle. Later he told the jury that he walked around to the driver's side of the car where I got out of the car and passed him the money. Again he claimed he could remember it as I had difficulty getting out of the car with my leg impediment. This is contrary to evidence given by the police observation team who stated Snakeshaft did not go anywhere near the driver's side of my vehicle and nor was there any money exchanged at the scene. Why was Snakeshaft lying so blatantly? It's because his head was so fucked up with all the information the police had pumped into him that he could not remember what he said or when he said it and under intense cross-examination his pitiable façade of witness respectability was beginning to crumble for all to see.

Another significant issue focussed upon the two mobile phones that Snakeshaft possessed. One was for legitimate work and the other for criminality and contacting his many police handlers. Snakeshaft described himself as a run-around, a gopher and patsy. He claimed he was not in the big league and yet according to police intelligence reports he was the major subject in a police operation that focussed upon the large importation of class A drugs. The police could not have it all ways, the image the police were trying to portray of Snakeshaft as a mere 'gopher' was at variance with intelligence reports and the fact that he was able to go and source, locate and deliver an Uzi submachine gun, nearly 400 rounds of ammunition and all its accessories. The overarching question that perturbed me was where did this monstrous weapon actually come from?

Another network of lies revolved around the issue of who exactly removed the mobile phone chip from Snakeshaft's phone after my arrest? In the pre-debriefing Book 112, Snakeshaft claimed he took the chip out and destroyed it. In the debrief notes Snakeshaft claimed Wendall took the phone chip out and destroyed it and also later in the debrief notes that I took the chip out and destroyed it. The chip was allegedly destroyed sometime between 2 and 3 pm on the day after my arrest. This is all poppycock because when I took possession of Snakeshaft's home landline itemized telephone billing, the landline contacts Snakeshaft's mobile phone at 16:32 for 1 unit and again at 16:56 for 3 units. So how could Snakeshaft's mobile phone chip still be operational up to two hours after he said it was destroyed. I did point this important point out to leading counsel. He dismissed it as we would have to call representatives from the telephone companies to verify the point. Personally, I felt that it was a very good point as it yet again proved that Snakeshaft was an unmitigated liar who was hiding the truth at every turn in the case.

Snakeshaft did admit, however, to knowing the Cambridge area but only through following West Ham United football team to away matches. Other than that he had not been to the Cambridge area. Again this was proved to be inaccurate as Snakeshaft had been to Royston, which is south of Cambridge where he had contacts in the cannabis smuggling trade.

The QC also explored the distance and time frame involved in Snakeshaft travelling to and from Islington to collect the Uzi from Rob the Porpoise and his business partner Elvis. Snakeshaft admitted that he collected the firearm sometime between 8 and 10 am and did not get to his house until 12:30 pm, some two and half hours later. Snakeshaft could not recall the route he took or how he got back to his home. Despite going against the rush hour traffic he said there was a lot of traffic and he could not recall the route that he took. This is a pathetic excuse, which I believe did not endear him to the jury as he had been pre-programmed not to try and explain this part of his story. The truth is, in my opinion, corrupt police officers supplied the firearm to Snakeshaft and they gave it to him between 12:05 and 12:30 pm on the day of my arrest.

Taken altogether the QC had cornered Snakeshaft on numerous occasions and tried to get him to admit that he was lying, but Snakeshaft had been well groomed over the months he had been in police protective custody whereupon he would only repeat his answers in a set manner. This was to Snakeshaft's detriment, however, as it only made him appear even more foolish and conniving. More damagingly, Snakeshaft would not take responsibility for any of his actions preferring to lay the blame at someone else's door. Nothing was ever his fault. He always did things because he was forced to do them by someone else. By now the jury realized, I felt, that they were dealing with a pathological liar who would say anything that paymasters ordered him to. In short, Snakeshaft was a police puppet, a thoroughly dangerous man that had to be stopped.

THE CROWN CALLS DC CURTIS

Basically this detective's evidence went as follows: he claimed that he was on observation duties on the 5th June 2001 as part of a police operation called 'Salieri', the main focus of which was subject one called Daniel Snakeshaft. He was keeping observation outside Snakeshaft's house when at 12:31 pm he saw Snakeshaft pull up on his driveway and enter his house. He then saw two white males enter the house at 12:33 pm. The two white males left the house at 12:36 pm and walked back the way they had come from. Snakeshaft left his house at 12:37 pm "carrying a blue bag over his shoulder and the bag appeared to be weighty." Under cross-examination this witness stated that he did not see Snakeshaft take anything inside his house when he pulled up on his driveway. He claimed, "As far as I am aware I did not see him carrying a bag into the house."

Q.   It was not the sort of bag you could not see if he was carrying it?

A.   I disagree, it depends on how he was carrying it. Snakeshaft may have been carrying it down by his side.

DC Curtis agreed that the two white males were inside Snakeshaft's house for only 3 minutes and also claimed he knew who Wendall was on that occasion. The witness was then asked to refer to his statement.

Q.   You have not put in your statement the name of the person you saw on that occasion, Mr Wendall? How would anybody know

240

who that person was if you do not name him, it could be anybody?

A.   It is up to my discretion whether or not I put the person's name in the statement. There are no rules to say that I have to put Wendall's name in the statement. Like I said it is my discretion.

Q.   How long have you been watching Mr Snakeshaft?

A.   3 months.

Q.   Why was he being watched?

A.   For drugs.

Q.   What type of drugs?

A.   Class A and B drugs. The operation focussed upon the supply, importation and distribution of drugs.

Q.   What type of quantity?

A.   Multi-kilo dealing.

RE-EXAMINATION BY THE PROSECUTION

The witness added that Snakeshaft was the main subject under observation that day and because he was the focus of the operation it did not mean the subject held any particular rank or place in the hierarchy of the operation. Mr Wendall was not a subject. It did not mean the main subject was a Mr Big. It just meant he was the number one target on that day of the operation.

To summarize this detective's evidence we learned that he did not see Snakeshaft carrying a bag inside his house and despite this being a major observation it was up to him whether or not he inserted the name of a so-called top London villain in his statement. Why would he not want to put Wendall's name in the statement? It is because, at the time this police officer composed his statement, it had not been decided what they were going to do about the Wendall imbroglio. As an informant they wanted to save him and the only way to do that was to leave his name out of the paperwork. Otherwise, when the paperwork was served upon me in prison and if Wendall's name had been in it, I could have said to people, "How come his name is blazoned all over these statements and he was not arrested, charged and remanded in custody with me right now?" It was a pathetic scenario, an elite police surveillance squad watched a top London villain take part in the supply of a lethal firearm and let him and his accomplice walk away from the alleged transaction and then consciously refrained from putting his name in official statements. And more than that they did not officially charge him with any offence until five months later?

More interestingly, the prosecution is trying to portray Snakeshaft as nothing more than a gopher or patsy and yet this detective proclaimed that Snakeshaft was part of a major police surveillance operation into multi-kilo drug supply, importation and distribution. The prosecution was asking the jury to swallow this nonsense. It was obvious by now to the jury that Snakeshaft was a fixer, a puppet for the police, who had recruited Wendall as a partner in exchange for 5 years parole and they had set about framing criminal friends and associates. But this time it had gone disastrously wrong and the police were trying to salvage the situation and save Wendall from the hall of shame and infamy.

THE CROWN CALL PC BISHOP

This police officer was also on observation duties on the 5th June 2002. He supported everything said by DC Curtis but also covered events which occurred at the BMW in Eyhurst Close. He claimed that he saw me and Wendall talking at the rear of the BMW. Diamond was standing by the open boot and Wendall was on the footpath. When Snakeshaft came down the road with the blue bag, I went to the driver's side of the vehicle and Snakeshaft placed the bag in the front passenger side of the vehicle. He saw Snakeshaft tap on the roof of the BMW and then it was driven away.

Under cross-examination this witness claimed he had been on observations regarding Snakeshaft before and although he had seen Mr Wendall before he did not know him by name. Asked why he did not insert Wendall's name in his statement he said because he may have not known his name at the time of the offence. He said he had a reasonable view of the BMW and he did not see Snakeshaft go to the driver's door of the vehicle at anytime nor did he see me give Snakeshaft a pouch or see Snakeshaft put the pouch in his back pocket. The witness was excused.

Once again this revealed serious inconsistencies in Snakeshaft's evidence. Snakeshaft stated in his evidence that I gave him £2500 in a pouch at the driver's side of the BMW? This could not have happened! Why would Snakeshaft need to blatantly lie over this issue? I am the one arrested with the £500 he gave to me in my pocket and Snakeshaft disappears with the £2500 that I am alleged to have given him. All utter nonsense!

THE CROWN CALLS PC PEIRCE

This police officer was part of the SO11 observation team on the 5th June 2002. He claimed that he was driving an unmarked police vehicle and followed the BMW continuously for three miles from Eyhurst Close to where it was finally stopped and the occupant was arrested. There was no serious cross-examination of this witness and he was excused.

THE CROWN CALLS PC DALY

This police officer was in an armed response vehicle codenamed Trojan 251 with PC Morley and PC George. He stated that he moved off from Bornchurch Police Station and took up position at the rendezvous point near Snakeshaft's address. He followed a W-registration BMW and was part of an authorized non-compliant stop of the BMW at the traffic lights at the junction of Whalebone Lane South and Wood Lane, Dagenham, Essex.

He claimed he was an armed officer with live ammunition and he shouted at the driver of the BMW to get out of the vehicle who complied with his instructions. He was asked to look at photograph 4 in the police bundle and confirmed it was the blue bag that he saw in the vehicle. After Diamond was arrested he went back to Havering Police Station for the debriefing.

Under cross-examination he confirmed that at 12:37 pm Trojan 251 received a briefing from PS Gladstone in the control ARV "to follow any person or vehicle away from the address and stop them."

Q.   Who followed the silver Vauxhall Vectra? (Wendall's vehicle).
A.   I received no news of a Vauxhall Vectra.

Again we learned that the ARVs were instructed to follow and stop any person or vehicles away from Snakeshaft's premises and this officer stated that he was not aware of any other vehicle. The defence were refused the opportunity to look at this officer's notebook as it was claimed that it had sensitive material in it. No doubt this referred to the initial briefing at 12 pm and the subsequent radio messages outlining the stage-by-stage progress of the set-up.

THE CROWN CALLS DC COLE

This police office was the arresting officer in both the Macitto amphetamine case and the Uzi case. He was one of a number of officers linked to the Cranham Crime Squad that took over the arrest once I had been stopped by the SO19, the armed response police. This police officer was taken through his original statement and the defence did not seek to disprove his evidence because the conversation with DC Cole on arrest at the BMW supported my case that I had just picked up the bag for someone and that I did not know conclusively what was inside the bag. What is interesting to note, however, is the number of police squads used in this investigation. There were police officers from SO11 the surveillance branch of New Dockland Yard, the firearms unit from SO19, the Flying or Robbery Squad from SO7 and also up to six police officers from the Cranham Crime Squad. This was quite a formidable array of law enforcement officers and it was obvious that someone was guiding them with their finger on the pulse of the set up.

THE CROWN CALLS DC ANDY LARK

This police officer was also present at the scene of my arrest. Once I had been handcuffed and gone through the pantomime of "what have we got in the bag" at the BMW, he escorted me to a police vehicle with other officers and searched my pockets. From my pockets he retrieved a black wallet and a quantity of money. He accepted that there was £500 in used £20 notes and £230 consisting of one £50 note and eighteen £10 notes. He agreed that these were placed in separate bags at the police station on the advice of the desk sergeant for evidential reasons. There was no serious challenge to his evidence as once again it supported my account of events on that day.

THE CROWN CALLS DC CHRIS LOGAN

This police officer was involved in the search of the blue bag found in the passenger foot well of my vehicle. He stated that as he carefully opened the bag he could see a cream-coloured towel at the top of the bag and that he had to pull the towel away before he could see the handle of a gun and its trigger. Later back at Bornchurch Police Station he listed all the items found in the bag and also a map of Cambridgeshire found in the glove compartment, a mobile phone attributed to me and a slip of paper found in the centre console with a phone number written on it, which was later attributed to the confirmed police informer Snakeshaft.

Under cross-examination, this officer agreed that no photographs were taken by the scene of crime officer at the scene of the arrest. Also when there were photographs taken of the bag and its contents at the police station there were none taken of the gun wrapped in the cream-coloured towel. The witness was excused.

DAY SEVEN OF THE TRIAL

Before the commencement of proceedings, counsel for the defence asked for time to go through the interviews with the prosecution to edit any detrimental material because the Crown had prepared their case with Wendall as a co-defendant and it would be damaging to the defendant. The Judge replied that he was not prepared to allow any more time than a 10-minute adjournment, as "this case is very straightforward." Amazingly this was the first time that anybody had said that this was a "straightforward case". As I had been in prison custody for nearly year while the real perpetrators of the crime had been conspiring big time how to fuck me, it had been anything but a straightforward case.

THE CROWN CALLS DETECTIVE INSPECTOR GARY FISHER

This Detective Inspector was attached to the Criminal Intelligence Branch at New Dockland Yard, also known as Special Operations 11. His role was to gather and disseminate intelligence. He stated that he arrived at Bornchurch Police Station at 11:10 am on the 5th June 2001 in the company of Chief Superintendent Linley. There he met other officers from different areas of the Metropole Police Force. He stated that he was part of a briefing process at that time. It was to be an armed operation. Later he was part of the operation at Snakeshaft's home address where Mr Wendall and Mr Diamond walked in and out of Snakeshaft's house. Soon afterwards an Uzi submachine gun was recovered from Mr Diamond's BMW car.

DI Fisher explained that on the 19th January 2001 Snakeshaft was registered as a police informant. On the 30th May 2001 (six days before my arrest) it was cancelled. And on the 15th June 2001 (nine days after my arrest) Snakeshaft was de-registered as an informant.

Judge: Does cancelled mean that you no longer work for the police.

A.   Yes, Mr Snakeshaft was informed that he was cancelled and he signed a form to say that he had been cancelled as an informant.

(This was all nonsense as we were already aware that on Tuesday 6th June, the day after my arrest, Snakeshaft was still phoning his handler asking what a man called Terry Diamond was saying in the police station because he was fearful that his cover might be exposed at a later court hearing? Remember Snakeshaft had knowledge of this scenario as he did the same thing in the Brooms cannabis case and named an informer to get the case chucked.)

CROSS-EXAMINATION BY DEFENCE COUNSEL

This officer stated that he was not present when Snakeshaft signed his cancellation. He only became aware that Snakeshaft was an informant on the 19th February 2001. The decision to cancel Snakeshaft's informant status was not taken by this officer. He claimed Snakeshaft was subject to scrutiny by the Criminal Investigation Branch as he was suspected to be involved in the supply of drugs. Snakeshaft was registered as an informant with Serious Crime Group East, SO1. The information that he was giving regarding drugs was not passed onto his department. "We have a flagging system in the Met. Snakeshaft was flagged to our department. SO1 would not have known that he was flagged by us. I do not know what information Snakeshaft was passing onto the police. The SO11 operation, our operation was called 'Operation Salieri'. We would be unaware of what information Snakeshaft was supplying to the police. There is nothing on computer on the 30th May 2001 to say that Snakeshaft had been cancelled as an informant. The use of police sources is a secretive issue. I have not seen any records, which told us why Snakeshaft was being cancelled as an informant."

The witness was then asked to look at a bundle of relevant observation logs and police intelligence reports. The witness stated that Operation Salieri began on the 12th September 2000. Snakeshaft became a suspect on 30th January 2001. The witness was asked to look at page 162. The witness agreed that the police intelligence report made reference to heroin, but added that throughout the investigation Snakeshaft was not concerned with heroin.

Another report stated that it was believed Snakeshaft was working for a man called Terry Broom. It alluded to an arrest for cannabis with Mr Broom two years ago.

Q. Did Mr Snakeshaft have access to a lock-up garage in Anchor Hope Lane SE10?

A. It was on record, but no lock-up was ever found.

There were a large number of operations carried out in relation to Operation Salieri and Snakeshaft had become one of many targets for that. There was a series of observations, approximately 22 over a five-month period. A number of observations started at Snakeshaft's address. On the 14th May 2001, police began observations on Snakeshaft's address and later two men called Macitto and Roberts were arrested for a quantity of amphetamine. The observations were of Snakeshaft delivering drugs to Macitto. Macitto drove to meet Roberts and they were both arrested. Mr Snakeshaft was not arrested that day. There were observations of a man driving a silver Vauxhall Vectra on that day (Wendall's vehicle). I don't know if the package was on its way back to Snakeshaft. I cannot comment on that, as I do not have the paperwork on that! I was aware that Snakeshaft was reporting to the local police station. The decision was made to keep Operation Salieri going. Mr Snakeshaft was a small part of the operation. Snakeshaft's behaviour on that day was in respect of low-level amphetamine. The decision was to wait and see if Mr Snakeshaft was involved in something more serious. I did not check to see if Snakeshaft gave this information to his handlers.

Q. On page 636, on the 16th May 2001, intelligence suggested that Snakeshaft was part of a group called The G Bar?

A. Yes, that matter was being investigated.

Q. The connections of persons connected with Operation Salieri were nothing to do with the supply of low-level amphetamine? Had officers overheard this group of men discussing drugs in the G-Bar?

A. Yes, number 32 refers to a person. Telephone analysis shows that person 32 and 78 are active and there is established telephone contact between 32 and 78 and Snakeshaft. The investigation was to discover whether Snakeshaft was working for this particular group of people.

Q. Page 639 – Danny Snakeshaft and Tony Formby have contacted the following ...?

A.   Yes, Mr Snakeshaft is a close associate of Tony Formby. They were in contact by phone. This is only information. It is a hypothesis that the police put together to try and establish a pattern of contact.

Q.   Did Tony Formby have a nickname of David Dixon?

A.   Yes!

Q.   Please turn to page 699. Mr Formby, amongst other things, has previous on at least three occasions for armed robbery? Mr Formby carries a firearm at all times? Sarah Bolton was arrested for possession of a firearm provided by Formby. When this police intelligence report was written on the 5th April last year, was Robert Knowles a target in your operation?

A.   I don't believe I should answer that, your Honour!

The jury were asked to leave the court to discuss a legal point. It was then stated that Robert Knowles was not a target of Operation Salieri and the jury were notified of this fact. So why DI Fisher would not answer the question in the first place is baffling. There was no value in him not answering the question straight away because if he was not a target then it was no big deal. The delaying tactics in answering the question spoke volumes. Was Knowles a target in Operation Salieri? If he was it meant that Snakeshaft was giving information to the police about him also, as he had already made several contact sheets referring to Knowles. To agree that Knowles was a target in the operation would have been seen as a fundamental weakness in the prosecution case, as it would have meant, as I believed, that Snakeshaft was an integral part of Operation Salieri and it would further show the observations of Snakeshaft were merely a smokescreen to conceal the fact that he was working in tandem with SO11.

Q.   Please turn to page 617. It states that a silver Mercedes pulls up outside Snakeshaft's address and the occupants are one male and one female. Was that vehicle followed?

A.   No!

Q.   The vehicle returned at 17:16 pm and it is believed the journey was with numbers ?? and ?? to see another target to view the stuff? What is the stuff? (The numbers were deleted).

A.   The commodity would be indeterminable.

Q.   Why would a mere runner need to view the stuff?

A. This is the entry of the criminal intelligence department I do not know the answer your Honour!

Q. From the investigation over the months there is nothing in the debrief which does not correspond to the material we have against Mr Snakeshaft?

A. We were monitoring him for six months. From January 2001 until his arrest on 6th June 2001.

Q. But none of the enquiries lead anywhere? Are you in charge of Operation Salieri?

A. Yes. Snakeshaft was investigated to see whether he was connected with this organization.

Q. All you saw was on the 14th May 2001 was a low-grade amphetamine matter and then the arrest in the firearms matter? Can you tell us what the stuff was?

A. No!

Q. On the 4th June (the day before Diamond's arrest) observations were carried out on Snakeshaft?

A. Yes, he was followed to the Isle of Dogs.

Q. Did he go to an address in Bing Street?

A. Yes.

Q. Did he then go to a car park and meet someone driving a black Ford Escort and leave 'empty-handed'?

A. Yes, the officer made an entry that he was not carrying anything. Criminal intelligence was important to know whether he had anything with him. The log states that he came out of the vehicle 'empty-handed'!

Q. The log states that Snakeshaft then goes to Carpenters Road, E15?

A. Yes, the surveillance terminated after that at 8:40 pm.

(It is interesting to note that Wendall phoned me by mobile phone at 9:36 pm on the same evening and stated that Snakeshaft could not do the drop that night as there were too many Old Bill about – not that he could not acquire the parcel!)

Q. Were you in anticipation that something was going to happen that day when Mr Snakeshaft had got into the black Ford Escort?

A. Intelligence indicates that something was to happen that day!

Q.   The intelligence did not specify as to the time or place?

A.   A firearm was the subject of the intelligence, your Honour.

(At last the police are admitting that they have access to constant information about the firearm and the people involved.)

Q.   Did the police arrive at Snakeshaft's address the next day at 11:00 am?

A.   Yes.

Q.   Did the police have intelligence that day about a firearm?

A.   Yes.

Q.   Was Snakeshaft the subject of observations prior to 11:00 am that day?

A.   No.

Q.   What was the number of armed police officers called on that day to assist?

A.   There were three Armed Response Vehicles – Trojan vehicles – with maybe two or three armed officers in each vehicle.

Q.   Was there a dog carrier there as well?

A.   Yes.

Q.   In terms of your squad how many police vehicles were available at Snakeshaft's address?

A.   There were five officers in three unmarked police vehicles.

Q.   When Mr Diamond drives off, Mr Snakeshaft walks to a silver Vauxhall Vectra motorcar?

A.   Yes.

Q.   Do you know if a vehicle check was done on that motorcar?

A.   I don't know, your Honour!

Q.   Was a check done later?

A.   Yes, it was registered to a Mr John Wendall.

The court was adjourned for lunch – always when we get close to the juicy bits.

Q.   Have you ever been a handler of Mr Snakeshaft?

A.   No.

DI Fisher then added, "I was personally at Bornchurch Police Station on 5th June 2001 and also present while the operation was going ahead. I was made aware that Mr Diamond had driven off in a BMW. I was not made aware at the time that Snakeshaft had driven off in a silver Vauxhall Vectra. Our priority was to follow the bag and the recovery of the weapon. I am not aware that anyone followed Snakeshaft."

Q.   Why did not someone follow Snakeshaft and Wendall?

A.   Because we did not have the resources.

Q.   Why not arrest him after you had arrested Diamond?

A.   It was my decision to arrest him the next day, as we knew where he lived.

Q.   Did you consider that he might do a runner?

A.   We did, but we had been watching him for many months and we knew his habits. My decision was based upon facts that we did not have the resources that day.

Q.   Did you not have the resources after Diamond's arrest at one o'clock?

A.   My resources were involved in making sure the evidence was being secured properly. The procedures take many hours to sort out and come into place after the arrest.

Q.   When was Snakeshaft arrested?

A.   Snakeshaft was arrested the following day at his home address.

Q.   What about the address the Vauxhall Vectra was registered too, did you try there first?

A.   No, it is not always linked to where the person lives. Wendall was subsequently arrested your Honour.

RE-EXAMINATION BY THE PROSECUTION

The witness was asked to explain the meaning of 'flagging' to the jury. He said that varying levels of authorization have access to a flagged person. "I did not initially know that Snakeshaft was an informant. I would agree that there is a culture of secrecy between our department and the informants department and about Mr Snakeshaft. I did not tell SO1 Serious Crime Group East that I knew Snakeshaft was an informant. The reason for this is because I did not want the Serious Crime Group East to know what our investigation was about. I saw Snakeshaft as a low-level suspect and possibly able to penetrate a bigger organization. The umbrella of the Salieri Operation was largely about drugs but it also dealt with firearms."

Q.   When a man like Snakeshaft is registered as an informant is he given some terms and conditions?

A.   That is correct, it an agreement which he has to sign. It is a contractual agreement.

Q.   Are there aspects where he may be given a minor criminal role, which is authorized to further the matter under the investigation?

A.   Yes, some police informers are given permission to use 'verbal enthusiasm' to encourage a crime and this has to be authorized by a Commander of the Police.

Q.   Is it to give informants protection from arrest?

A.   Yes, Snakeshaft was authorized to use 'verbal enthusiasm'.

Q.   Was he authorized at the level of, for example, participating in the organizing of this firearm?

A.   He was not authorized to go higher than using 'verbal enthusiasm'.

Q.   If a person goes higher than the level which he has been authorized as an informant, the informant can be brought before a court and prosecuted.

A.   Yes.

The witness was then asked to turn to page 456/457 dated 14th May 2001. This was the day of the Snakeshaft, Macitto and Roberts drug transaction. It stated that at between 10 and 12 o'clock Snakeshaft was observed at a premises called Sleek Fitness. The Vauxhall Vectra was registered to Mr Wendall, the white Ford Escort to Snakeshaft and a Volkswagen Golf to Macitto. Mr Snakeshaft was interviewed and charged for this offence on the 23rd July 2001.

Q.   Turn to page 617. The car that Mr Snakeshaft got into was an S registration Mercedes. There was nothing more to suggest that he was merely showing them the way?

Counsel for the defence objects!
I am afraid that is misleading! Unless my learned friend can confirm the reason for the entry in the observation log for that statement then it is misleading.

Q.   Why did you not arrest Wendall and Snakeshaft directly after you arrested Diamond?

A.   There are a number of things that have to be done throughout the day after an arrest. There is a lot of paperwork that needs to be completed.

RE-CROSS EXAMINATION DEFENCE

Q.   How many people in numbers, apart from Macitto, Roberts, Diamond, Wendall and Snakeshaft, were arrested under the umbrella of the Salieri Operation?

A.   Two others.

Q.   Out of how many targets?

A.   Around ten.

Q.   The others have been arrested and charged?

A.   Yes, they have been convicted.

Judge: So seven suspects have been arrested and charged?

A.   Yes.

End of cross-examination. The witness was excused.

On a personal level, I noticed that this witness was very frustrating in providing direct answers. Similar to Snakeshaft's evidence, when we got near to an incisive or important question he would parry it away and claim that he was not aware of it or he was not in a position to answer the question. From a prosecution point of view, he was very good as a witness as he had obviously had lots of experience at giving evidence in a very formal manner while at the same time evading the dodgy questions.

What was very interesting, however, was the exposition of the contractual terms and conditions of being a registered police informant. I have always wondered why the police employed two informers to set me up and then when things went boss-eyed due to my 'prepared defence statement' they decided to arrest and charge – albeit belatedly in Wendall's case – the two police informers involved. After hearing Detective Inspector Fisher's evidence today it all fell into place.

It transpired that Wendall and Snakeshaft's contractual terms and conditions of being a police informer had only allowed them to use 'verbal enthusiasm' to encourage other criminal associates to commit crime, as seen when Wendall kept coming to my address on release from prison and asking me to commit a wide variety of crimes. We now learn that they had not been given '*participatory status*'. Therefore when the Flying Squad came in and took over the case, due to the 'cab rank' philosophy of policing, I was their man. They then looked at the evidence, and more especially the contractual terms and conditions of Wendall and Snakeshaft, and quickly realized, through either insidious encouragement from their senior police handler or the seemingly blasé and untouchable nature of their position, that they had transgressed the terms and conditions of their contract. That explains why the Flying Squad took their highest ranking police officer, Acting Detective Chief Inspector Baines round to Snakeshaft's house on the 6th June to arrest him.

When the Flying Squad took over the case they quickly realized that they were taking over a set-up and if they did not act on the basis of my 'prepared defence statement' and the police surveillance reports they were going to be made to look extremely foolish in court. Basically they had two options, give me police bail and send the paperwork off to the CPS for advice, or charge me and arrest Wendall and Snakeshaft as they had *de facto* committed a *bona fide* crime. They chose the latter because, if they had given me police bail, I already knew that I had been set-up and those responsible would have been ruthlessly exposed. So they decided to prosecute me and embark upon a damage limitation exercise.

What is even more interesting is the senior police controller or handler in this case. He must have known that he was asking Wendall and Snakeshaft to participate in a covert police operation that transgressed their authority to do so. This is where we have a combination of factors at work. In my opinion, we have the corrupt and depraved disposition of the senior police handler who was blinded by the prospect of gunning down or at the minimum arresting and imprisoning a top East London villain. We have the personal jealousy and resentment of Wendall who begrudged the fact that I made something of my life while he vegetated in prison and he held me responsible for that, as I had got him out of the prison van in 1984. And lastly, we had the perennial most toad-spotted traitor Snakeshaft who would betray anybody for personal gain and self-advancement. He was not content with his comfortable family lifestyle in Bornchurch. He wanted the wealth and status that his drug-dealing associates had, but inwardly he knew, deep in his heart, that he could never attain such rarefied heights as he was a wanker of the highest order. If it were essential, he would betray his own flesh.

THE CROWN CALL DS PETER HERBERT (FLYING SQUAD)

This witness agreed that he was the officer in charge of the case. He stated that he was called in after a tour of duty at 7 pm on the 5th June 2001 and had to go to Bornchurch Police Station with two other officers to take over the case.

This officer was taken through the previous convictions of Formby and Wendall. In Formby's case it was stated that he had previous for robbery for which he was sentenced to eight years imprisonment and the possession of two firearms for which he received a sentence of eight months imprisonment.

In Wendall's case the jury were agog at his antecedents which included armed robbery, escape from lawful custody, using a firearm to resist arrest, hijacking, kidnapping and wounding with intent. Then DS Herbert was taken through my police taped interviews, conducted the day after my arrest on the 6th June 2001. DS Herbert asked the questions while the prosecutor read out my replies. The interviews were too voluminous to retrace word for word here, save to state that I was unwilling to divulge the names or location of those involved in the set-up as I was dealing with dangerous villains and my life and that of my family were in danger. Basically I said that I would love to elaborate on matters but my family came first and it was my duty to protect them. Before this witness could conclude his evidence-in-chief we had run out of time and the court was adjourned until the next day.

DAY EIGHT OF THE TRIAL

The hearing continued where it left off yesterday. The reading of my police taped interview. Although I did not answer all questions put to me by DS Herbert I felt the interview came across well to the jury and they could sense that the only one telling the truth in this case was me. DS Herbert was excused.

Then there was a formal reading of witness statements rather than calling them to give evidence in person. The first statement to be read was that of DS Herbert's partner in the interviews, DC Noel of the Flying Squad. Much of this evidence was dealt with earlier by DS Herbert. Then we had a statement read by the police fingerprint expert, David Farrell, who carried out various fingerprint tests, the most significant for me was that there was no 'identifiable fingerprints' found on the firearm. Next to be read out was the statement of Michael Kemble the firearms expert who claimed that the weapon worked faultlessly and that it did indeed contravene the Firearm Act of 1968. There was also a statement by David Sturges, a DNA expert who claimed there was no DNA found on the weapon belonging to me. Taken altogether, despite Snakeshaft's evidence, which stated that Diamond assembled and dismantled the Uzi submachine gun without wearing any gloves, the prosecution had to concede that there was no DNA or fingerprint evidence linking me to the gun. Once again it proved Snakeshaft to be an unmitigated liar.

At the conclusion of the prosecution case, the jury were sent out and the prosecutor asked permission from the Judge to let the jury hear my previous convictions, the most serious convictions were for malicious wounding, two offences of armed robbery and escape from lawful custody. I strongly believed that this is where I would get rumped and the Judge would let my form out, but to my utter amazement, he declined the prosecutor's application as, up to yet, the defence had not accused the police of any wrong doing or malpractice. This was the brainchild of Mr Gallant QC who claimed that there was no point charging in like a bull in china shop and accusing the police of masterminding the set-up. It was much better, he said, to excavate and expose the facts of the case and leave it to the jury to make up their minds.

I must admit, I was a little apprehensive about this approach as if it all went boss-eyed it would be me who would be slowly rotting in the dungeons of Her Majesty's prisons for a decade or more. Inwardly, I was wondering if there had been a secret deal between the Judge and my counsel to the effect that 'Providing Diamond does not slander or accuse the police of malpractice I will not let the jury hear his previous convictions'. Admittedly this is only conjecture, but I did feel it was odd that my form was not exposed. On the other hand, however, if my form had been disclosed to the jury, I had nothing to lose in the witness box and I could go for the jugular, as it was quite obvious the police do not set-up seemingly straight people fresh off the street.

The basis of the set-up was I had been out of prison and more importantly out of trouble with the police for six long years. The police suspected me of committing a major armed robbery in the docklands area of South East London and that is why they recruited Wendall and his accomplice Snakeshaft to set me up. Whatever you may believe is true or not, the facts are that this is the motivation and reason for the set-up and if my form did come out I was going to open the flood gates to the omnipotent freedom of truth and honesty. For I believe lies cannot be sustained forever. By their very nature lies are destined to be exposed by the truth and no matter how many layers of misrepresentation are used to conceal the truth, it will come out eventually. I possessed an inner strength and faith that no matter whatever jury sat and heard my case and my evidence in court I could convince them about the set-up as when the truth stares people in the eyes they know it, feel it and can sense its compelling force. Wendall, Snakeshaft and their senior police controller – who was conveniently kept out of the case despite being in control at the scene of my arrest – could not live with me! I was a juggernaut of truth coming through a rain swept motorway of lies and depravity and they were not going to stop human decency and morality from reaching its god-given destination.

THE DEFENCE CALLS THE DEFENDANT TERENCE GEORGE MICHAEL DIAMOND

As anyone will tell you, for those who are not versed in giving evidence in a court of law, it is a very nerve-wracking and debilitating experience. As a former professional armed robber I have had my fair share of pre-robbery butterflies and nervousness, but once I am in gear and firing upon all cylinders I become the sweetest engine in existence. There is no denying I would much prefer to commit a robbery all day long than give evidence in a court of law in front of a jury, more especially when it is your own life on the line. The experience is terrifying but once again I had two weapons up my sleeve.

Firstly, during the last six days of the trial I had purposely allowed myself to become acclimatized to the courtroom ambiance and atmosphere and secondly, I had the grand master of truth on my side. It was my first opportunity to ask questions and to get some real answers. As is their wont in such cases, the police and the gangsters of language and dalliance at the CPS had unveiled as little information as possible throughout the build up to this case and now it was time to get some real answers in front of an all-seeing and all-knowing jury. But first I had to be taken through the evidence-in-chief by the defence counsel. This was a slow and tedious process where the Judge, junior prosecution counsel and defence clerks were scribbling down every syllable of speech and content.

Shortly before the Judge entered the courtroom and the jury were summoned to their positions, I looked up at my wife Stacey in the public gallery. I could see the stress and strain of the trial was getting to her as we had been in this position before. To comfort her I recalled the time, many years earlier, when I was going into an important Open University examination and my friend said to me, "No one has put more work into the course than you. This is your day so go in there (the examination room) and show off!" The same principles applied here too! No one knew the case better than me. This was my day and I was going to go for it. I looked up at my wife in the public gallery and whispered so that she could lip-read me, "It's our day today, you watch me go!"

I started my evidence by explaining all that has been written in the previous chapters. How Wendall had came home from prison in earlier April 2001 on parole and how I wanted to help him reintegrate back into normal society. I stated how I had given him some money, clothes and a vehicle and offered advice to him about how to handle the being dumped back into society with strangely no opportunity of resettlement.

I explained how after two weeks of being home Wendall came out with the absurd notion that he wanted to start robbing again and that I had said "No!" I explained about how he wanted me to commit an armed robbery with his friend – now a confirmed police informer – Danny Snakeshaft. And how when I refused this offer he asked me to acquire him a large consignment of cannabis resin, then acquire him a firearm because a black guy had allegedly fired two shots at his twenty-one year old son who had become embroiled in a dispute over a half-caste girl. The list went on and on, even to the extent how Wendall had lied to me about the reason why he changed his mobile telephone because of the Macitto amphetamine sulphate arrest. I explained how he kept coming to my family home with these absurd requests and how my wife Stacey and I had nicknamed him 'The Pest'!

I was then asked to explain how I had become involved in collecting and delivering the 'valuable printing presses' and how I was to become a part of a money counterfeiting operation. I was taken through my 'prepared defence statement' and asked to explain how Wendall and Snakeshaft had it all planned for me to collect the printing presses the day before my arrest and get nicked, but because of a prior commitment I could not accommodate their wishes. I explained the reasons for making several phone calls, my relationship with my friend in Cambridge, how I had been lured, steered and chaperoned to Snakeshaft's house by Wendall and how Snakeshaft had given me the £500 in used twenty pound notes in his house and insisted in bringing the parcel around to my vehicle without me checking it. Also, on placing the blue bag in my car I opened the drawstring to the bag and saw a yellow towel wrapped around what I believed to be the 'valuable printing presses'. This part of my evidence went quite smoothly as I was being taken through it very slowly and purposely by my counsel. Far from dreading the cross-examination from the prosecution I was eagerly awaiting it. I wanted get my teeth into some fast flowing questions as this was my golden opportunity to get at the truth of this putrescent affair and lance the boil of nastiness so that everyone could smell its all-pervading rottenness.

After my evidence-in-chief, the Judge adjourned the case until the following day so that the prosecution had time to absorb and analyse what I had said. Basically the central planks of the defence case were; firstly, that I trusted Wendall implicitly and that I had no reason to distrust him; secondly, that I had either been had-over, duped, conned, or even set-up by Wendall and Snakeshaft; thirdly, that I did not know what had gone on in this case and that I was hoping to get some answers during cross-examination and; lastly, because of my knowledge about the suspicious way in which Macitto had been arrested, I had tentatively checked the blue bag in my car to reassure myself that there were no drugs in the bag.

DAY NINE OF THE TRIAL

Since giving evidence the previous day I had been embroiled in an intense inner-conflict over which way to present my evidence today. I had been warned by counsel to stay away from the 'Wendall is a police informer issue' because we didn't need to prove that he was a state-registered informant. I was told that we had enough ammunition to undermine and discredit the prosecution case and that if I went down the Wendall-is-an-informer-road my previous convictions might come out and jeopardize the defence case. This may have been sound advice, but I felt that if I could corner the prosecutor without coming across as too tricky during my testimony I would go for it as it was my life and should the case be lost and I had not follow my instincts I would forever remain in purgatory as the dopiest person in criminal history.

So there it was, if the prosecutor opened the gates to the underlying truth I would not need a second invitation. I would go for it!

PROSECUTION CROSS-EXAMINATION OF THE DEFENDANT

Firstly, the prosecutor provided me with a copy of my 'prepared defence statement'. I agreed that it was my own statement and that it was composed by my solicitor who was acting on my behalf. I agreed that I knew it was an important document and that I had to explain events and that it may be used later such as it is now.

Q. Do you stand by what you said to the police officers during the interviews?

A. Yes.

Q. Did you have time alone with your solicitor to prepare your statement?

A. Yes.

Q. Is Mr Wendall about 50 years of age?

A. Yes.

Q. And how old are you?

A. I am 43 at the moment.

Q. How long have you known Mr Wendall?

A. I have known Mr Wendall since about 1980, maybe a bit before that!

Q. To a certain degree, did a close relationship develop between you two?

A. Yes, I knew him very well.

Q. Did you know about his past?

A. Yes.

Q. When he came out of prison and he kept coming to your house, you say that you were like a therapist to him, is that correct?

A. Yes.

Q. When he came out he asked you to take part in an armed robbery, is that correct?

A. Yes.

Q. You knew him to be a professional armed robber?

A. Yes.

Q. A top villain?

A. Yes. He came out of prison and asked me to commit an armed robbery and I told him that I am not robbing nor are you!

Q. Do you need a good team to commit an armed robbery?

A. Yes.

Q. You need people in that team who you can trust?

A. Yes.

Q. You need people who can hold their head?

A. Yes that is correct, but when he came up to me and asked me to commit an armed robbery, things did not add up with him. Here is a man who has just been released after spending seventeen years in prison and within two weeks of his release he is asking me to commit an armed robbery! It did not make sense.

Q. When you spoke to Wendall, when he came to your house, you spoke to him outside your house, is that correct?

A. Yes.

Q. Why?

A. I did not want to speak in front of my wife and children?

Q. Why not?

A. Because it would be better to speak to him outside my house.

Q. This could amount to talking about crime out of earshot of others?

A. Listen I do not profess to be an angel, but I did not talk about crime, it was Wendall who wanted to talk about crime and I did not want to discuss such things inside my house.

Q. How did Wendall initially come to your house?

A. I invited him to my house to help him be reintegrated back into society and to make sure he hadn't gone mad! When he came round to my house I soon realised that he was ancient and caught in a time warp and wanted me to commit armed robberies.

Q. Had you met Daniel Snakeshaft by then?

A. No!

Q. Did Wendall mention Snakeshaft's name about committing armed robberies?

A. Yes.

Q. Did you ask about Snakeshaft?

A. Yes I did, I said who is this fellow Snakeshaft? And Wendall said he is a good friend and that he is skint and he wants to commit an armed robbery with me!

Q.	Is there some form of hierarchy in the criminal world?
A.	Yes.
Q.	Do you know a Mr Knowles?
A.	No.
Q.	Do you know of him?
A.	Yes, by reputation.
Q.	Do some people do other people's work for them?
A.	Yes.

The jury were then asked to leave the court after an objection from defence counsel. Defence counsel objected to the insidious nature of the prosecutor's line of questioning, asking about the client's knowledge of the criminal underworld.

Judge: The prosecution is entitled to ask questions about Wendall.

The jury were brought back into court.

Q.	Do people do things for other people in the criminal world?
A.	Yes.
Q.	Are you familiar with the term of collector also known as a runner?
A.	Yes, a runner is someone who collects things!
Q.	What about the term patsy?
A.	The term patsy is vague to me.
Q.	I mean the term patsy in the rank of criminal work. You were trying to tell the jury that you were going to be a gopher in the delivery of the printing presses?
A.	No, not a gopher, once the counterfeit operation was up and going I was going to be a part of the enterprise. My initial role was to deliver the presses to the Midlands. Mr Wendall introduced me into the printing project because I was good to him when he was released from prison.
Q.	Why didn't Mr Wendall ask Mr Snakeshaft to deliver the printing presses?
A.	Because he wanted someone reliable and dependable, plus I had also given him the Vauxhall Vectra motor car.
Q.	How often did Snakeshaft's name come up in your conversations

with Wendall?

A. Quite frequently.

Q. How frequently.

A. Well I knew that they were close friends and after I received their mobile phone records I could see that they were phoning each other like lovers!

Q. Did you know Snakeshaft had been visiting Wendall while he was in prison?

A. I was not aware of it until Wendall came out of prison.

Q. I suggest that you know Snakeshaft more than you say?

A. I do not know him. I have only met him once before.

Defence Counsel:

Objection, in the evidence of Snakeshaft he stated that he only met Mr Diamond once at a football match.

Prosecution:

Point taken.

Q. You have spoken about printing pressing of counterfeit notes?

A. Yes, it was Mr Wendall's idea not mine.

Q. Did you know about the time scale in making this money?

A. No I did not, I was not there to ask questions I was there to make some money.

Q. Wendall's first request was for you to be involved in armed robbery?

A. Yes.

Q. Wendall's second request for cannabis?

A. Yes, he asked me if I could put him in touch with some people who could supply cannabis and I said no! We called Wendall "The Pest" because he kept asking requests of people. I did not want to get involved with Wendall in this issue, because if anything goes wrong, it will be my fault as I had vouched for Wendall. As far as I was concerned, I had given Wendall a car, clothes and some money and that was enough. I did not need to help him any further.

Q. Did Wendall tell you about his son Willy, that someone had shot at him?

A. Yes, he asked if I could get him a gun.

Q.   Why do you think he asked you to get him a gun?

A.   Most probably because he trusted me and that he had only recently come out of prison. During that time of my life everything was rosy and if Mr Wendall had not come home from prison when he did I would not be in this courtroom today.

Q.   I suggest that you were involved in collecting an Uzi that day and not printing presses as you say.

A.   No, that is not true. I was asked to collect and deliver the printing presses because I was trustworthy and reliable.

Q.   Did you know that Snakeshaft was involved in getting the printing presses to Essex?

A.   According to Wendall, yes!

Q.   And Mr Snakeshaft was to pay you?

A.   Yes, he paid me.

Q.   Why did he pay you and you hardly knew him?

A.   Mr Wendall and Mr Snakeshaft were very close. I did not know which one of them the money was coming from only that it was Mr Snakeshaft who gave me the money.

Q.   I suggest that you are lying and you really knew that you were to collect an Uzi firearm that day?

A.   I am not lying. I have been in prison custody for a year now, banged up for up to 23 hours a day. This has been a nightmare ordeal for my family and me. I wake up in the morning and this case is on my mind. The last thing at night before I go to sleep this case is on my mind. All I want is to get to the truth Mr Maskell, let's you and me work together and try to get at the truth, because even now I do not know exactly what has gone on in this case.

Q.   If you accept the truth that you knew about the Uzi then this will be all over for you?

A.   That is not the truth.

Q.   Well you are saying that you have been fitted-up, set-up Mr Diamond! That is correct isn't it?

(At this stage I was fearful that I might say the wrong thing and my previous convictions would be produced to the jury. I hesitated and soon realized that I could not avoid the question. I had to answer the question in an unequivocal and emphatic manner. This was the question

I had been waiting for and the door to the truth was beginning to open, I had to go for it and to use a firearm analogy I let him have with both barrels.)

A.   Yes, I have been set-up by both Wendall and Snakeshaft but I am not the only one who is saying it.

Q.   Well who else is saying it?

A.   The police are saying it as well. The Flying Squad put it to Wendall during one of his taped police interviews. They said, "I put it to you that you are the one who has set this up, you have set Terence Diamond up in cahoots with Daniel Snakeshaft, what have you to say about that? Wendall, no reply! Do you deny any knowledge of that? Wendall, no reply!" What is going on Mr Maskell? Even your own police officers are accusing Wendall and Snakeshaft of setting me up.

Q.   I have already told you that there are no participatory police informers in this case and I neither confirm or deny that Mr Wendall is a police informer.

A.   You have not told me that!

Q.   Well, I have told your counsel.

A.   Well, I have a theory about that!

Q.   Well, let's hear it Mr Diamond?

A.   Well, we have already heard from DI 'General' Fisher of SO11 in this courtroom that there exists a culture of secrecy in the Metropole Police Force where one squad does not know or tell what the other squad is doing or whether or not they are working with a police informer. I suggest that if I was a top policeman working with a top police squad, let us say for example The National Crime Squad, and someone like Wendall, who is a top London villain was a registered police informer, I would not want to tell anyone, not colleagues, people in the CPS and most of all not even you Mr Maskell. I would not even tell you! It would be hidden from everyone.

(As I said this I looked to the jury and I caught one or two of them nodding in agreement.) The prosecutor then decided to get off this thorny line of questioning as it was becoming very embarrassing.

Q.	So you thought the bag contained printing presses?
A.	Yes.
Q.	Snakeshaft has given evidence that you did know the bag contained an Uzi?
A.	I did not know what was in the bag that is why Snakeshaft wanted to put it inside my car himself!
Q.	We know that Snakeshaft brought the bag home to his house on the 5th June 2002.
A.	Yes, but Snakeshaft lied to me about the contents of the bag!
Q.	We know Snakeshaft knew the bag contained an Uzi?
A.	Yes.
Q.	We know that he had the Uzi inside his house?
A.	Yes.
Q.	We know that he took the Uzi out and put it in your car?
A.	Yes.
Q.	We also know that he didn't know he was being watched by the police. We also know that Snakeshaft was arrested for it. We know that Snakeshaft has pleaded guilty to his part and we also know that Snakeshaft was not being paid for this crime. So what benefit did he have to set you up?
A.	He is a stated registered police informer!
Q.	But he did not benefit from it?
A.	Yeah, because he has been caught out!
Q.	Mr Wendall must have known that there was an Uzi in the bag if he and Mr Snakeshaft were to set you up?
A.	That is correct as he wanted me to collect the printing presses the night before, but could not do it, so I contacted my friend Brian in Stratford and asked him to pick them up for me but this was unacceptable to Wendall as he could not make on-the-spot-decisions. It seemed like he had to consult with someone else first before making any decisions. As far as I was concerned he wanted me personally to collect them. Why does Wendall chaperone me to that house? Why don't the police arrest all three of us in the quiet suburban back street where there is no risk to the public and take us all down to the police station and ask us what is going on? I know we have been told that there are no participatory police informers in this case, but why does Wendall come with me to Snakeshaft's

house on the 5th June to where the gun is? I suggest he knew that he could not get nicked!

Q. Where was Mr Wendall situated inside Snakeshaft's house?

A. He stayed downstairs with me.

Q. So Wendall does not get away from the gun?

A. Yes.

Q. Mr Wendall is on the gun all the time. He is following the gun? I suggest that he wanted to distance himself from the gun because he was on licence wasn't he? What happens when Mr Wendall is arrested? Is he not charged with the offence of possessing an Uzi?

A. Yes.

Q. Then where is the benefit for him setting you up?

A. That is a good point. Why does it take the police five months to arrest Mr Wendall? Let's look at the facts. I am arrested on the 5th June 2001. Wendall and Snakeshaft are allowed to walk away from the scene of a serious crime despite the police watching knowing both their identities. Then on the 19th June 2001, two weeks later Wendall is placed on the Police National Computer as wanted. Wendall is out on four and half year's parole. As a condition of that parole, his Probation Officer has to know where he is living. Then on the 20th July 2001, Snakeshaft is taken out of Wentonville Prison for seven days by the police for a debrief. Two days later on the 22nd July, the elite Flying Squad who are renowned for kicking down doors and putting guns at their suspects' heads refine their tactics and decide to put a hand delivered letter through Wendall's door claiming, "Please can you contact us as we would like to speak to you about a serious matter!" What is going on Mr Maskell? Then two days later, on the 24th July, Wendall walks into Wilford Police Station where the police put to him that he set me up. Wendall is then given police bail on a monthly basis through August, September and October until November when he is finally re-arrested and charged. What is going on, as I was being penalized by the police and CPS inaction in this case?

Judge: Was it your impression that Mr Wendall wanted to keep his distance from criminality?

A.   Yes, he did not want to be hands on involving criminal products, but at the same time he was asking me to commit armed robberies that does not make sense.

At 11:50 am the court adjourned for a morning break. At 12:07 pm the court reconvened and the cross-examination continued.

Q.   So you were involved in delivering the printing presses for £500?
A.   Yes.
Q.   And you were to be involved in the scam later on as well?
A.   Yes.
Q.   Wendall could have asked someone else couldn't he?
A.   Yes.
Q.   He could have asked Mr Snakeshaft, because he went to South London to pick the printing presses up didn't he?
A.   Yes.
Q.   This is all a pack of lies?
A.   It is not a pack of lies.
Q.   Who paid you?
A.   Snakeshaft.
Q.   So Snakeshaft is a paymaster too? But not good enough to go to Cambridge rather than Wendall getting you to go?
A.   Must be.
Q.   It is a pack of lies?
A.   Is it, according to Mr Snakeshaft's evidence he is no good at reading road maps?
Q.   Have you heard of the Bermondsey job?
A.   Yes, it was an armed robbery committed in South East London. It was common knowledge about the robbery in South East London.
Q.   Tell me about the time you went to Snakeshaft's house?
A.   I went to Snakeshaft's house, Wendall knocked on the door. We exchanged some pleasantries and I asked for the money, the £500. Snakeshaft gave me the £500. I then said where is the parcel? Snakeshaft asked where I was parked. I said that I was parked in nearby St Nicholas Road, so he said you go to your car and I will bring the parcel around to your car.
Q.   Did you look in the bag?

A.   No.

Q.   So you took the bag on trust?

A.   Yes. If there is a patsy involved in this case, it is me!

Q.   What do you do for a living?

A.   I am a private car trader.

Q.   Do you pay tax?

A.   No.

Q.   Are you a registered company?

A.   No.

Q.   How did you pay for the black BMW that you were arrested in?

A.   I part exchanged a red BMW 750i and gave the dealer a cheque for £13,000. The £13,000 came from the sale of a previous BMW M3 that I sold for £25,500. I had the black BMW that I was arrested in sold to my friend Mr Black in Cambridge.

Q.   And what does he do for a living?

A.   He runs his own security company.

Q.   That is the person referred in the phone records as David Marson?

A.   Yes.

Q.   Why does he use a mobile phone that is registered in another person's name?

A.   I believe it may be a company phone as he is out and about all night long supervising his staff.

Q.   Mr Wendall did not ask you to take the printing presses to Cambridge did he?

A.   Yes he did, but we all know that I was never going to make it there.

Q.   Who were you told to meet?

A.   I had to meet someone called Alex.

Q.   Is there anyone that can support your belief that it was printing presses?

A.   Yes, my wife Stacey and the relative that came to my house while Wendall was there Danny Fearon.

Q.   I suggest that the prepared defence statement that you made is a pack of lies.

A.   No, it is the actual truth.

Q.   Then why didn't you elaborate on matters?

A.   My solicitor at the time told me that when you make a prepared statement you just put down the bare bones of the defence case. It was my idea to elaborate on matters, but my solicitor advised me to keep it short.

Q.   But you have not admitted in the statement to committing a criminal offence?

A.   I think that I covered all the areas in the prepared statement that I wanted to.

Q.   What happened when Snakeshaft placed the bag in your car?

A.   I leaned over the centre console and pulled the drawstring of the bag open a little bit and put my fingers inside. I felt some towelling like material and it was hard. I was making sure that it was not drugs.

Q.   Why do you say in your statement that you felt something metallic, which could actually mean that you felt the metal?

A.   I felt something hard through the towel and I was reassured that it was the printing presses. (I rapped my knuckled on the side of the witness stand as emphasis of the objects hardness) I thought it was the printing presses.

Q.   I suggest to you that this is all a pack of lies and that the reason you did not give your name to the police when you were first arrested is so that you had time to think up this story about the printing presses?

A.   That is not true, because as soon as I was arrested when I reached Bornchurch Police Station and the desk sergeant was counting my money, I told him that the 18 ten pound notes, £180, and the solitary £50 note was my money, and that the £500 in used £20 notes was the money that the man gave to me.

(Upon hearing this, the prosecutor complained to the Judge claiming that this was not mentioned during the evidence in chief. Defence counsel said that it was in his notes from the client but that it had been an oversight on his part. In short, this meant that I could not have been lying because as soon as I was arrested I was pointing the police to evidence that proved that I was telling the truth).

End of the prosecution's cross-examination.

RE-EXAMINATION OF THE DEFENDANT BY THE DEFENCE

Defence counsel provided me with several documents and asked me to explain exactly what they were. These were my annual subscription to the car trade's bible Glass's Guide, a receipt for a car advertisement in the Sunday Times, an Abbey National bank book that related to some of the aforementioned car transactions and lastly I was handed a copy of the police interview with Wendall where it is claimed that he set me up in cahoots with Snakeshaft. This was the *coup de grace* of my defence case as I was not the only one proclaiming that I had been set-up by these pernicious villains. All these documents were handed to the jury and made exhibits for their perusal during their deliberation of the evidence.

Before I was formally excused as a witness in the case the Judge asked me one last question.

Judge: The printing presses Wendall told you about were for counterfeit money. Did it cross you mind that you were involving yourself in crime?

A.   Yes.

Q.   Would you put making counterfeit money in the same league as robbery or being in possession of this firearm?

A.   No, it is not in the same league, nowhere near it.

End of re-examination.

The jury were asked to wait outside as the prosecution had a number of points to discuss with the Judge. The prosecutor asked that he might start his closing speech the following morning and that he wanted leave to call one witness as rebuttal evidence. This was to do with PC Lark who was present when I said "That's the money (£500) the man gave me" at the police station on arrest. The Judge granted both these requests. The court adjourned a 12:50 pm until 10:15 am the following morning.

Down in the bowels of the courthouse all the legal team came to see me. Both junior and leading counsel were cock-a-hoop at my evidence. They said that the prosecutor had done a poor job and had left the door open for me to elaborate on the theories of set-up and had let me ask questions in order to get at the truth. Apparently, the prosecution only intended to have me in the witness box for half-hour but I was in there from 10:30 am to 1 pm some two and half hours. Junior counsel said that it was one of the best 'performances' he had seen in the witness box, but on reflection we all agreed the term 'performance' was not the correct word to use as the evidence was from the heart and it was not an act. Later I spoke to members of my family who were in the public gallery and they agreed that everyone could tell that I was telling the truth. Mr Gallant QC proclaimed that if ever he needed another junior counsel he would like me. He said that once the Judge refused to let the jury hear my previous convictions the prosecution case lost all sense of direction. Credit for this supreme tactical manoeuvre must go to leading counsel who compelled me not to accuse the police of any corruption or wrongdoing as all the prosecution had to say "This is history repeating itself, Wendall and Diamond had got back together after a long absence and were preparing to commit robberies again!" Obviously this was not the case, but it was nonetheless a powerful argument and explanation.

During our discussions leading counsel summarized his thoughts about Snakeshaft by saying that Snakeshaft was not entirely stupid. He possessed a streetwise cunning. He was not that bright and indeed looked like a patsy. He added he could easily see how the previous jury fell for his lies with that effective hangdog expression he used in the courtroom, but really he was quite clever.

Despite being optimistic about the case after giving evidence I had an intuitive feeling that until the prosecution had started their closing speech anything could happen. What was worrying me was my solicitor had still not taken defence witness statements from my wife Stacey and her relatives who were present when Wendall came to my address and asked me to collect the printing presses the day before my arrest. He had the best part of six months to take these statements and in spite of continual reminders on the phone, in person and in writing he had still not carried out this elementary legal exercise. Why? Admittedly shortly before my evidence leading counsel said that he did not want to call any defence witnesses but nevertheless the defence team should have been prepared for any eventuality. This episode and other shortcomings that I have mentioned in this book left a bad taste in my mouth about my solicitor. Was he a good solicitor merely lacking in drive and gumption or were there more sinister motives behind this wilful incompetence? Given the level of power and corruption behind this bungled set-up I was forced to keep an open mind.

Finally, at 2:45 pm when I was been escorted by prison officers back to Cellmarsh Prison via its underground link or tunnel, I saw an old cellmate of mine being escorted himself from the legal rooms to his holding cell in another part of the building. Immediately my mind began to race – what was he doing here? I recalled that I initially shared a cell with this guy for three days while I was in Wentonville Prison. This was the only cellmate I ever had as I was transferred to Cellmarsh Prison soon after my arrest and was made a category A prisoner where I was housed in a single cell. As far as I was aware this prisoner was halfway through a four and half year prison sentence for a particularly vicious attack and robbery on a homosexual in his home. It was a distasteful crime and previous prison experience had taught me to be wary of such unknown characters and not talk about past or future crimes. Also as far as I was aware he had no further charges or court appearances to face so what was he doing here at Thamesmead Crown Court on the day that my evidence had concluded? I recalled earlier that morning when the prison van taking me from the HSU inside Cellmarsh Prison to the underground tunnel link, the radio controller told the escorting screws to hold me there for a while as other prisoners from the main prison were being taken through the underground link with the court.

Taken altogether, as is the case where the police want a conviction at all costs, they seek to strengthen their case with a cell confession to another prisoner who is in turn offered an alternative incentive such as early release to give evidence against the defendant. This is an old trick used by the police and despite its purpose and intent being transparent to those in the judiciary and the criminal fraternity it is still being used today and in the future to persuade gullible juries that the defendant is indeed guilty. I had no concrete evidence that this ex-cellmate was to give evidence in rebuttal against me that is why I have not named him, but on the balance of probabilities it looked highly likely that he had been primed to give evidence against me but the prosecution reconsidered its position in the light of my evidence.

DAY TEN OF THE TRIAL

The prosecution recalled PC Lark of Cranham Crime Squad as rebuttal evidence. PC Lark claimed that he did not hear me say to the desk sergeant at Bornchurch Police Station on arrest "and that's the money the man gave to me!" When cross-examined by the defence, PC Lark claimed that he was able to remember this event but not how long I was in the custody area of the police station. Mr Gallant QC sat back down in disgust and I believe the jury were having none of it either.

Then the prosecution made some submissions regarding the exhibits for the jury to have, namely police photographs, police plans, indictment and the Uzi itself.

THE PROSECUTION CLOSING SPEECH

"Mr Smith's defence in this case is that he has been set-up by Wendall and Snakeshaft. Wendall is not a participatory informant in this case. Wendall had no benefit in setting Diamond up as he claims. There was no benefit for Snakeshaft either because as an informer he has received no reward for this case and he has been charged and is due to be sentenced.

If Mr Diamond is right in that Snakeshaft set him up, all Snakeshaft had to do was go to his handlers and tell them what was going down, for example the time and place of this crime. Even if you disbelieve Snakeshaft, it still does not matter as Diamond was still in possession of the firearm.

It is logic and common sense that Diamond could not have been set up by Wendall and Snakeshaft. This is a man trying desperately to shine the spotlight elsewhere and will not accept responsibility for his actions. Is his claim of set-up really credible? Let's examine Diamond's claim of set-up – it is fatally flawed. Why would Wendall and Snakeshaft want to set up Diamond as they were not going to benefit from it, quite the reverse, they were prosecuted for their participation.

Police informants are essential and necessary in the investigation of serious organized crime. This case involves serious villains and they don't play by the Queensberry rules. They are capable of abusing people, threatening people and intimidation. They are capable of manipulation and fabrication. We know that Snakeshaft has broken the hallowed code of behaviour but it isn't, as Diamond says, his personal gain for printing presses. It is the real world of the furtherance of self-interest.

We know that Snakeshaft has told lies. I am not going to cherry pick and I will not shirk from that! But when has any or all of the lies had an effect on the issues of this case. We know that there is sensitive material and intelligence in this case and there has been some cloak and dagger stuff going on. There is such a thing as serious crime and sensitive material is essential. Material has been edited from documents and it has been provided to the defence. His Honour the Judge is aware of it and has presided over it to ensure fairness. It is not a new process! It has been going on for years. It is a process that everyone in this room is familiar with. Criminal intelligence and the gathering of it is a necessary part of criminal investigation. Sometimes there is a need to keep it from the jury as it is for their own interest.

Let's look at a new topic – Snakeshaft's evidence – what I am going to say in the opening and closing speech is not evidence. Once Snakeshaft decided to give evidence for the crown he was involved in a debrief process, a cleansing process where he volunteered to give evidence against Mr Diamond. He admitted that he was no angel and has admitted committing drug, handling, burglary and perjury offences. Snakeshaft had lied to a jury in order to get acquitted where he has attracted criticism. He blamed his solicitor and his lawyer's advice. If you don't believe anything Mr Snakeshaft has said then acquit Mr Diamond now. But Mr Snakeshaft volunteered to the police that he committed perjury. If he did not admit it no one would have known about it. But even if you take away all of Mr Snakeshaft's evidence, Mr Diamond is still left with the bag in the car.

With regard to the phone evidence, for all we know Wendall could have contacted Snakeshaft after Diamond's arrest by using a telephone kiosk which would not be traced. Snakeshaft did make 81 calls to Diamond after he put the bag in Diamond's car and there is evidence that there were calls between Snakeshaft, Diamond and Wendall. So what is good for the goose is also good for the gander. Having seen both Mr Snakeshaft and Mr Diamond in the witness box who seems to be the gopher or delivery boy, Mr Diamond or Mr Snakeshaft? There is some intelligence on record that Snakeshaft had a lock-up garage but this was never found.

As for Mr Snakeshaft's involvement in the arrest of Macitto and Roberts on the 14th May 2001, as DI Fisher stated, the drugs were of a low quality and Snakeshaft could always be arrested later on. If you think there was skulduggery going on and the police officers did not arrest Snakeshaft – just remember there was no evidence to support his arrest.

We also heard how Snakeshaft got into a silver Mercedes with three others and were going to look at 'the stuff' in what was called a high-ranking drugs deal. All in all, there were 22 occasions where Mr Snakeshaft was observed and there was no evidence to bring him in. As for the Knowles debt, someone had to be held responsible for it and it was Snakeshaft. If you were Snakeshaft would you obligingly go to Knowles or would you prefer to be a patsy. Snakeshaft is nothing more than a patsy and he played a low level role in Operation Salieri.

As for the abortive pick-up of the Uzi on the 4th June 2001, the observation log supports Mr Snakeshaft's account where he is seen coming out of a black Ford Escort car 'empty-handed'. The Uzi and the 5th June: Snakeshaft did not look at the contents of the bag when he collected it. The prosecution do not accept Mr Diamond's version of events. Snakeshaft took the bag out of his house at the request of Diamond. Mr Snakeshaft was not in charge. He did not know that he was under police observation. Mr Snakeshaft said Diamond got into his car and then he got out of the car and paid him £2500. Either Mr Snakeshaft misremembered or the police missed Snakeshaft going to the driver's door to collect the money from Diamond.

As is the case with the evidence of DC Curtis who saw Snakeshaft go into his house, but he did not see him carrying anything into the house. But we know, it is not disputed by the defence, that Snakeshaft must have taken the bag into his house. Alternatively, Mr Snakeshaft could have easily said Diamond paid me inside the house.

Also at the time Mr Diamond stated in his police interview that he touched something metallic in the bag, he would not have known at the time that his fingerprints were not on it and therefore he was laying the ground in case his fingerprints were on it. Regarding the bullets and accessories for the weapon – neither Wendall nor Diamond requested the accessories. If Snakeshaft wanted to lie he could have easily said that Diamond had requested the accessories also.

In relation to the 38s, Mr Snakeshaft went backwards and forwards in his account of the 38s. We know that Snakeshaft's credibility is at the heart of this case and he is not asking for a get out clause but Snakeshaft said I have been asked to say many things over the months and I may have made a mistake. In any case the 38s have nothing to do with this case. It is a peripheral issue. We also know that Snakeshaft lied to his handler on the 6th June 2001 and Snakeshaft has admitted that he lied to his handler. The assessment of witnesses is entirely a matter for you. Some of the things a person may say, which may be a lie or a mistake, may not be issues that you have to try on.

You also have the forensic evidence. Wendall's fingerprints appear on the inside of Diamond's BMW. Neither Diamond's nor Snakeshaft's fingerprints were found on the money, the £500 found in Diamond's possession and Diamond's fingerprints do not appear on the gun. There were no identifiable fingerprints found on the gun, not one!

Now we move on to the criticism of the defence case. It has been established that between the 4th and 6th June that Diamond, Wendall and Snakeshaft were in contact with each other.

You may think Diamond would blame the absent Wendall in this case. Is what Diamond says true? Is his evidence corroborated or supported by anyone? Diamond claims on arrest that he said to the station sergeant "I got the money (£500) from the man." Mr Diamond may have put the £500 in his pocket in case of his arrest. Mr Diamond claims he was asked to deliver the printing presses because he was reliable and dependable. He said Snakeshaft was bringing the printing presses from South London and that Snakeshaft was paying for the delivery. Diamond portrayed himself as a patsy. Mr Snakeshaft's debrief took 700 odd pages and if what he said is correct, he has been criticised for it.

Mr Diamond is quite capable of making up every single word of his defence. You may even come to the conclusion that he is reasonably intelligent, quick and a little funny.

When DC Logan searched the bag inside Diamond's BMW he touched a wooden handle, but when Diamond put his hand in the bag he touched metal through the towel. In evidence Diamond stated he felt metal through the towel and yet in his interview at the police station he stated quite clearly that he touched metal, not through a towel. There is a small twist in Diamond's evidence and his version of events only changes when he knows that his fingerprints were not on the gun.

Mr Diamond had a piece of paper in his car with Snakeshaft's mobile telephone number on it. Not the phone number of Alex who he was supposed to meet, the person to whom he was taking the printing presses and he had to phone in case something went wrong. No, he only has Snakeshaft's phone number!

We heard in DC Noel's interview of Wendall that he set up Mr Diamond. That is not true, Mr Wendall was accused of setting up the transaction not Mr Diamond.

When we examine Mr Diamond's account it may be said how can

he be making it up? Mr Diamond states he was advised to say "no comment" by his solicitor in his interview. It was Wendall that came to him and asked him about committing a robbery, about cannabis and acquiring a gun for his son's problems. Do you really believe Diamond was scared of Wendall or Snakeshaft, a mere gopher, a delivery boy who Diamond would cast aside? The Crown says the defence has too much detail and yet none of his defence is complicated to make up. He has been pondering over his defence for over a year and he has clothed the Uzi in an air of respectability. For example a professional criminal Wendall going to Diamond to deliver printing presses. It is all a ruse, a false claim. Mr Diamond has marshalled his resources but he has been hoist by his own petard. He uses the fit-up theory but there was no gain in it for Wendall and Snakeshaft. The person who fits someone up does it for personal gain, this is not the case here. The fitter-upper wants the person to get done and he himself does not get done.

Neither Wendall nor Snakeshaft was a participatory informant in this case. Wendall asked Snakeshaft to obtain a gun. Diamond knew Wendall from old. He saw and paid for the gun. He knew what was in that bag, he knew! The prosecution invite you to say that he and Wendall were in possession of that gun with intent to endanger life. The prosecution say you can be sure so that you are sure. If you find Mr Diamond guilty of Count 1 possession of a firearm with intent to endanger life, he is no doubt also guilty of Count 3 the possession of a firearm."

End of the prosecution's closing speech.

THE DEFENCE CLOSING SPEECH

"Let me start by saying that this case is very simple. It is a question of do you believe Mr Snakeshaft? It is not the defence duty to find the defendant innocent, it is the prosecution's role to find the defendant guilty beyond any reasonable doubt. They must prove the case against the defendant so that you are sure he is guilty.

With regard to Mr Snakeshaft's account of events, not only does Mr Diamond say it is not true, but the police do not agree with his version either. In evidence Mr Snakeshaft said that Mr Diamond was in his house for at least ten minutes when it is alleged that Mr Diamond assembled and dismantled the Uzi submachine gun and all its component parts. But we know from the police observations outside Mr Snakeshaft's address that they were in that house for three minutes or less. Mr

Diamond said that when he was inside that house he had a short conversation, Mr Snakeshaft gave him the £500 and he asks where Mr Diamond's car is parked and added that he would follow him around to his car with the package. Mr Diamond did not have the time to do all that Mr Snakeshaft claims he did!

(The jury are asked to look at a road map of the area around Snakeshaft's house in Bornchurch, Essex)

On the map are two coloured lines that show the route taken by Wendall and Diamond and that of Snakeshaft. The blue line distinctly shows Snakeshaft's route up to the passenger door of Diamond's BMW parked in Eyhurst Close and then he walks back the way he came to Wendall's parked vehicle.

According to the police evidence in this map, Mr Snakeshaft never goes to the driver's side of the car, never receives the alleged £2500 from Diamond. The only area where Mr Snakeshaft was not observed was when he arrived at his house earlier that morning and DC Curtis was unable to say whether he saw Mr Snakeshaft carrying anything into his house.

Even if the question is, who do you believe Mr Snakeshaft or Mr Diamond or Mr Diamond or the police? How on earth do you know that Mr Snakeshaft really picked that gun up at all? According to his evidence it took him somewhere in the region of 2 ½ to 4 ½ hours to get back to his address at Bornchurch from Stoke Newington where it is alleged that he collected the gun from the mysterious Rob the Porpoise and his business partner Elvis! Mr Snakeshaft is an unmitigated liar.

Regarding the set-up, Mr Diamond's defence is that he was not set-up, but that he was duped, tricked or conned and has been set-up in that sense by Mr Wendall and Mr Snakeshaft. You will be able to see this when you get a chance to look at and examine Wendall's interview with DC Noel. Where he states, "I put it to you, you are the one that has set this up, you have set up Terence Diamond in cahoots with Daniel Snakeshaft, what have you to say about that?" In this interview, DC Noel uses the phrase "set-up" to mean duped, I was duped, had-over by a man I trusted. Mr Diamond's defence is that I was had-over, misled and conned by these two men.

That man – defence counsel points to the defendant in the dock – has been in prison fretting over this case for nearly a year, banged-up for 23 hours-a-day where he has studied every punctuation mark and comma in the case papers. It has been on his mind continuously. You saw him when he gave his evidence. He was genuine. He could not understand how this could happen to him? I have no doubt that you saw and sympathized with Mr Diamond. I am not suggesting that the police were up to no good, but there is plenty of material and evidence to support that he was had-over.

If we could have an audience with Daniel Snakeshaft, a bit like the TV celebrity shows and invite all the people he knew or spoke about in his debrief process, some 50 to 60 people and they could ask him questions, Mr Snakeshaft's only answer or response would be, "I've already answered that question!" or "It wasn't my fault!" that was the way he performed in giving his evidence.

Or imagine if you were up there in the public gallery and your relative or friend was sitting there in the dock and you heard all the evidence in this case. You would be thinking, "What the hell is Mr Diamond doing in the dock based upon the evidence of an unmitigated liar?"

I am not saying Mr Snakeshaft is a criminal mastermind. He is a man who is very dangerous, wholly unprepared to accept responsibility for what he has done, where he blames everybody else.

The next point is what was the gun for? We heard in evidence from Mr Snakeshaft that he had committed perjury at Knaresbrook Crown Court in the case regarding a quantity of cannabis. He conned the jury and was acquitted along with his co-defendants the Brooms. To do this he put an innocent man in the frame and alleges that the man was a police informant. Mr Snakeshaft is the prosecution's star witness. He managed to con a jury. That is the man that you are dealing with! If the jury were sitting in this court today they would be gutted because they allowed themselves to be duped. He puts an innocent man in the frame to serve his own purposes. Mr Snakeshaft is a con man. He would grass his own grandmother for his own purposes. He claims in the witness box that he has no answers to all these lies. It is not impossible to ask a man of his ilk to put an innocent man in the frame.

Let's explore the Snakeshaft fantasyland. You will remember the whole sorry saga of the 38s? Mr Snakeshaft got himself in a position that he was so tangled up with his lies that Mr Diamond had asked him for two 38s? He says that Terry Diamond asked for two 38s after he put the bag containing the Uzi in the car? He said, "I just nodded, I was petrified as he is not the sort of person that you say no to! It's getting out of hand and I was going to phone a policeman that I know straight away afterwards!" We later learned that it is all made up, not a word of that is true. It is all a lie. He would not accept responsibility that he had lied. He makes up the whole story about Mr Diamond. Again this is the prosecution's star witness. The Crown simply try to push it under the carpet and try to defend his evidence. How can you hang a dog on this man's evidence? It is a disgrace. This is all before we get to the real facts of this case. God help the next person he does this to!

Mr Snakeshaft did the Brooms a favour in that cannabis case at Knaresbrook Crown Court where he blames it on a grass called Stilson? As an expression of gratitude, the Brooms pass the debt onto the mysterious Robert Knowles. Mr Snakeshaft claims Mr Knowles said that I owe him the debt for the loss of the cannabis, some £100,000 to £150,000.

We learn that Mr Snakeshaft became a police informant on 19th January 2001. Not once does he ask the police to protect him from this man. He does not ask for police protection. A curious thing is not once in all that time that he spends with Mr Wendall on his release from prison in April 2001 does he ask Mr Wendall to help him, to protect him from this man? He had six weeks to ask Mr Wendall for help almost on a daily basis and he does not? Here is a man that said 75% of his mates that he mixes with are villains? It's all rubbish and it does not bear scrutiny!

Who was that gun for? He says that it was for Terry Diamond? Why is he so keen to make up that incident in the back bedroom of his house? Why do you need an Uzi submachine gun with nearly 400 rounds of ammunition with a shoulder stock and silencer? Who was the end user of that gun? How do we know that what he tells you about the Brooms, Mr Knowles and Mr Formby is not true?

We know that Mr Snakeshaft became a police informant at the end of January last year. At the end of January DI Fisher elicited that Mr Snakeshaft was in contact with the Brooms and that he was an associate of Mr Formby. Mr Knowles was not a suspect. The Brooms are not people who Mr Snakeshaft has turned his back on! No, he associated with them even though they passed the debt onto him for Mr Knowles? In March 2001, the police associated a link between Daniel Snakeshaft and Mr Formby. What is going on? Formby is arrested for firearms."

The jury are asked to look at the contact sheet page 117.

"This was made on the 23rd March 2001 where Mr Snakeshaft told his handlers that he was ordered to go down to the Magistrate's Court by Knowles to stand surety for Mr Formby who had been arrested with two firearms? The one place where you could not discover who the guns were for because Mr Formby was held in the cells below the court and he was not allowed to see him. And yet at 11:45 am on the same day Mr Snakeshaft telephones his handlers and says who the guns are for? It is all made up! Why is he doing this? What is it all for? I will tell you why, because there is a war going on. Mr Snakeshaft is such a liar that we don't even know what side of the war he is on. Formby was nicked with two guns and taken out of circulation. Snakeshaft was left with the Uzi and then he puts it in Diamond's car and then claims that he was going to phone the police. This gun was meant for a gang war. A war that has nothing to do with Terry Diamond. The man who really had that gun with intent to endanger life is Daniel Snakeshaft. You are never going to get the truth from Mr Snakeshaft, but we are able to get an insight into the man. Criminal intelligence claims Formby always carries a gun.

And yet Mr Snakeshaft is prepared to go and stand surety for someone that he says he is supplying firearms to a man that is allegedly threatening him for a £100,000 debt? How are we to believe all this? It does not make sense. Once again this is the prosecution's star witness. Mr Diamond was simply a courier for Wendall and Snakeshaft and he has been had-over."

The court adjourned for lunch 13:00 hours. We are called back into court at 14:00 hours. Defence Closing Speech continues ...

"Do you really believe how Mr Snakeshaft came by that Uzi? On the evening of the 4th June 2001 – the day before Diamond's arrest – Mr Snakeshaft ends up in Bing Street on the Isle of Dogs where he was observed by the police getting into a black Ford Escort and he spends 10 minutes with a man called Rob. Why is it this man Rob, from the Eastside Gymnasium, had to meet Mr Snakeshaft? Why not just say the gun is not ready in code over the phone? We heard that Rob the Porpoise has owned that gun for over two years? What is it about that gun that it is not ready? Maybe the ammunition and the silencer were not ready?

Obviously you cannot speak about those things over the phone and perhaps that is why they had to meet? Mr Snakeshaft knew what was coming and that is why it made sense to make up what happened in the upstairs back bedroom. Mr Snakeshaft knew that this gun was for war, not robbery, that's why there was the meeting on the Isle of Dogs?

We learn that Mr Wendall does not telephone Mr Diamond until two hours after his arrest. This is not Terry Diamond's gun! He is simply a courier that is why Mr Snakeshaft gives you the elaborate story about the back bedroom!

We also heard that there was not one of Mr Diamond's fingerprints found on that gun? If I pick up this book – counsel picks up a book – you would expect my fingerprints to be all over it wouldn't you? Well if I had to construct and dismantle an Uzi submachine gun and all its component parts, I would have eight fingers and two thumbs all over that gun. My fingerprints would be all over it. Again Snakeshaft is a liar!

What lesson do you think Mr Snakeshaft would have learnt—that delivering things can seriously damage yourself! After getting arrested with the cannabis in the van with the Brooms, Mr Snakeshaft would not go anywhere near any other deliveries. He would get someone else to do it. Take for instance Mr Macitto with the kilo of amphetamine and now Mr Diamond with the Uzi! What we learn from this is when Wendall and Snakeshaft want to deliver something that they don't do it themselves. The easiest way would have been to give the gun to Wendall at the Eastside gym and then Wendall give it to Terry Diamond. Why did they not do that? I will tell you why, it is because they have to get someone else to deliver it, Terry Diamond, Wendall's old friend, so they dupe him!

Mr Diamond was asked by his friend Wendall to do this and he trusted him. He did not check the contents of that bag thoroughly as he trusted him. A perfect analogy is that of the airport suitcase. If a stranger asked you to take a suitcase through the custom's checkpoint you would, and rightly so, be very suspicious and probably refuse to do it. But if a close friend asked you to do it you would probably do it because you trust that person. You don't check the contents of something when a friend asks you do something. I don't check the contents of my wife's laundry when she asks me to drop it off at the dry cleaners, because I trust her. Mr Diamond trusted Wendall and look where he is now!

We don't know when Mr Snakeshaft picked up that gun on that morning or even where from. Mr Snakeshaft claimed in evidence that he was merely a patsy, yet he was able to source, obtain and supply an Uzi submachine gun, nearly 400 rounds of ammunition, a shoulder stock, magazine and silencer from the first person he asked who happens to have one sitting in his cupboard for the last two and half years? Nothing Mr Snakeshaft says about that gun should be taken for granted."

The jury are asked to look at the debrief transcript of Snakeshaft pages 276-277.

"This is the occasion when Mr Snakeshaft is describing what happened when he picked up the gun from Elvis's flat. I will read it out for you.

DC Lawson: Was the bag opened in your presence?

Snakeshaft: Ah?

DC Lawson: At *um*, I think you said it was at Islington or *um* where you picked the gun up from?

Snakeshaft: Yeah the gun was opened in my presence yes.

DC Lawson: It was, was it?

Snakeshaft: Yes.

DC Lawson. Who showed you it there?

Snakeshaft: Rob and his friend Elvis.

DC Lawson: Did they actually show you, did they open the bag, take the gun out and show you?

Snakeshaft: No, opened it up like that, and said look that's what's in there.

DC Lawson: What, and you just looked inside the bag?

Snakeshaft: Yeah.

DC Lawson: And it was assembled then?

Snakeshaft: No.

DC Lawson: Right.

If that version of events is right, members of the jury, where did the yellow towel come from? Because Mr Snakeshaft wrapped up that gun in the towel. And why was that? So that when the man collected it – Mr Diamond – he wouldn't know what was in the bag. You also have the business with the gardening gloves. Mr Snakeshaft said that he had the gardening gloves on so that he wouldn't get his fingerprints on it. Then he changed his mind and said that the gardening gloves were for Terry Diamond.

Also Mr Maskell (prosecution counsel) cannot explain how to reconcile the evidence of Mr Snakeshaft going to the driver's door of Mr Diamond's BMW and allegedly collecting the £2500 when even the police observing him did not see him do that?

We know that Mr Diamond drove off from Eyhurst Close at 12:40 pm. The very next phone call Mr Snakeshaft made on his mobile phone was at 13:29 pm but he could not say who that call was to? Mr Snakeshaft said in evidence that when Mr Diamond drove away from him the Uzi transaction 'was a done deal'. But then we have enigma of 81 calls to Diamond. Why did Snakeshaft phone Diamond 81 times on his mobile phone? The only sensible construction you can place on this is that Mr Snakeshaft is trying to get hold of Mr Diamond. Look how many times Mr Snakeshaft phones Mr Diamond within the first hour after Diamond's arrest, 10 times? Why? Because he says Wendall told me to. There is not a single call from Wendall to Diamond. In total 81 times Mr Snakeshaft tries to call Diamond. Why, because Mr Snakeshaft did not sell a gun to Diamond, he was couriering a gun for Snakeshaft. He was obviously worried why Mr Diamond was not answering his phone. Maybe it is because Mr Diamond had discovered what he was actually carrying? Daniel Snakeshaft is a liar. What more can I do to demonstrate that he is a liar!

The prosecution have to prove so that you are sure, all I have to prove is that there is doubt. Mr Snakeshaft's evidence is inconsistent with the telephone records, the police evidence and Mr Diamond's evidence. He is a man who has duped a jury. This man is dangerous and he should be stopped.

Mr Snakeshaft threw away the chip in his mobile phone. Having told the police he threw it away, he then changes his mind and says Wendall threw it away. You are supposed to convict Mr Diamond on the word of Daniel Snakeshaft. I suggest that it would be an outrage to convict this man.

What fault did Mr Maskell find with Mr Diamond's prepared defence statement? Do you not see the difference between a solicitor giving advice in a police station to a solicitor giving advice to concoct a bogus story as in the case where Mr Snakeshaft tells a pack of lies to a jury to get himself and others acquitted.

Mr Diamond has been tortured for a year while he has been in prison as to how this has happened. I beg you do not convict this man. Short of cutting open Mr Snakeshaft's head and dragging the truth out we are not ever going to know the truth or where this gun has come from. Mr Snakeshaft is a deceitful, unscrupulous and unmitigated liar. We cannot trust him and I repeat this man is dangerous and he has to be stopped. He has duped one jury and implicated an innocent man to fool them and all I ask is that he is not allowed to fool you."

End of defence closing speech.

Judge: I shall sum up on Monday.

Court adjourned 14:50 hours.

DAY ELEVEN OF THE TRIAL
THE JUDGE'S SUMMING-UP

"Let me begin by saying that there are 13 Judges in this courtroom. There are twelve Judges of the facts – you the jury – and one Judge that deals with the law – obviously that is me. The facts deal with the truth in this case and it is not a game. It is the enquiring of the truthful evidence. The law is a matter for me. You have to decide whether or not the facts agree or disagree with your view of the case. You have a duty to reject the facts if you disagree.

The prosecution have a burden of proof. They have to prove the case beyond any reasonable doubt against the defendant. The definition of possession is that the defendant had control over that firearm and that he knowingly had possession of it. The vital issue in this case is whether the defendant knew that he had possession of that gun. Snakeshaft knew full well what was in that bag and has admitted the offence.

There is the issue of shared possession. A submachine gun was found in the BMW. The issue is whether the possession is between Diamond and Snakeshaft. We know that there may be in reality possession between Snakeshaft and Wendall and if you are sure that their possession is joint possession it may throw some light on the case, but not on the first issue. The first issue is whether he was knowingly in possession, either in single or joint possession. Knowing possession of the Uzi, you must be sure he had the gun in possession to endanger life. For instance, he may have used the gun for entertainment or use the gun as a decoration over his mantelpiece. If the gun was being purchased for robbery then there would be an intent to endanger life. All that involves is an enquiry by you as to what Diamond was doing in obtaining the submachine gun?

You know that the cost of the gun was £2500 and that Wendall kept his distance from the gun, telling Snakeshaft that the gun was for Diamond. If you are sure that the gun was meant for robbery then you are invited to find the defendant guilty of Count 1 – possession with intent to endanger life. If you are sure of the element of possession but not that of intent to endanger life, then it is open to you to decide on Count 2 of purchasing or acquiring a gun. There is also the second limb of Count 2, a gun that was adapted to fire more than one bullet while the finger was pressed on the trigger. Count 3 is a person prohibited by the Firearms Act from acquiring a firearm.

If you decide the defendant is not guilty of Count 1 then you may consider Count 2.

Next is the concept of joint enterprise. If two or more people are involved in this offence then each must be party to the common design. If it took three people to purchase the firearm then they are all guilty of the offence.

You are allowed to draw inferences in your deliberations only if it helps you in the conclusions of fact. Only draw inferences and seek to rely on circumstantial evidence when you the jury consider it to be just and right and fair.

Snakeshaft is an accomplice in this criminal enterprise. Snakeshaft has told you that he pleaded guilty to the offences in relation to this submachine gun. He has pleaded guilty to Counts 2 and 3 on the indictment. I strongly advise you to look at his evidence with close scrutiny and care. There are many conflicts in his evidence and you have to look at his evidence with the greatest possible care.

The prosecution's case is that Wendall asked Snakeshaft to get the gun for the defendant Diamond. Wendall is a friend of Snakeshaft and Diamond. We heard from Snakeshaft that Wendall had just been released from prison and was returning to his criminal ways. If you take an adverse view of Wendall this should not reflect on the defendant Diamond. There is no such thing as guilt by association. You should be sure from the evidence of Snakeshaft that Wendall was involved and it does not in anyway mean Diamond was in on it. During Wendall's interview he made 'no comment'. He was advised by his solicitor to say 'no comment'!

You have been asked to read through three exhibits—statements. Some are briefing notes and contact sheets—which are not evidence in this case unless you decide to adopt them. They are statements made out of court to police officers and you heard about them. If Snakeshaft says different things at differing times it may reduce the value of his evidence or destroy his evidence. They are not evidence in the case at all. Do not accept anything in those notes unless adopted and agreed to in reaching your verdict. You must be satisfied that first it was a deliberate lie and that it relates to a material issue and motivation of guilt in fact of truth. The centre of this matter is the printing presses. If you come to the conclusion that is a lie then you need not go into other points of the case. It is at the heart of the case.

The facts as to the finding of the gun. We heard from police officer Daly who was involved in the stop of the BMW. That officer went to the nearside of the BMW and shouted 'armed police' and to get out. Officer Daly opened the passenger front door and saw the blue bag. He had no knowledge that there was another car involved at Barren Drive, the Vauxhall Vectra.

We also heard from DC Logan on finding the gun. He saw the black BMW stationary. He saw the bag. The defendant was brought to the opened door so that he could witness the search. He opened the bag and towel and saw the handle of a gun. To see the gun he had to pull back the towel and he saw the handle of the gun and trigger. A number of other items were also found in the car which have been exhibited. The vehicle was further searched from 16:50 to 17:45 pm back at the Police Station.

You heard from Officer Cole. He goes to the driver's side of the BMW and he says, "We've got reason to believe that you've got a gun in here?" Diamond's reply, "A gun - no way!" The officer says, "Is that your bag in the passenger foot well?" Diamond, "No, I just picked it up for someone!" The officer, "What is in it?" Diamond, "Don't know I never looked!" Diamond was then arrested and cautioned by DC Cole. Officer Lark then took the cash from the defendant's pocket. DC Cole was attached to the crime squad at Cranham.

We now come to the nature of the gun. We heard the forensic expert Kemble that he test fired the gun and found that it worked faultlessly in both fully and semi-automatic mode. There were 29 cartridges in a magazine that held a total of 32. The submachine gun was a prohibited weapon under sections of the Firearms Act. The silencer was also prohibited as an accessory under the Firearms Act. He also received a bum bag containing ammunition. A total of 375 unfired calibre cartridges of Czech origin. In a test firing of 50 cartridges, 28 misfired and 22 were live. The gun was in good working order and the ammunition was a bit rusty.

Turning to Snakeshaft's evidence. We heard that he knew Wendall since he left school. Snakeshaft gave Wendall £3000 on release from prison and Diamond gave him a Vauxhall Vectra car. He asked Rob for a gun in the Eastside Gym. The gun was supposed to be ready on the 4th June 2001 but it was not. Snakeshaft said Diamond knew Wendall very well. Wendall visited Diamond at his house and Diamond gave him the Vectra. Wendall asked Diamond if he wanted to commit a robbery with him and Snakeshaft. Diamond said – no! Wendall asked Diamond if he could get him some cannabis. Diamond refused. Wendall asked Diamond to deliver some printing presses for £500 and it may be a regular run. Wendall had just come out of prison and did not want to get involved because he was on licence. He asked Diamond to deliver printing presses to a man called Alex on the A14. Wendall said Diamond was unable to pick up the printing presses that day and he met Diamond at Upminster Station the next day. He gave Snakeshaft's phone number to Diamond and he phoned Snakeshaft. Diamond said that he did not take the gun out of the bag and he did not give him £2500. Diamond believed that it was printing presses. Diamond was stopped three miles away by the police. Someone is lying and is lying hard.

During Snakeshaft's evidence he told you he had been in custody since he had been arrested. He is 38 years old and he is married with two boys aged 10 and 14 years. He had known Wendall since he left school. He had met Diamond at a football match. He only knew one Terry Diamond. He has pleaded guilty and awaits sentence.

He said "I saw Wendall and gave him £3000. Diamond gave him a car. I went to the Eastside Gym and I met a 6 foot 2 inch black guy called Rob. I went there regularly and heard Rob talking to someone at a table about guns. I told Wendall. I told Rob what I asked for – the Uzi – was wanted. Wendall told me the Uzi was for Terry Diamond. I followed Rob to Islington and I went to Elvis's flat. He is half-caste. I did not check the bag. I went with the bag in the car. The green bag had a label on it. It was like a duffle bag with a drawstring on it. I was to meet them around my house at about 12 noon. They came into my hallway of my house. Diamond and me went upstairs. We went in the bedroom and Diamond looked into the bag. He assembled the gun and put the gun waist high and pointed it. Then dismantled the gun. He said, "This will do a good job like the Bermondsey job!" He paid me £2500. I took the money to the gym and met Rob. I went to the park nearby with Wendall and his wife for tea. Then I went to the Eastside Gym.

I did not know that Diamond had been arrested and I kept trying his phone number. I met Wendall the next day and he was angry. He said that Diamond had been nicked and it smelt dodgy. He took the chip out of my mobile phone and destroyed it."

Snakeshaft has pleaded guilty to three firearms charges and asked that a number of offences be taken into consideration. These are the supply of cannabis resin five times in 1998; between the 1st January and the 30th April 2001 the supply of cannabis resin three times; also the supply of amphetamine sulphate; handling of stolen goods in 1996 – TV sets and jeans; again he has admitted five times the supply of cannabis in 1998. What is Snakeshaft's motivation in all this? He also pleaded guilty to perjury in relation to a drug offence. Then he got involved with the Uzi – bullied by a man called Knowles – he said "I owed him £150,000. I was charged with the offence at Knaresbrook Crown Court. I paid £30,000 off the debt. I thought if I do this Uzi deal Diamond and Wendall may get Knowles off my back". Snakeshaft has no convictions since 1983. He has had convictions for offences prior to 1983.

"The money Billy Milton gave to me was included in the £3000 that I gave to Wendall. Milton has nothing to do with the gun. I met Terry Diamond at a football match. He told the court that he was a regular visitor to the Eastside Gym – 75% of the people I know are involved in crime. The people I meet at the Eastside Gym are involved in drugs. The Bermondsey robbery was four miles away from the gym. I was charged with offences of cannabis with the Brooms and stood trial at Knaresbrook Crown Court.

I became a police informant in January 2001. I got involved with the Uzi and cannabis to get Knowles off my back. I was given two handlers and I committed perjury. Knowles is not a drug dealer, he is a collector. Knowles sells diesel oil. I know the slang for drugs – if a dog won it meant the drugs got through the Customs. If a dog fell it meant the drugs were intercepted."

Snakeshaft made police reports that were called 'contact sheets'. Why did he go into police informing? The court heard how another branch of the police force did not know who were watching him. In the report number 28 in January 2001, Snakeshaft said he thought that he was being watched by the police. In report number 60, he said Robert Knowles wants £50,000 by this Friday. On the 9th February 2001 he told his handlers for the first time how the debt had arisen. In report number 202 dated 23rd March 2001 he said, "Robert Knowles wants me to go to the Magistrate's Court regarding the Formby and Donald firearms arrest." He said Formby is my wife's brother-in-law. You have the pages of this report numbers 117 and 119. The guns found in possession of Formby were two 9 millimetres. "Formby does not have the bottle to use guns but Knowles has the capability. I heard there was a war going on between Knowles and Billy Milton. The Uzi was not intended for Milton to wage war against Knowles. The gun was not for Knowles. Knowles is 37 to 38 and big built."

Report number 212 – Snakeshaft was reporting on a regular basis – he said, "I didn't see the police after May 23rd 2001. I was getting worried about how many police handlers I was seeing. I was told on a number of occasions not to get involved in crime." He was authorized to use 'verbal enthusiasm' and not to get involved in actual crime. Snakeshaft was not given permission to get involved in the Uzi or the amphetamine cases. He was not given *carte blanche* to commit crime.

On the 6th June 2001 he contacted his controller just before he was arrested. We learn Snakeshaft had been involved in the commission of a firearm offence. He lied to his controller. He asked his controller how Terry Diamond had been arrested. He said Diamond may think it was him tipping off the police. Diamond was not just a courier carrying the bag. Diamond drove off at 12:40 pm and was stopped by the police at 12:55 pm.

"At 13:13 pm I was telephoning Diamond to get in touch with Wendall. I rang Diamond 81 times – I did not know that Diamond was arrested. Rob let me have the gun on a sale or return basis. Diamond did not wear gloves in the house. Formby used to work for Billy Milton. Knowles was having a war with a man called Carrant over 800 kilos of cannabis. Formby was getting guns for Knowles.

Rob's alias is 'the Porpoise'. Rob didn't have the 38s. No I did not ask Rob for the 38s. Wendall asked for the 38s as well as Diamond. Diamond never asked me for the 38s. It is not a lie I must have got it wrong. Wendall asked me!"

When the police summarized Snakeshaft's version of events in the debrief, they summarized it as if Diamond did ask for the 38s. The bullets and silencer were just chucked in with the Uzi. It was just an Uzi for a friend Terry Diamond! Once the Uzi was got he was then asked for the 38s. There is a very serious conflict about what Snakeshaft says about the 38s!"

Morning break 12:20 hours
Return to court at 12:35 hours.

Judge summing-up continued.

"He just passed the money to me in the car. No the money did not go through the window. I put the money in my back pocket. In the debrief statements it states how the money passed to me was wrong. In evidence Snakeshaft said Diamond got out of the car to give me the money. I did not give him printing presses. Diamond was not given £500 to make a delivery." In the debrief statements Snakeshaft said, "When Terry Diamond got nicked I took the chip out of my mobile phone and threw it away." Then later he said, "Wendall threw the chip away. I was wrong. It was a mistake. I don't know how I got it wrong. Yes I had two mobile phones. One was a 1-2-1 phone. I bought the phone in May 2001 to commit offences. To find out about drugs – I was an informant. Wendall knows I would never go on an armed robbery. In January to June 2001 I was running drugs around. This is a serious breach as an undertaking informant. I've admitted my crimes. I did not use Diamond. A collector means to come and get something or collect something. I was at the bottom of the ring – I am a patsy, a runabout.

I knew Diamond knew Wendall for a long time. I couldn't ask Diamond for anything. I do not have that kind of clout. I was running drugs about. I had about 4 to 6 police handlers. I had not spoken to Wendall to see what he might do to Knowles to get him off my back."

When you look at Snakeshaft's evidence, you have to consider what his motivation was in confessing, helping the police and giving evidence? Or is the whole thing in connection with what will happen to him, for example, in relation to whatever sentence he will get? If you think his motivation is to help himself by admitting a spate of offences, how does it help him to invent a wholly dishonest account of events? If it was about the printing presses then Snakeshaft is telling a serious pack of lies. Is it the presses or guns? Is it a cock and bull story? The matter is entirely a matter for you members of the jury.

Snakeshaft does not know Diamond but he knows Wendall very well. This puts Wendall at the centre of it. Why would Snakeshaft want to put Diamond in it? He doesn't know Diamond very well. The evaluation of Snakeshaft's evidence is really important.

On the 5th June 2001 the police were observing 205 Barren Drive. At 12:36 pm two males went into 205. On police time the males were in that house for three minutes. They did not see Snakeshaft carrying anything into his house. The police had been watching Snakeshaft for three months. He was known as D1 – watching for involvement in class A and B drugs. This covers the importation of multi-kilo consignments. The police report on Operation Salieri states that Snakeshaft had been under observation since February 2001. We heard from officer Bishop. He was in Barren Drive from 11:20 am. At 12:39 he saw Daniel Snakeshaft carrying a blue bag over his shoulder and take it to the passenger side of the black BMW. He put the bag in the car. The man in the yellow T-shirt got into the car and Snakeshaft tapped on the roof. For some reason the log did not name Wendall. At no stage did Snakeshaft go to the driver side of the vehicle!

Officer Lark found the money on Diamond when he was arrested. The £500 was separated from the £230. He said that there was no comment made by Mr Diamond when the money was taken. He said it would have been recorded by the custody officer if Diamond had made a reply.

The gun was subject to analysis – none of Mr Diamond's fingerprints were found on the gun. There was no analysis on the gun by which DNA could be made."

At 13:15 pm the court was adjourned for lunch.
At 14:15 pm the court reconvened and the summing-up continued.

"We heard evidence from DI Fisher. He attended Bornchurch Police Station to brief the firearms branch. He said on 30th May 2001 Snakeshaft signed a paper for his cancellation of being an informant. Snakeshaft was a registered informant for SO1 – Serious Crime Group East. There was nothing in his cancellation document to say why he had been cancelled.

There was no lock-up garage found in Anchor Hope Lane. Snakeshaft was a subject of observation since 31ˢᵗ January 2001. There were 22 observations of Snakeshaft. A number of these observations started at Snakeshaft's address. In May 2001 we had the Macitto and Roberts saga. Macitto was found with a kilo of amphetamine sulphate. Snakeshaft was not arrested for this.

Operation Salieri was investigating class A and B drugs. The G-Bar was one meeting place for criminal associates. Snakeshaft was their runner. Knowles was not a target of Salieri. There is no material in the debrief that did not correspond with our investigation of Salieri. Intelligence suggests something has to have happened on the 4ᵗʰ June 2001 regarding a firearm. DI Fisher did not find out that Snakeshaft was an informant until February 2001. His role was of minor participation – permission to use 'verbal enthusiasm'. Snakeshaft was charged with the amphetamine offences in July 2001. DI Fisher said on the 5ᵗʰ June 2001 that he did not have enough officers to proceed with the arrest of Wendall. There were three main targets with regard to Operation Salieri. Wendall's palm prints were found on the interior door of Mr Diamond's BMW. That print put Wendall inside Diamond's car. The telephone analysis by Mr Wiles said that the telephone schedule was accurate and correct.

Now we turn to the evidence of the defendant. He was living in Canvey Island with his wife and four children. He said he knew Wendall for many years. He added Wendall had come round to his house and spoke about prison. "He came regularly to my house. I said that I had some money for Wendall or a car? Wendall said he wanted the car. He also asked me if I wanted to commit a robbery with him? I said no! Then Wendall asked me if I could get him some drugs and I said no! Then he spoke to me about his son being shot at by a black guy and he asked me if I could get him a gun and I said no! Wendall said that he wanted someone reliable and dependable to run some parcels to his friends in the Midlands. I believe that he chose me because I had given him the car. He told me about the printing presses.

I bought the black BMW on 1ˢᵗ June 2001. I part exchanged a BMW 750i for £13,500 and added another £13,000 by cheque. I visited Mark Black on the 2ⁿᵈ June 2001. Black was using a mobile telephone in the name of David Marson. I bought the black BMW to sell on again to Black. I spent a few hours with Black.

Wendall lives in Rainham. At 14:09 p.m. on the 4ᵗʰ June Wendall phoned me and asked me to collect the printing presses. He was adamant that I collect the printing press on the 4th June but I could not as someone was coming to my house to buy my jet ski. Wendall telephoned me at 9:36 pm and stated that I would not be able to pick up the printing presses that evening. The next day I met Wendall at Upminster Station. Wendall came and got in my car. Wendall said Snakeshaft was bringing them now. Wendall gave me Snakeshaft's phone number. I telephoned Snakeshaft. I went to Barren Drive. Wendall dropped his wife Carol at a park and we went to Barren Drive. I asked Wendall for the £500 and he said that he didn't have it and I should ask Snakeshaft for it. We went to Snakeshaft's address. Snakeshaft gave me £500. I never touched a gun. I did not give him £2500. Snakeshaft did not come round to the driver's door. I looked in the bag and saw a towel. I put my fingers in the bag and felt something metallic through the towel. I thought it was the printing presses."

When DC Cole asked 'what is in the bag?', Diamond said that he didn't know. PC Lark took £500 from Diamond on arrest at the police station. "Wendall is a dangerous man. I did not purchase a gun. I did not purchase any ammunition."

Diamond had a solicitor at the police station who gave advice to make a prepared defence statement. Diamond said, "Wendall is a top villain that needed a trustworthy friend. We would go for walks and he would talk about crime. He spoke about crime to me. There is a bit of a hierarchy in the criminal underworld. A collector is a runner that collects things. I don't accept the term 'patsy' as it is a bit vague. I accept the term 'gopher'! I visited Wendall while he was in prison, twice in 1995. I knew that I was getting involved in crime regarding the printing presses and counterfeit money."

We have heard there are no participating informants in this case. Wendall could have asked Snakeshaft to deliver the presses. It was common knowledge about the Bermondsey robbery in South East London.

There are a number of areas that you need to look at in regard to Diamond's evidence. You saw both Snakeshaft and Diamond give evidence. You have to judge them and see where the essential matters are. The prosecution say Diamond was a sophisticated and intelligent man. Which is the delivery boy? Diamond said counterfeit money is not in the same league as robbery or possession of a firearm. If the account of the printing presses is a cock and bull story then why did he lie? If you reject it as lies to cover his possession of the gun then the question is why? The prosecution must prove the defendant's guilt. You must only convict if you are sure. On the totality of evidence, if you don't believe the defendant the prosecution must succeed. If what the defendant said may reasonably be true or is true then the prosecution must fail.

END OF THE JUDGE'S SUMMING-UP

The Judge then directed the jury that he would only accept a unanimous verdict. The usher was sworn in at 15:03 pm. The jury retired to consider their verdict at 15:04 pm.

While the jury were considering their verdict my solicitor's clerk, leading and junior counsel all came to visit me down in the cells. We all agreed that the Judge's summing-up was not only long, but also very boring. I alluded to it as a 'rambling monologue' and felt disappointed that there were no extra warnings to be ultra cautious about the evidence of a confessed perjurer. Moreover I felt the Judge should have said that if the jury disbelieved Snakeshaft's evidence then they should look for corroborating evidence elsewhere? But on second thoughts how could the Judge have directed them to do that when there was no other evidence to dispute my account of events. Even the police evidence supported what I had said in the prepared defence statement, police interviews and evidence. Leading counsel stated that he felt that the Judge's summing up was very pro-defence and that he covered all our points. He also added that there were not sufficient grounds for appeal should the trial be lost. Inwardly I disagreed with this view, as we had still not been told in open court whether or not Wendall was a *registered informant*. We accepted and I agreed that it was possible that Snakeshaft and Wendall were not 'participating informants', but the mere fact that Wendall was a registered informant and it was not disclosed to the jury was, in my view, at the heart of this case and it was compelling grounds for an appeal should I be convicted.

Junior counsel added that he could not see how a jury could possibly convict on Count 1, possession of a firearm with intent to endanger life, but he added juries are the worst people to try to understand. Rather than speculate we should all wait and see.

At 16:15 pm, the jury were called back into court and sent away until 10:15 am the next day. Meanwhile I was whisked away to the bleak confines of the HSU at Cellmarsh Prison to await my fate.

DAY TWELVE OF THE TRIAL

Back at Thamesmead Crown Court today after a sleepless night pondering over the trial and its attendant nightmare ordeal. I awoke about 6 am that morning. Generally throughout the trial, I had been waking up somewhere between 5 and 6 am. My dreams had taken on an added intensity since the trial started and although I could not recall what they were about they appeared fraught with underlying angst and nervous energy.

I was really worried about today, especially being a Tuesday as Tuesdays have come to symbolize momentous days in my life for me. For example, it was on a Tuesday that I was arrested for this offence. It was on a Tuesday when I was rammed on a motorbike by a member of the public in a car whilst making good my escape from a bank robbery in June 1986 where I nearly lost my life and was arrested. It was on a Tuesday that I was released from prison for that offence back in 1995. Being increasingly superstitious, Tuesdays have therefore become a day to beware of and I was fearful that the jury would come back with the verdict today.

At 10:15 am we were called into court and the Judge sent the jury out to consider their verdict at 10:17 am. While the jury were left to their deliberations I was left to mine down in the court cells. Surrounded by thick concrete walls and cold bars my mind began to race. The obvious thought processes of a defendant facing a verdict that could result in an automatic life sentence of imprisonment is to try and predict what the outcome will be and to try to extrapolate the unknown workings and rationalization of a jury room. The process of predicting the unpredictable leads to self-torture and torment in the extreme. I tried to divert my attention elsewhere, but there is an unwholesome tendency to focus upon the totality of events should things go disastrously wrong. Somehow I had to eradicate these negative doubts and concerns because not only was it making me depressed, but also I felt as if in some bizarre way my negative thoughts and feelings may shape and affect the outcome of the verdict.

All through this nightmare ordeal I willed myself to keep strong and positive about the outcome of the case and I was not about to melt now. Deep down inside, I knew that there were some powerfully expressive individuals in that jury room and they were not going to let the police and their pre-programmed police informers send me to jail for umpteen years. It was nothing to do with the support of the underdog syndrome, it was based upon natural intuition and a neutral grasp of the pervasive lies as vented by the prosecution's star witness Daniel William Snakeshaft!

I felt as if there were people sitting on that jury who sensed and knew where the truth lay in this case and they were not prepared to let the State persecute and punish the defendant in the dock. This was not some whimsical belief or assumption, I just knew that there were some jurors rooting for me. They had seen me give evidence in a most intense and heartfelt fashion which was peppered with pervasive and coherent arguments and reasoning. Perhaps the most pervasive arguments for acquittal focuses upon the three minutes that I spent inside Snakeshaft's house where it was claimed that I assembled the Uzi, commented upon a robbery and then dismantled the firearm without gloves. The time frame of this exercise, the unconvincing verbal comments about the Bermondsey robbery and the complete dearth of fingerprints and DNA evidence should ring alarm bells in the jury room.

How could a jury convict on this evidence and several weeks later, while consuming their delicious Sunday roast dinner, begin to have gut-churning doubts and misgivings over the verdict? I really believed, the defence case aside, that there were too many flaws in the prosecution case. The list was almost endless. For instance, here we had a man who was able to source, obtain and supply an Uzi submachine gun, 375 rounds of ammunition, a shoulder stock, a loaded magazine and a silencer from the first person he asks – the mysterious Rob the Porpoise – who just happens to have one lying around in his cupboard for the last two and half years? We have the three minutes in the house issue. The fact that Snakeshaft stated that he looked in the bag and saw a dismantled weapon only for it later to have a towel wrapped around it when it was discovered in my car. The lack of DNA and fingerprints on the gun after it was alleged that I handled it extensively. A star prosecution witness who was not only a self-confessed perjurer who puts an innocent man in the frame to save his own skin, but also was a state registered police informant who was motivated by financial gain.

On top of all that there was a drugs war going on between rival gangs in East London where it was alleged the star witness was obtaining firearms for them. We have a defendant who only met the accuser once before. The defendant was found with a map and £500 on him, whereas the £2500 it is alleged the defendant gave to Snakeshaft has never been traced. We have the underlying reason and motivation for the set-up – the police believe the defendant committed a major armed robbery in the South East London area where they recruited two informers to set-up the suspect and reap the benefit of a substantial financial reward. We have the flapdoodle about the 38s issue. A star witness who was not only involved in the importation of class A and B drugs, but also admitted on oath that he lied to his police handler. Finally we have the police themselves who put it to the star witness's accomplice – Wendall – that he was responsible for the set-up. If ever a definition of 'reasonable doubt' was needed in a case, this was it!

After the jury were left to their deliberations, junior counsel, James Goodwyn, and my solicitor's clerk, Phil Bunter, came down to the court cells to visit me. I wanted to discuss 'The Wendall issue' again as – god forbid – if the verdict did go against me I wanted to lay the groundwork out for an appeal now. I stated yet again that the question that the Judge asked the prosecution about Wendall at the beginning of the trial, i.e. to disclose only if Wendall was *not* a police informer had not been answered. Counsel agreed that he was not entirely happy with the answer. He indicated that usually the defence would get 'a nod and wink' from the prosecution as to whether or not they were on the right track, but this had not happened in this case. Counsel agreed with me that Wendall had most probably been at it, but not formally in this case, or that if he was at it, it had been doctored in some way to protect the informant. Either way, he said, he felt if we could not get a definitive answer about the Wendall issue at this court, it was highly unlikely, in the event of a conviction, that the Judges at the Court of Appeal would divulge that information. Nonetheless, James said he was prepared, if required, to submit grounds for appeal on 'the Wendall issue' as we never got a definitive answer. This pleased me, as I knew if the jury did convict I needed a glimmer of hope that one day I would prove that there had been a severe miscarriage of justice in this case.

After the legal conference, back in the cells I thought to myself, 'What the fuck am I doing here? There is a jury upstairs considering whether not I am guilty of this offence and their decision dictates whether I am going to prison for life! How did I allow myself to become involved in this nightmare scenario, what a sucker I have been!' It all seemed so surreal as if it was happening to another person but in fact it was ME!

While we were in conference we were unaware that the jury had

TWO STRIKES AND YOU'RE OUT!

requested to see all the exhibits 1-7 in the case, including the Uzi and the ammunition. Was this a good or bad sign? We would have to wait and see.

At 15:40 p.m. the Judge called the jury back into the court. At this stage they had been deliberating for 5 hours and 23 minutes. The Judge released the jury for the day and told them to be there the following day at 10:15 a.m.

Defence counsel:

> Will your honour be giving a majority direction at 10:15 hours tomorrow?

Judge: No!

Court adjourned at 15:42.

DAY THIRTEEN OF TRIAL

After another sleepless night I sensed that this was the day that I would learn of my fate. I had been getting several favourable looks from some of the jury members but I did not encourage this as the last thing I wanted was the scheming case officer DS Herbert who was present throughout the case to accuse the defendant or his family and friends of skulduggery with the jury.

Over the years I had heard about cases where a trial was going so well for the defendant that the police tried every trick in the book to halt the trial. Even if this meant getting depraved and dishonest detectives involved in the case to masquerade as villains and threaten jurors into an acquittal. Or by claiming to the trial Judge that that they had received a reliable tip-off from an informant—*a la* Snakeshaft—that the jury had been nobbled. Anything was possible for these 'legalized gangsters' who thought of themselves as above the law.

At 10:15 a.m. the Judge asked the jury to retire to consider their verdict. No direction was given regarding a majority verdict.

At 12:00 I had a legal conference with leading counsel David Gallant QC and my solicitor Andrew Conrad. To take our minds off the case we discussed previous trials and experiences of the lawyers. David rather unassumingly alluded to himself as merely 'a blagger's brief'! I wholeheartedly disagreed with this description and redressed the balance by calling him 'the God of Strategy and Tactics'! The overarching reason for this was throughout the trial I had been observing his oratorical style, behaviour and intellect very carefully and although I thought that I knew everything about the case, David seemed to understand and interpret the case on a deeper three-dimensional level.

When I first met Mr Gallant at the beginning of the trial I found him somewhat arrogant and supercilious in his approach to the case, as he wanted to run the case his way. I had to stop him and point out in metaphorical terms that this was a 15 round contest and we had already gone through 12 bitterly contested rounds and he was only entering the fight in the 13th round. I stated, much to his initial chagrin that he had to learn about what had gone on in the previous 12 rounds before he could start to dictate the terms of our defence. David seemed a little shocked at my forthright behaviour and views, but emphatically added that he could do more damage to the star prosecution witness Snakeshaft under cross-examination than I could do to him with a gun! This was the type of talk and determination that I wanted to hear and it helped to clear the air between us. It was only then, albeit reluctantly, that I agreed to listen to what he had planned for the defence case. The idea was not to start accusing the police in the case of wholesale corruption and wronging as this would play into the prosecution's hand whereby my previous convictions, especially for armed robbery, would come out. The idea was to say that I had been misled, duped, tricked, had-over or even set-up by Wendall and Snakeshaft and let the jury work out for themselves what kind of relationship these scumbags were having with the police. This subtle defence tactic severely undermined the prosecution's approach to their case as they had been expecting a resolute salvo of anti-police invective and accusations regarding their questionable role and behaviour in the case. Once the salvo amidships was not forthcoming, the prosecution's case began to fall apart and disintegrate. They were left there waiting for a physical battle and all they got was 'the god of Strategy and Tactics' who relied upon the natural judgement and commonsense of our peers on the jury panel.

At 14:15 pm the Judge called the jury back into court and asked them if they have reached a verdict on any of the counts? The foreman of the jury said they had not. The Judge then gave them a majority direction and explained that is a verdict in which at least ten of them are in agreement, for example he will accept a 11-1 or 10-2 majority verdict. The jury retired at 14:18 pm. At this stage, the jury had been deliberating for 10 hours and 35 minutes.

As I went back to the cells I worked it out that if the jury came back within the next 30-60 minutes it must be an acquittal because counsel and I fancied that we had at least three of the jury members on our side. If that was the case and most of the jury were in favour of a guilty verdict their deliberations would continue for a lot longer than 30-60 minutes.

While I was in the cells below the court my mind began to race again. I rationalized that this was it! I wanted the jury to come back quickly. I heard the telephone ring in the screw's office but it was a false alarm. Then, at 15:01 pm, the telephone rang again and the screws told me that I was wanted back in court, the jury were back. They say that there is nothing as unpredictable, not even the weather, as a jury. My head and heart were beating acquittal, acquittal, acquittal, but until we heard the formal verdict I was still in utter purgatory.

When the jury came in to the court at 14:04 pm they had been deliberating for 11 hours and 8 minutes. As they took their places on the panel one of the jurors winked at me and smiled and then I sensed that the nightmare ordeal was finally over. I looked up to my wife Stacey, family and friends in the public gallery and tried to look as confident as possible to reassure them that everything would be all right.

The clerk of the court addressed the jury, "Have you reached a verdict?"

The young fellow on the front row who had been looking at me throughout the trial stood up. "Yes!" he replied solemnly.

"On Count 1, Terence George Michael Diamond on the 5th day of June 2001 had in your possession a firearm, namely an Uzi submachine gun with intent by means thereof to endanger life. How do you find the defendant guilty or not guilty?"

The jury foreman, "NOT GUILTY!"

I looked up to the public gallery and smiled and was relieved that I would not be going to prison for life. It was imperative, however, that I was also found not guilty of the Count 2 otherwise it would mean a very long prison sentence.

"On Count 2, Terence George Michael Diamond on the 5th day of June 2001 without the authority of the Secretary of State, purchased or acquired a firearm, namely an Uzi submachine gun, which is so adapted that two or more missiles could be successively discharged without repeated pressure on the trigger. How do you find the defendant, guilty or not guilty?"

The jury foreman, "NOT GUILTY!"

By now everything was becoming a blur and became as surreal as the sunny day that my vehicle was stopped by armed police where I stood with my hands in the air and wondered, 'What the fuck was going on?' By now I realized that the verdict regarding Count 3 would be a formality.

"On Count 3, Terence George Michael Diamond on the 5th day of June 2001 being a prohibited person had in his possession a firearm, namely an Uzi submachine gun. How do you find the defendant, guilty of not guilty?"

The jury foreman, "NOT GUILTY!"

Upon hearing the last verdict I looked up to the public gallery and my wife Stacey, family and friends were smiling profusely and punching the air in triumph and jubilation. But inwardly, I knew that this was no victory, it was the end of a nightmare ordeal. Before the verdict I had promised myself in the event of an acquittal there would be no over-the-top celebrations in the dock. I decided to keep a dignified demeanour and put my hands together in prayer fashion and bow to the jury as they were discharged by the Judge and left the court to go to their room. For it was the jury who had released me from this unadulterated hell and torture! It was the jury who were able to see through this absurdly obscene case, where enormous amounts of public funds were used to release a dangerous long-term prisoner on parole to work in cahoots with depraved and dishonest detectives and set me up. I thank all eleven of the jury who found me not guilty and as for the juror that was undecided or thought I was guilty I forgive you and hope and pray that neither you nor any of your family and friends have to go through what my family and I have been through.

At 15:08 pm the Judge ordered the defendant to be released and he thanked the counsel for their efforts.

I was told that I would be released from the cells below the court. I was escorted back to the cells where the screws telephoned Cellmarsh Prison and told them the outcome of the trial and acquired authorization to release me. I grabbed two large plastic prison bags of personal property and was escorted through a network of passages until I was released from a nondescript doorway into the lower levels of the courthouse. I was astonished to find out that no one was there to greet me. I asked a stern looking security guard where Court 1 was and ran upstairs to greet my family. As I swung open the doors to the waiting area outside the courtroom I walked into a sea of smiles and euphoria. I flung my brawny arms around my loving and devoted wife and swept her off the floor. The look in her eyes said it all, she was ultra-relieved to have me back again as another long and debilitating prison sentence might have been the end for us. As I was absorbing the unrestrained joys of acquittal I noticed my 18 month old son Sonny crawling on all fours around my feet. I picked him up and held him aloft and listened to his dulcet cries of "Daddy, Daddy, Daddy!" It was pure bliss!

Slowly, one by one, I embraced everyone and noticed as I embraced my leading counsel that he had a tear in his eye. I thanked him and the solicitor's clerk profusely and slowly walked with my family and friends to the car park. The only ones not present to witness the outcome were my junior counsel, James Goodwyn, who had started another trial at the Old Bailey and my solicitor, Andrew Conrad, who was visiting another client at the nearby Cellmarsh Prison.

Then it was all back to a pub in Canning Town to celebrate. I drank deliciously chilled lagers and champagne for a couple of hours with an ever-increasing crowd of family and friends in the pub and decided to get home to Essex and spend some 'quality time' indoors with my family. Some of the well-wishers took my acquittal to heart and did not return home to their wives until two days later, citing "Well it is not everyday a member of the family gets acquitted of a blatant set-up!" Over the coming weeks, I received some feedback regarding the case, the most salient allegedly coming from Snakeshaft proclaiming, "You'd be surprised if you knew who the real grass was in the case!" The most disturbing comment for me was when someone said that I was lucky that I had been given my life back! This was all bollocks, as it had nothing to do with luck. In my opinion, this was a police-constructed crime from the very beginning. It was a highly manufactured crime and an arrant abuse and misuse of lawful authority and power. I decided in due course to make a formal compliant to the Police Complaint's Authority about the police conduct in this case.

Sometime after the acquittal, I was reading a very interesting and detailed book about police corruption. The author claimed due to the ever increasing numbers of criminal prosecutions being directed against corrupt and depraved detectives in the Metropole Force, "it was decided to set up a special unit at CPS headquarters in Ludgate Hill, a short walk from the Old Bailey, dedicated to dealing only with police corruption cases." It is uncanny how my nightmare case was switched from the Crown Prosecution Offices based at East London, to a special case female lawyer at CPS offices in Central London. When I asked my solicitor to find out the significance of this switch he never did find out! Moreover, where did this wretched firearm come from? I will leave it to you to decide!

CHAPTER 39:

WAS MY SOLICITOR FRIEND OR FOE?

The day after the acquittal I received a phone call from my solicitor regarding my personal property that had to be returned by the police to me. He said that he had spoken with DS Herbert and he claimed that the Judge did them no favours in the trial and that I was very lucky because the police had more stuff on me that they didn't use! My solicitor replied that the prosecution were always going to have problems with a star witness like Snakeshaft and a defendant with some intelligence. As for the 'more stuff' that the police could not use, what could it be? Could it be covert video and listening devices inside Snakeshaft's address that may have pointed conclusively to a police constructed set-up and, by extension, implicated Wendall in the set-up if it were disclosed? Or could it have been a spurious cell confession while I was held in Wentonville Prison? Whatever the case, the police and prosecution were in a deep hole as the more they revealed about the case to secure a conviction the more they would have to expose about its genesis and development and those that were running the show.

Two weeks later I went to my solicitor's office to collect some personal property and documents that would be needed to write this book and we had a general chat about the case and my solicitor handed me the six-page letter dated 25th April 2002 that he had composed in response to my pre-trial accusations that he was 'wilfully misleading' my family and me about certain issues surrounding the case and its defence.

Naturally being a defendant involved in a murky case of this nature one has a tendency to be wary of everyone and everything. Appreciable distrust and cynicism is increased, however, when the defendant sees and senses that the square pegs are being forced into round holes. From the very beginning of the case I wanted to have a hands-on approach and to learn about the way the judicial system had evolved into the monster that it is today. In many respects, my solicitor was very helpful in this area. He saw that I was willing to learn and understand the complexities of law and provided me with material and texts to aid this process. But somewhere inside me lay the feeling that I was getting rumped too by my trusted legal advisor. This may seem a harsh thing to say in the light of the acquittal but let's look at the evidence.

In all fairness, when I first appointed my second solicitor to act for me, he was young, vibrant and had a wealth of fresh ideas about the case. He was a very prolific letter writer and pestered the CPS continuously for more disclosure material. On my request, he composed and submitted a very comprehensive Defence Case Statement to trigger more disclosure material and it seemed, he genuinely sympathized with my plight, that I had been the victim of a set-up by the police and police informers. He was always available on the phone to discuss things and visited me to prepare the case on a regular basis. After taking over the case from the louche female solicitor, he continued working with the barrister of my choice James Goodwyn and secured the venerable services of David Gallant QC to lead us into battle against the gangsters of language and deception at the CPS. All in all, on the surface level, my solicitor appeared to be an asset to the defence and in reality I could not wish for a better legal advisor.

On the debit side, however, all that glitters is not gold. I first realized that things were not right when all the glowing ideas and promises about the defence case were not forthcoming. For instance, he said that he would get an independent firearms expert to examine the Uzi submachine gun in order to trace its origin in case the weapon had been seized by the police during another operation and had been logged down on police records somewhere. Apparently I was told the independent firearms expert did examine the weapon, but to this day I have never seen the report.

Similarly, we were to get a retired police expert to examine and analyse the codes with regard to the internal CAD and KRIS reports. This was never carried out. We were also to obtain professional video footage of the distance between Snakeshaft's address to my BMW in order to show the jury the extent to which a police informer would go to plant the firearm in my vehicle. This did not materialize either.

Then there were my continuous requests for my solicitor to visit the Eastside Gym in Canning Town to secure the personal details and possibly a photograph of Rob the Porpoise. In the end I had to put this request in writing, as his reluctance to carry out this mission was very disturbing. He asked if I could get a middleman to deliver the material to his office but this was unacceptable to the proprietors at the gym. Alas, when he did finally visit the Eastside Gym he came away empty-handed.

Then there were the essential requests for him to write to the CPS and ask for the mobile phone records of the confirmed police informer Snakeshaft and his willing accomplice Wendall. Over the prison payphone, my solicitor warned me that should I formally ask for this material it would give Wendall further ammunition to denounce me as a grass. This was absurd, so I sent letters to the trial Judge, CPS, The Flying Squad, my solicitor and two broadsheet newspapers – as insurance – asking for the material. Eventually I was successful in acquiring this material and it became an invaluable part of the defence case. Rather uncannily, the unjustified accusation of being a grass did come to pass from the scowling lips of Wendall!

Once the mobile phone records were obtained, we were to employ the services of a private investigator to check out several suspicious phone numbers in order to show and expose the method of communication between Wendall, Snakeshaft and their senior police handlers and controllers. Once I realized that these promises were not forthcoming I paid for this to be done privately. Post-trial my solicitor claimed that he did carry out this exercise but as yet I have never seen any reports or records to support his claim.

Then there was the occasion that I have previously mentioned about my home landline phone record being given to me in the surreptitious manner in two bulging A4 lever arch-files. When I checked the contents of the phone records I found two incriminating calls had been inserted on the phone record. Was this a pure coincidence or abject paranoia? I don't know but it certainly was suspicious!

Then there was the issue of the undated and un-addressed handwritten 'letter' found in Wendall's wardrobe on arrest. When I asked my solicitor to write to the CPS and inquire about the missing exhibit number and the letter's contents I was told not to worry as it would be interpreted as a 'self-serving letter' by the court and deemed inadmissible as evidence. Far from it, as we know, the first I knew of its contents was when it was read out in open court during the prosecution's opening speech thus not giving the defence time to argue against its admissibility as evidence. Was this pure oversight or something more sinister?

It was the Time Custody Limits saga that really shattered my faith and confidence in my solicitor! After three months of continuous delays in organizing the hearing, my solicitor told my family and me that we were to have a Judicial Review at the High Court on the 11th April 2002. On the 10th April, however, this was cancelled due to counsel not being ready. A week later we were told that there was never a Judicial Review hearing in the name of Diamond to be heard on the 11th April nor was one cancelled. The clerk in the listing office told us that if our solicitor could not produce a reference number for the case then we should start worrying. There was no reference number. What was going on?

As a result of this, two weeks before the trial was to begin, I sent a letter to a new solicitor asking if he would be prepared to take over the case and also a letter to the High Court listing's clerk seeking confirmation that there was no Judicial Review hearing booked for the 11th April. Both these letters did not reach their destination and I believe that they were intercepted by someone at the prison, most probably the police liaison officer at Cellmarsh Prison who has the authority to censor all incoming and out-going mail at the jail.

Finally, after months and months of continuous nagging for my solicitor to take crucial witness statements from my wife and two relatives that could support the defence case that Wendall came to my address the day before my arrest and gave me a map, this was not done! Admittedly, at the fag end of the trial, on counsel's advise, we did not call any defence witnesses but any solicitor worth his or her salt should have obtained these statements and been prepared for any eventuality. Why was he so reluctant to obtain these witness statements? It doesn't make sense!

Taken altogether, the cumulative effect of the above observations was enough to make even the most optimistic and relaxed defendant succumb to the travails of rampant distrust and paranoia. It is not for me to accuse my solicitor of professional incompetence or wilfully misleading and hindering the defence case, I merely relate the facts and leave it to you the reader to make up your own mind and allow you to cast your judgement accordingly.

In my solicitor's defence, I have reproduced an abridged version of his six-page letter of 25th April 2002 that was handed to me two weeks after my acquittal.

RE: YOUR CASE FOR JUDICIAL REVIEW

Dear Terry,

I write to confirm that your claim for Judicial Review was issued with the Queen's Bench Division of the High Court on the 23rd April 2002 and has been allocated a reference number of RO/1898/2002.

For your information I enclose a copy of the Application for Permission to Proceed with a Claim for Judicial Review, the grounds of our application and the statement of facts upon which our application is based.

I further confirm receipt of your letter of the 18th April 2002. Since receiving that I have also spoken to you over the telephone.

Firstly, let me state that I was very upset to hear your concerns regarding the way in which I have conducted your case. I am happy to respond to the matters that you have raised with me, but before I do so I would like to provide you with my guarantee that I have not, nor would I ever have, any wish to mislead you or your family. I regret that you feel as though I have wilfully obstructed the progress of your case and have betrayed your trust, and I would emphasise to you that is simply not the case. I have always been very grateful to you for instructing me in relation to your case and I feel that your case is extremely important bearing in mind the belief that both you and I share as to the corrupt and illegal manner in which the investigation against you has been conducted.

I accept that it is difficult for you to appreciate the extent of my work on your behalf when you are only able to discuss matters face to face with me on occasions that I visit you in custody. Your ability to provide clear and comprehensive instructions independently of my visiting you has meant that I have not needed to visit as often as ordinarily I would have. I have always felt that my time would be better spent in the office preparing your case and organizing the way in which we would seek to challenge the Crown's case against you.

I would say, however, that whilst it is extremely frustrating to learn that you have lost faith in my intention to act in your best interest, I would never oppose any application that you would make to obtain alternative representation. If indeed that were your intention, my main concern would be that the transfer of your case to another solicitor would be contrary to your interests and would be to the detriment to your case. Even so, if it is the case that you do not feel able to trust me with the conduct of your case, I would not feel it appropriate for me to continue to represent you.

(The letter then deals with the reason for the absurd delay in getting the Judicial Review hearing heard, a PII application, telephone evidence and the submission of a new Defence Case Statement.)

Finally, I wish to conclude the letter in the same way it commenced:

It pains me deeply to hear the concerns that you have raised as to the way in which I have conducted your defence. I truly regret the fact that the difficulties encountered, particularly with regard to the judicial review proceedings, have caused both you and your wife considerable frustration. Upon reflection, I would accept some responsibility for not pushing ahead with having the matter listed without securing representations from Counsel instructed in relation to your case. Unfortunately, it appears as though you and I are the only people who have faith in the merits of the argument, which is why I was particularly pleased to be able to inform Counsel that Mrs Justice Ferndale agreed with us and granted leave.

Most importantly, I wish to emphasise that I was extremely distressed to hear that your frustration with your situation has resulted in you beginning to suspect my motives. When I began this letter I felt it appropriate to respond to your concerns in a formal manner. However, to do so would not provide you with any indications as to the sincerity of my feelings. Since I first became aware of your concerns I have thought of little else. You will be aware from first hand experience that it is not unusual for someone in your position to suspect the motives behind the actions of his solicitor. Obviously there are occasions in which a client may be correct in his suspicions, however, it is more common for a client's suspicions to be aroused by a combination of misunderstandings between himself and his solicitor, deficiencies or difficulties in the way in which this case is being conducted combined with the pressure and anxiety associated with being held in custody with the possibility of being convicted of a serious offence.

Professionally, your distrust of my motives does cause me some concern, however, this can obviously be shrugged off as something that happens to all solicitors at some point in their career. It is not for professional reasons that the prospect of losing you as a client causes me such distress. It is for personal reasons that I am so alarmed at such a prospect. I have not drafted this letter in an attempt to persuade you to retain me as your solicitor if we have reached the stage that you have lost faith in my abilities or no longer trust my motives. In such a case it would be totally inappropriate for you to continue to instruct me.

Regardless of your decision, it is important to me that I have the opportunity to explain my feelings and leave it open to you as to whether or not you accept the sincerity.

I was excited at the prospect of representing you and have been 'hooked' by your case since our first meeting and since that time my faith in you as a defendant and my belief in the power of your case has only been strengthened. The case itself is fascinating from a legal perspective, however, this is insignificant when measured alongside the importance of your case from the perspective of justice.

Unfortunately corruption and corrupt practices are often encountered in cases such as yours, however, I have never come across a case that represents such a flagrant abuse of power by the Police revealing the cynical and disgusting way in which they feel it appropriate to conduct investigations.

I have no doubt of the fact that we are correct in our belief as to the way in which this case has been constructed, indeed everything that has arisen since the time of your arrest merely confirms this. The prospect of revealing the repugnant reality of this investigation and the persons involved in fabricating evidence to achieve your arrest is not only my motivation for doing everything that I can to prove your innocence but is also the whole motivation for me doing this job at all.

I appreciate that you are under a considerable amount of pressure and are deeply frustrated by being incarcerated for these allegations and consequently limited in your ability to defend yourself. I apologise if I have been inconsiderate in not fully appreciating how important it was for you to have the proceedings in the High Court conducted as quickly as possible.

In particular I apologise for the fact that the situation has caused your wife and family considerable anxiety, and at such a difficult time that it is impossible for someone in my position to be able to contemplate the significance of these proceedings.

I sincerely hope that you accept this letter and my apology to yourself and your family in the spirit in which it is intended. I hope that I will be able to come and see you and discuss matters face to face. Should you decide to obtain alternative representation I hope that you would not choose to do so on the basis of believing that I have deliberately sought to obstruct your case or otherwise acted against your best interests.

Furthermore, I assure you that my commitment to your case would continue and I would offer every assistance to any successor that you should choose to instruct to ensure your best defence.

It seems appropriate in such a bizarre case that I find myself in the unusual position of writing to a client in such terms, but I feel that it is important to respond to your concerns honestly and sincerely bearing in mind the amount of trust that both you and your family have placed in me.

With hope for the future.

Yours sincerely,

Andrew Conrad

As you can see this is a very emotive and compelling letter. It contains some 2,817 words and although it was never sent to me (as it had to be censored by Andrew's boss) it still doesn't detract from the fact that because of the bizarre nature of the case I was justified in believing that my solicitor *may* have been taking instructions about the case from someone else. In my view, this case was very important to the dishonest and depraved detectives who manufactured it and it would be at our peril if we were naïve enough to think that their tentacles of power and influence could not reach the hallowed portals of a solicitor's office in order to subvert and derail my defence. I do not accuse my solicitor of any malpractice or wrongdoing in this case, I merely wish to convey the state of mind I was in during the nightmare ordeal.

THE EPILOGUE

In early October 2002, my erstwhile friend and co-defendant John Wendall appeared at Thamesmead Crown Court in front of His Honour Judge Atkinson QC for a pre-trial hearing. Unremarkably, the public gallery was closed and the hearing was adjourned until the afternoon to allow the prosecution time to 'truncate the issues'!

After the lunch break, a deal had been struck between the prosecution and defence counsel. Count 1, possession of a firearm with intent to endanger life—that carried an automatic life sentence and; Count 2, purchasing or acquiring a prohibited weapon—maximum sentence 10 years were to be left on file or in layman's terms 'dropped'! Wendall was to plead guilty to Count 4, possessing a firearm when prohibited. He was sentenced to 3½ years imprisonment. This was to run concurrently with the 29-year sentence that he was already serving before he was released on parole. We learnt the sentence would not surpass Wendall's earliest date of release of February 2006. In effect, Wendall – the main player of the set-up – had received a slapped wrist from the State and was warned not to over step his remit the next time.

Several days later, amidst tight security and secrecy, Daniel William Snakeshaft appeared at the same court and was sentenced for his role in the Uzi set-up and other offences. Snakeshaft was sentenced to 4 years imprisonment and received a nominal Drug Trafficking Order to pay a £1000 fine.

In general, I was pleased with the outcome because if Wendall had received a hefty prison sentence that reflected the 'going-rate' at the time for possession of a firearm – let alone a firearm of this awesome firepower and accessories – many observers would have begun to question and doubt my claim that I was ruthlessly set-up by this person. When we compare and contrast their respective prison sentences we learn Snakeshaft was a state-paid, state-registered police informant who admitted a catalogue of crimes in his cleansing process and had given evidence for the Crown against a co-defendant. He was sentenced to 4 years imprisonment where the halfway release policy does not apply.

On the other hand, however, Wendall was considered a big time London villain with previous convictions for shooting people, armed robbery and kidnapping. He received 3½ years imprisonment where the halfway release policy did apply.

On a judicial level, to a great degree, the upshot is that the lenient prison sentence given to Snakeshaft may be justified and legitimised through the active assistance and cooperation that he gave to the police and the Crown Prosecution Service. What, however, is the justification for Wendall's nominal prison sentence? What has Wendall got going for him that his accomplice Snakeshaft hasn't? I will tell you.

Wendall was the real police informant in this sad case where, through his perverse desire to suck-up to his senior police handlers for practically airlifting him out of prison early and his equally distorted wish to see my family and me suffer, he wilfully transgressed his contractual remit as an informant authorized to use *'verbal enthusiasm'*. Instead he acted illegally as a *'participatory informant'* and, rather poetically, all that he and his sad accomplice succeeded in doing was setting up themselves and acquiring another spell in prison. It was a toxic combination of natural evil and over-zealousness that was Wendall, Snakeshaft and their bungling senior police controller's fatal flaw. They broke the law and had to be nicked by the new elite police squad that were brought in to take over the case. *Sic transit gloria monde.*

As for me, I returned to the home of my loving family and licked my wounds and wrote this book. Shortly before Wendall and Snakeshaft were sentenced I made a formal complaint to the Police Complaint's Authority (PCA). Initially I was told that the complaint was out of time as there is a 12-month window during which a complaint has to be made after the offence. I claimed how could the complaint be out of time when the case was still *sub judice* regarding the protagonist Wendall and Snakeshaft? The PCA forwarded my complaint on to the Chief Officer of the Metropole Police and I sincerely thought that because of the serious nature of the complaint and the number of very senior police officers and detectives involved that the investigation would be given to an outside police force to investigate. No, it was initially given to an Acting Detective Inspector in their own back yard at the Internal Investigations Command in North-East London. I have provided them with a 10,000 word personal statement which concludes ...

"Should the police complaints department decide to thoroughly investigate this complaint I would like them to take into consideration the following observations and issues.

Firstly, it is submitted that those responsible for misleading me into collecting the 'printing presses', Wendall and Snakeshaft provided false information to the Police and were able to do so through either the co-operation, connivance and misconduct of certain persons within the Police.

Secondly, the investigation from the outset conducted by DI Helliman and later by DS Herbert of the Flying Squad did not employ proper safeguards and was being misdirected by false information.

Thirdly, it is alleged that valuable evidence was lost as a result of bad decisions by those conducting the investigation. The Police have ignored or failed to investigate several lines of enquiry and not sought to gather evidence that was obtainable and may have assisted me in proving that this was a combined police-crook constructed set-up, i.e. allowing Wendall and Snakeshaft to walk away from the scene with evidence and an inadequate response in tracing the provenance of the firearm.

Fourthly, it is alleged that certain specified senior police officers have wilfully manipulated the investigation to prevent the revelation of matters adverse to their interests or intentions, and . . .

Fifthly, it is submitted that because of the wilful disregard for police codes of practice and conduct in this matter it made it harder for me to establish my innocence. By that, I mean, the secrecy that surrounds senior police controllers and handlers and their cherished informants meant that disclosure of the relevant defence material was almost impossible, and when it was disclosed regarding Snakeshaft it had been presented and manipulated in such a way as to continue the case against me.

All in all, whoever manufactured and instigated the set-up against me needs to be accountable for their actions as, in my view, this was an outrageous misuse and abuse of police powers and resources and we need to stop the main players involved in this case as they are extremely dangerous individuals and they appear to be acting above the law.

The overarching reason for this complaint is that I am fearful that those involved in this case and their vast network of informants will be plotting revenge of some description in the future. I understand that I am taking a risk in making this complaint but I feel a strong sense of personal and public duty that these 'legalized gangsters' must be stopped before they get beyond control which, who knows, appears to have already happened."

Finally, in November 2003, some fourteen month after I made a formal complaint to the Police Complaints Authority I received this reply.

"Having considered the circumstances of this complaint I am not satisfied that there is a realistic prospect that a tribunal would find that the conduct of any officer under investigation fell below the required standard and conclude that misconduct proceedings cannot be justified."

Moreover, I also made a detailed complaint to the little known independent 'Investigatory Power Tribunal' which adjudicates whether or not a suspect's human rights have been infringed through the abuse and misuse of intrusive surveillance techniques, i.e. surveillance being carried out in relation to residential properties, vehicles, the interception of post and telecommunications, etc. Twenty-four hours after the PCA reply, I received a letter proclaiming, *"The Investigatory Powers Tribunal has now investigated your application and has asked me to inform you that no determination in your favour has been made on your complaint."*

It is now late February 2005 and as a final update, I heard that Daniel Snakeshaft has now completed his sentence in the cushy confines of police custody. Under the Witness Protection Scheme he and his family have now been given new identities and are living at a new secret location.

As for Mr Wendall, he is still hanging on to his previously good name and reputation by a slender thread. He was being held at Smitemoor Prison in Cambridgeshire where he told other prisoners that he was serving six years for the Uzi offence and that he shook my hand in the cells beneath Thamesmead Crown Court. He also bragged to other prisoners that on his release he is going to kill me. What else could he say?

Not surprisingly, at this time of writing, in the last few days, I have heard that Mr Wendall has been awarded parole yet again. He has been released 12 months early, no doubt to carry on with his nefarious police-inspired activities.

As for the prison death threats, if he was a proper man, a proper villain with a proper name I would undeniably be concerned. But he is forgetting one crucial fact, I know, and now you know, through this story exactly what he is. May God have mercy on his soul!

GLOSSARY

1. ARV: Armed Response Vehicle.

2. ATM: Automatic Transaction Machine, i.e. Cash Machine.

3. Being bottled or get on his bottle: being followed.

4. CAD report: Computer Assisted Data reports which monitor police radio communications of an incident.

5. Charlie: cocaine.

6. CHIS: Covert Human Intelligence Source, i.e. an informant.

7. Cozzer: slang for a policeman or detective.

8. CPIA: Criminal Procedure and Investigation Act.

9. CPS: Crown Prosecution Service.

10. *ex parte* : Latin, a legal term meaning on the part of one side only. i.e. an *ex parte* PII hearing generally connotes the prosecution speaking to the trial Judge in chambers without the defence present in order to suppress sensitive or other material.

11. On his toes: disappear so the police cannot find or arrest a suspect.

12. HSU: High Secure Unit i.e. a top security prison within a prison.

13. KRIS report; an internal computer progress report on an investigation by an officer involved in the case.

14. MDMA: a chemical substance used in the making of ecstasy tablets.

15. Nonce: generally a sexual offender in prison or elsewhere.

16. PCA: Police Complaints Authority.

17. PII: Public Immunity Interest.

18. PNC: Police National Computer.

19. Q.E.: Queen's Evidence, or giving evidence for the prosecution.

20. Screws: prison officers.

21. SIS: The Special Intelligence Section which gathers intelligence on the higher echelons of criminality, as they affect London, for offences which include; multiple high value thefts; the importation of large quantities of class A drugs, human trafficking; organized immigration crime and multi-million pound money laundering in relation to the proceeds of organized crime.

22. SO 1: Serious Crime Group East.

23. SO 10: Also known as the "Infiltrators." Special hand picked deep undercover police officers that infiltrate the criminal underworld.

24. SO 11: From experience, dedicated police observation teams that collect, collate and disseminate intelligence on suspects before arrest by appropriate crime squads.

25. SO 19: The name given to the department which provides firearm-related support to the rest of the Metropole Police i.e. crews for ARV and teams of Special Firearms Officers who deal with pre-planned firearms operations.

26. SO 8: Formerly the Flying Squad now know as the Serious Organized Crime Group.

27. Stay or keep schtoom: say nothing.

28. Text: A legal term for list of information given to the police by an state registered informant, usually given to a Judge in secret before the informant is sentenced for an offence.

29. TIU: Telephone Intelligence Unit: this unit includes assistance with subscriber identity and account details, itemised billing and other specialist services for serious crime investigations or critical incidents.

30. Turn turtle: turn Q.E. or become a police informant.